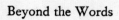

Beyond the Words

BEYOND THE WORDS

ELEVEN WRITERS IN SEARCH
OF A NEW FICTION
EDITED BY GILES GORDON

Hutchinson of London

Hutchinson & Co (Publishers) Ltd
3 Fitzroy Square, London W1

London Melbourne Sydney Auckland
Wellington Johannesburg Cape Town
and agencies throughout the world

First published 1975
© in this collection Giles Gordon 1975
Introduction © Giles Gordon 1975;
Foreword and extract from *A Long Trip to Tea Time*
© Anthony Burgess 1975; Essay and 'Wonderland' © Alan
Burns 1975; Note, 'Concerto' and Waiting for the Sun'
© Elspeth Davie 1975; Note, summary of Acts 1 and 2, and
Act 3 of *On Stage* © Eva Figes 1975; Portrait of the editor
as author, 'Alpha' and 'Omega' © Giles Gordon 1975; Note
by Michael Bakewell and extèacts from transcript of Fat
Man on a Beach © the estate of B. S. Johnson 1973, 1975;
Letter to the Editor and 'Contiguities' © Gabriel
Josipovici 1975; Note and 'Adam Kadmon' © Robert Nye
1975; Letter to the Editor and 'Preface' © David Plante
1975; Extract from *The Unmapped Country* © Calder &
Boyars 1975; Interview and 'Fire' © Maggie Ross 1975.
Thanks are due to the following for permission to reproduce
photographs in the text as line blocks: Jerry Bauer (Maggie Ross),
Fay Godwin (Giles Gordon), Oswald Jones (Ann Quin) and Jill
Krementz (Anthony Burgess).
The poems quoted in 'Fat Man on a Beach' are reproduced
from B. S. Johnson's *Poems* (Constable) and *Poems Two* (Trigram)

Set in Monotype Fournier
Printed in Great Britain by The Anchor Press Ltd
and bound by Wm Brendon and Son Ltd
both of Tiptree, Essex

ISBN 0 09 122270 2

IM

Ann Quin
1936–1973

B. S. Johnson
1933–1973

CONTENTS

8 Contents

INTRODUCTION

One of the hazards of writing an introduction to a book of this kind is that the editor's expressed intentions can all too easily be used as a weapon with which to abuse his contributors. I shall not, therefore, state here what in my view the eleven authors represented in these pages are specifically about.

A few words of background to the book may, however, not be out of place. In 1973, B. S. Johnson published a collection of short fictions, ironically entitled *Aren't You Rather Young to be Writing Your Memoirs?* In his introduction, he listed the eighteen writers he considered to be the present and even future interesting exponents of the art of fiction in Britain. And yet, with the exception of two or three of them, their work is nothing like as well known as it should be. The list includes six of the authors represented in this book. Two of the others were invited to contribute but were unable to do so.

After I had read Bryan Johnson's introduction, I suggested to him that he and I might compile an anthology of previously unpublished work by those we considered to be among the most worth while of contemporary British writers. We suggested to Messrs Hutchinson, our own publishers, that they might commission the book. On the day on which they agreed, I telephoned B. S. Johnson to inform him. The phone seemed permanently engaged. It wasn't until the following day I was told that he had killed himself a few hours before I tried to speak to him.

Charles Clark of Hutchinson persuaded me, absolutely against my feelings at the time, to edit the book on my own. Not all the authors I invited to contribute would necessarily have been in a book co-edited by Bryan Johnson and myself. Indeed, I doubt whether we would ever have agreed upon a mutually acceptable list.

It has to be remembered that in a book of this kind the editor is responsible only for commissioning the contributors. He is not responsible for what they write, which is one of the pleasures and hazards of compiling such an anthology. And he is not commissioning essays but pieces of creative writing. In short, everybody is at risk: editor, authors, publishers and readers.

When I first approached the prospective contributors I explained that the book 'would contain short fictions, previously unpublished, by about ten writers, each of excellence and also representative of different aspects of the new writing (which is, most emphatically, British; and not necessarily influenced by the work of, say, French or German writers)'. The authors whose words follow seem to me to be among the finest exponents of this new writing, a writing as much to do with the present, even the future, as with the past.

By its very nature the act of writing, the activity, is a nostalgic one; and therefore reactionary. What is immediate in the mind of the writer as he writes becomes, the moment he has written, part of the past rather than of the present or the future. Accordingly, it should not cause surprise that at any given time the majority of even serious writers (and I do not mean humourless writers) are, by inclination, traditional in their approach and response to their art. Nor is it surprising that so many of the pioneers of Modernism (Pound, Wyndham Lewis, Eliot, D. H. Lawrence) were as human beings reactionary.

The act and pursuit of writing doesn't immediately correspond to our image conscious and visually orientated era. Therefore the writer is, in effect, paying homage to a past. He or she must have a built-in sense of history, an awareness of a continuity between past, present and future. This must apply particularly to 'creative writing', to constructions or inventions of the mind and of the senses. Because the (serious) writer is likely also to be a (serious) reader, he or she is bound to be influenced by what has come before.

Reverting to my original letter inviting the authors whose work appears in these pages to contribute, I went on: 'The fictions would be preceded where the authors desired it by individual "statements", the writers giving perhaps their views on the new writing and their own contributions to it, relating it to the mainstream of English literature, to the other arts including cinema, television, painting, and to life as it is lived today . . . The book will be, in effect, a manifesto – but with a difference: exciting pieces of creative writing will be provided as well as theory.'

As will be seen, the contributors responded to this challenge in different ways. Some wrote fairly formal critical pieces, others less so. Some wrote about their own work – even their own methods of work – others about the writing of others. Two wrote open letters to me, one provided an imaginary interview with herself.

I would tentatively suggest that this book be considered as an antidote to Karl Miller's Penguin, *Writing in England Today* (1968). Of Professor Miller's authors, only Anthony Burgess appears in the present compilation. Incidentally, all the work in Professor Miller's anthology had been published previously. The book was influential, partly because it was published in paperback, partly because of Professor Miller's authority, particularly perhaps because it was the only major anthology of the last fifteen years purporting to be 'representative' of contemporary writing in the British Common-wealth. In fact, the book was not merely idiosyncratic, it was perverse. It omitted any writer whose abilities and inclinations were remotely divorced from the, so called, realistic; or, rather, any such individual piece of writing. Even Scotsmen (and certainly I include Karl Miller and myself as such) should have faith in the imaginative powers of the writer, of his visionary impulse. Where has 'being realistic' got the present decade? Where has 'social realism' got this century?

I wish it had proved possible to include in this book previously unpublished prose fiction by B. S. Johnson. Though useful to have in print, and extremely funny, the filmscript printed here does not, in my view, do full justice to the author's diverse talents. I am grateful to Michael Bakewell, who directed the film with B. S. Johnson, for creating a publishable script from celluloid and sound-track, a paradox the author would have relished.

Likewise it is sad to have to record that the novel on which Ann Quin (one of Bryan Johnson's chosen authors) was working when she died will remain unfinished. Judging by the opening chapter printed here, it could have been her most considerable work.

The difficulty with writing, as with reading, is words. Only the painter uses paint – not the spectator, not even the art critic; he uses words. Only the composer uses notes – not the listener, nor the music critic; he too uses words. The writer uses words, but so does everybody else. Therefore everyone believes he or she is a potential writer.

Most people, in daily currency, use words in what they think of as a fairly literal way. Consequently they are made uneasy if a writer does not use them similarly. They expect a novelist to know more words than they do, and to employ them with greater expertise than they can. Basically though, they expect a 'story' to begin at the beginning (wherever that may be). If the first four words aren't literally 'Once upon a time', the reader should be able to assume they're taken for granted. The story should continue through exposition, climax, denouement, until on the last page the author can write 'The end', and the reader may be confident there's no more to come, that nothing that should have been said remains unsaid.

The reader, then, expects to understand a work of fiction in the way he understands a conversation with his butcher, his bank manager, his wife, his colleagues at work, or even – in times of energy crisis – his candlestick maker or vendor. Or, pitching it a degree higher, he expects the fiction he reads to illuminate his own conversations with his hairdresser, his solicitor, his wife, his friends, even his Member of Parliament, because he knows that the author possesses 'imagination' while he probably does not.

We are conditioned to read thousands of words every day. There are probably more of them in a single issue of *The Times* or the *Guardian* or the *Daily Telegraph* than there are in the average new novel; and we're conditioned, because we lead such 'busy' lives, to read these words – whether in newspaper or book – as fast as we're able to assimilate them. In practice, this means a general understanding of the surface meaning, the 'factual' content, rather than being persuaded, beguiled, influenced, stimulated and altered by the words. But the craft of even our best journalist is one thing, the art of our better novelists quite another. Or should be.

In his introduction to *The Secret Life of Our Times*, a collection of fiction first published in the magazine *Esquire* (edited by Gordon Lish; Doubleday, 1973), Tom Wolfe points out that in the 1960s in America:

Journalists began mastering the same techniques of social realism that American short-story writers had depended on for so long. They began using them in quite sophisticated ways, in fact – and without ducking behind the screen of fiction. This was the movement or, better said, the development known as the New Journalism. These two forces – film and the New Journalism – would have probably been enough by themselves to deflect serious fiction writers onto a new course, much the same way that the rise of photography helped turn painters and sculptors against representationalism after the turn of the century.

Mr Wolfe goes on to suggest that the contemporary American short story is now evolving a system of poetics, or formal conventions, after the manner of the classical conventions that English poets – and English readers – observed in the eighteenth century: '. . . the characters are not tied to history, geography, nationality, or political subdivisions . . . They speak, if they speak at all, in a language that tells you nothing about class, regional or ethnic status.'

The journalist, the 'factual' writer, reports a world which his reader not only recognizes but identifies with, even if it is Chile, China or Afghanistan. This he can do uniquely well. The talented writer of fiction is much more subversive. As David Gallagher wrote recently in the *Observer*, reviewing a novel by the Chilean José Donoso: 'The only reality it posits is that of its own pages. There is no "real world", no specific context to which it refers, and it is subversive precisely because it denies the validity, or stability, of *any* context.' In other words, it is itself. A novel is a novel is a novel.

Traditionally, the British have been suspicious of theories of fiction, but at a time when many of the most intelligent and imaginative novels are coming from Latin America, North America and France, and when translation is making available to us more new books than ever before, we could do a lot worse than to pay closer attention to what critics are writing about non-British fiction. Though Tom Wolfe and David Gallagher in their remarks quoted here are writing about American fiction, we surely cannot afford to be so insular as to disregard what they are saying. Sooner or later, we must – as a fiction writing and reading nation – accept that unambitious but competent slice-of-life mediocrity (Joe Lampton Jim Dixon, Lewis Eliot) isn't all our novelists need be capable of.

In what seems to me a passage of the utmost importance to contemporary fiction criticism, Tom Wolfe in the introduction already quoted from suggests that the perpetrators of what he calls the new poetic in fiction are producing – legends, fables, parables, myths – neo-fables:

. . . realism has been *done*; it's finished. But how can I abandon realism and all of its extraordinary power and yet transcend it ? Why, by returning to a form that goes back to the very roots of literature itself, a pure and crystalline form, a form that does not depend on the soon outdated details of everyday life for its effects, a form that communicates directly with the consciousness of man, a form that is as timeless as language itself.

In spite of the universality of myth, for the writer of fiction today to create and invent neo-fables is, paradoxically, to make novel writing and reading a more private, more elitist activity than hitherto. It accepts both the limitations and the strengths of the position in which fiction now finds itself: that it is no longer a popular art.

I'm asking for a *more* critical approach to fiction – by authors, reviewers and readers, I'd like the reviewer or reader to say to himself: 'Mr X appears to be doing such and such. He knows his European literature, he's read his Cervantes and Sterne and Peacock as well as his Joyce and Proust and Beckett, and his Americans, not forgetting Borges. He uses words in his latest artefact in a way that, if not peculiar to him, is not how they are used in this sentence. He's intrigued and fascinated by them, by sentences, paragraphs, pages as sounds, shapes, rhythms as well as senses. His meanings aren't necessarily mine, but that's no reason to dismiss them.'

Let us be grateful to our all too few writers prepared to reveal in fictional terms their visions of the air-conditioned nightmare, and their parallel dreams, even day-dreams.

I am not asking for fiction which isn't immediately accessible in all its glories either to be praised lavishly or to be patronized with contempt or parody. If in terms of its own originality – whatever uniqueness it possesses – the reader of a book has difficulty immediately in interpreting its territory, why shouldn't this be regarded as a challenge? Henry Moore said recently: 'Cézanne, at one time, was completely unacceptable, and now he's part of the tradition. It's time that makes the difference.'

But I would not want to suggest that there is, in itself, any virtue in the writing of fiction in being 'experimental', assuming that were possible, which I don't believe to be the case if the author is serious about his art. If a novel is labelled experimental or avant garde by a reader, then it seems to me that the book has failed in its primary function, at least in terms of that one reader: to be a novel.

If content and form in fiction are inseparable, both essential aspects of a single artefact, a novel which with skill portrays its author's individual contemporary vision cannot be experimental or avant garde. It can only be itself, a work of fiction.

I hope readers will enjoy this book, and that once they have read it they will want to seek out further work by at least one or two of the authors represented here. What more can the writer do at any time than try to provide the reader (and himself) with a new experience? Literature, like life, should be a terribly big adventure.

GILES GORDON

ANTHONY BURGESS

Anthony Burgess was born in Manchester in 1917, the only son of a cinema pianist and a stage soubrette. He was educated at Roman Catholic schools in Manchester, and, after two years spent studying music and languages privately, mostly abroad, went to Manchester University. There he won a national short story competition, produced and acted, played the piano, and took his degree in English Language and Literature. From 1940 to 1946 he served in the army, ultimately with the rank of sergeant-major. He wrote poetry, but was determined to make his name primarily as a composer. He didn't abandon this ambition until 1955, having produced two symphonies, sonatas, concertos and other works.

After lecturing in England from 1946–54, he went as a senior education officer to Malaya, where he wrote his first published books. His first main work was a trilogy about the end of British power in the Far East, The Long Day Wanes. After Malaya, he went to Borneo as a lecturer, and wrote The Right to an Answer and Devil of a State, the first dealing with decadent England in the 1950s, the second with an imaginary East African caliphate resembling Brunei. Invalided home in 1959 with a suspected brain tumour, he was given a year to live and so wrote in one year as many novels as he could: The Doctor is Sick, Inside Mr Enderby, The Worm and the Ring, The Wanting Seed and One Hand Clapping.

The solemn warning of impending death proved groundless. Living in Sussex and London, he produced novels at a slower rate from now on but still with a speed that disconcerted some critics and readers. His later novels include: A Clockwork Orange (in 1972 made into a controversial and enormously popular film), Honey for the Bears, Nothing Like the Sun (a study of Shakespeare's sexual life), Tremor of Intent, Enderby Outside, MF, Clockwork Testament and Napoleon Symphony (1974). He has also written a biography of Shakespeare, and his literary essays have been collected in Urgent Copy. He has written a treatise on linguistics, a book on the modern novel, a study of James Joyce, and a shortened version of Finnegans Wake.

Married in 1942, his wife died in 1968. He is now married to an Italian philologist and translator, and they live mostly in Rome and Malta.

FOREWORD

I have not a great deal to say about the fragment of a children's story that, with proper tyro bashfulness, I present here. In this post-Freudian age we are all very wary of going down the rabbit-hole, because we know we are only visiting the unconscious and exhibiting obsessions that decency would prefer to remain hidden. The experience of writing novels for adults has taught me that the bulk of the work is done at the preconscious level, but I knew that already from the experience of writing music. But in adult art some kind of control is exerted by the conscious – the shaping mind, as it is called – while in a book for children one thing follows another by free association, and the result is a picnic for Freudian investigators. This children's book of mine has a key, but it is not a psycho-analytical one: it is what might be termed taxonomicoaleatory.

I wrote once in a long review of *The Oxford Companion to English Literature* that this is probably the most useful of all reference books to the professional writer. I also said, and I was not altogether joking:

I open at random: pages 446 and 447. These take me from Kennedy, Margaret (author of *The Constant Nymph*) to Kierkegaard, Søren Aabye. Good, I shall write a novel about an Anglo-Dane called Søren Kennedy, who lives in Kensington and is doing research on St Mungo (who is also St Kentigern). Discovering that this saint probably sojourned for a time on the Isle of Man (Keys, House of), he goes to Douglas, where he meets a beautiful Arab divorcee called Khadijah, after the first wife of the Prophet. She is very interested in Khusrau I, King of Iran (531–79), and they argue a great deal, despite an evident and inescapable physical attraction, about their irreconcilable faiths. A man called W. P. Ker, a fellow of All Souls on holiday, tried to heal their breach, urging that they see how ridiculous religious bigotry is by reading the episodes about the fanatical Kettledrummle in Scott's *Old Mortality*.

Khadijah falls for Ker, and Kennedy becomes violently jealous. But Ker is in love with a certain Ebenezer Balfour (*Kidnapped*), whom he is expecting to come to Douglas in a day or two. Balfour duly arrives, along with a certain Alan Breck, a con-man who pretends to weary for the heather and the deer, but whose Scots accent is suspect. But Balfour is under his power, and it is left to Khadijah to show the greatness of her love for Ker by exposing Beck as a mere adventurer who, when she pretends to wealth, at once starts to woo her and, when deliberately made drunk on a local whisky called Jack Ketch (or Captain Kettle), speaks in an American accent and proves to be a penniless descendant of Francis Scott Key of Frederick, Maryland, author of 'The Star-Spangled Banner'. The denouement brings in learned discussions of St Kentigern's miracles (it was on the Isle of Man that he revived St Serf's favourite robin-redbreast) and on proto-existentialism.

This little book from which I excerpt here is based not on a mere couple of pages in the *Oxford Companion* but on a whole letter-section. The letter will be obvious to the adult reader, but a younger reader will not bother about that – if any younger reader, of course, is willing to find the book acceptable. The letter-taxonomy ends up by being irrelevant: the real work of the author lies in bringing brief encyclopaedic entries to some sort of fictional life, utilizing the surprise element latent in juxtapositions arbitrary except for the initial letter, and trying to justify in terms of the logic of life (even if it is only fantasy life) what only makes taxonomic sense on the most elementary level.

I say no more of my own work, but I want to say a little about the much more important entity known as the experimental novel. I have very sadly in mind two young British writers who considerably extended the formal scope of fiction and ended up by taking their own lives. I greatly admired the books of B. S. Johnson and Ann Quin – not only for their willingness to try new things but also for their firmly traditional virtues. Both writers knew how to create character, to present a recognizably real world, to develop plot, to probe human motivation. Of Johnson I once wrote that he was a best-seller deliberately manqué. He could have churned out a novel every six months with all the surface properties that appeal to the tired reader in a railway compartment, but he had the courage and the devotion to the fictional art which makes a writer turn away from the obvious and the facile. Hence his restless searching after new things. He could have been popular, but he preferred to play some part in the development of the novel. I do not think his readers let him down, but I am sure that his critics did. He lacked an American audience, which was a great pity: in America he would have found a critical response more serious and painstaking than was ever possible in England, where there are many reviewers but few critics. He took his own life in an accession of despair, a state of mind experienced by all novelists except perhaps Harold Robbins, and I think time will show that, as often happens, the despair was premature: Johnson's *œuvre* is already about to receive the serious attention that it merits. Death is frequently a force that compels such attention; the living author is a sort of frivolity.

I feel strongly about Johnson and about the entire experimental tradition, if one may use such an oxymoron, in the English novel. After all, Laurence Sterne was a great avant-garde writer, and Johnson was one of the few modern novelists prepared to learn from him (another is William Burroughs). But experimental fiction is supposed to be a monopoly of the French, who, in my view, generally take to experiment because they lack talent. Michel Butor, Nathalie Sarraute, Robbe-Grillet and the rest have more intellect than solid interest in the current of life as it is lived; none of them has been able to create, as Johnson did and Sterne before him, a credible major character. James Joyce could afford to take mad risks (there is no madder risk than *Finnegans Wake*) because compelling three-dimensional characters of Shakespearian size stride through the thickets of formal experiment. For the sake of meeting Bloom or Earwicker one might even be prepared to read Joyce backwards. In other words, the novel develops as an art-form not through the jettisoning of the virtues we find in Fielding and Stendhal and Balzac but through adding to those virtues new elements of surprise, which means new devices for the presentation of the quiddity of time-and-space and what human souls really experience within that continuum.

I have never regarded myself as an experimental writer. Timidity or the need to pay bills has prevented me from moving too far away from received notions of plot, character, dialogue, diachronic presentation of action and so on. Perhaps as old age approaches, and it seems to be approaching now, I will be bolder. I have already written a novel on Napoleon in the shape of Beethoven's *Eroica* symphony, though this reads regrettably like orthodox historical fiction, and I plan to use the medium of verse for the telling of a long story (nothing new about this, except that, since *Aurora Leigh*, nobody has really dared to do it). In other words, I recognize that it is not enough to make things easy for the reader. The novel is still the major literary form of our time, and talk about its moribundity is only viable if the talk refers to novelists who are happy to be stuck in the nineteenth century (I will not mention names). Novelists like B. S. Johnson were keeping the novel alive. And now Johnson is dead.

1. from A LONG TRIP TO TEA TIME

1. Straight Through a Hole in the Desk

Edgar was heartily sick of the droning voice of Mr Anselm Eadmer, who was going on, through the last gorgeous spring afternoon before the start of the Easter holiday, about Edmund Ironside and Edward the Confessor and Edward the Elder and Edward the Martyr, and the rest of the boring kings of Anglo-Saxon England. Edgar's desk was pocked with tiny holes made by doodling compass or dividers, and he thought what a capital thing it would be if he could become small enough to creep into one of those holes and vanish – his real diminished self, that was – until the lesson ended, while this big bored self became a wide-eyed responsive machine, taking it all in about Anglo-Saxon royalty. Imagine his surprise, then, to find himself suddenly on a ship being steered carefully through one of those holes – the one nearest the D of his own carved and inked-in first name – and to hear voices calling in a language he did not understand. He was standing on deck, not very well wrapped against a piercing wind that cried in from the other end of the hole, and an old man was standing next to him, all white beard and oilskins, with a red-coaled pipe held firm in smiling jaws. The old man said:

'You, boy – are you on the crew-list? What's your name? Solomon Eagle? John Earle? Hareton Earnscliff? Atalanta, Perseus, Cupid, Psyche, Alcestis, Pygmalion, Bellerophon? Ah, that was a great ship, the Bully Ruffian we used to call her. Speak, boy, and answer.' But he did not seem really interested, and Edgar did not wonder, for the ship had at last come through the hole, or rocky tunnel as it really was, and into a wide sea where the gulls were crying 'Repent! Repent! The end of the world is coming!'

'Eagles they should be by rights,' the old man said, still smiling. And then, suddenly frowning, he called: '*Laxdaela!*' or something like it to a couple of members of the crew, who replied with sounds like *isk* and *bosk* and *etheldeth*. 'We put you ashore,' said the old man to Edgar, 'on Easter Island. There it is, on the port bow.'

Edgar had too many questions to ask. He asked one only. 'What language are they speaking, sir?' he asked.

'There it is,' said the old man, 'coming up now. Listen to the Easter bells.' And the sea air had suddenly become alive with a sweet loud jangling. 'But don't,' he said, 'expect the place to be full of eggs and hot cross buns, because it won't. The people there have very long ears, right down to their shoulders, and their gods are the same. Look, you can see some of those stone idols, all along the shore. To keep out intruders, that was the idea. But it won't keep *you* out, oh dear me, no.'

'Why do I have to be put ashore?' asked Edgar. 'Why can't I stay on the ship and go wherever you are going?'

'Eastward ho,' said the old man, who, it dawned on Edgar, must be the captain. 'That's where we're going. To see Sir Petronel Flash. Also Moses and the Devil and the great Orc. No place for you, boy. Ah, the boat's being lowered.'

So it was. They were still some way from the shore, all along which stone effigies stood, and Edgar did not really enjoy climbing down the nets to the two rowers who awaited him, men who had stripped off their oilskins for the sudden heat and were now half-naked, though, in a sense very fully clothed in tattooings. On the chest of one of them was the blued-in face of a rather pretty girl, her presumed name Rhoda Fleming etched in beneath. 'Hallo there,' said the face, to Edgar's mixed fear and amusement. 'Vanity of vanities, all is vanity.'

'Don't you listen to her,' said the other man, whose chest and stomach were covered with a very fine map of Hindustan, all twinkling lights and bullock-carts moving along the roads. 'It's for me she's saying that, not you. What you might call a long-standing feud, my name being Bob Eccles. So, then – off we go.' And they both plied lustily with their oars. The man who had not yet spoken now spoke, though jerkily and rather breathlessly with the effort of rowing:

'You watch out, son, for the mother of the Blatant Beast. If you see a lady there that's a bit like a snake from the waist down, then you'll know it's her.'

'No, no,' cried Edgar with sudden panic. 'Take me back. Take me back to school and Mr Eadmer and the kings of Anglo-Saxon England.'

The two men laughed, and Rhoda Fleming laughed too, all blue teeth.

'Why,' said Bob Eccles, 'bless your heart, son, she's nought to be afeared on. Worn out she is now, having been mother to no end of monsters – Chimera and Orthrus and the Sphinx of Egypt itself. Also Cerebos and the Hydrant.'

'Haven't got them two last ones quite right,' said the other man. 'But never mind. Sing us a song, young un, to keep us in trim for the rowing.' So Edgar sang a song he knew, when he started, he did not know, but knew that he would know when he started. It went like this:

> A forrard leak on the garboard strake
> And the harbour bar o'erflowing,
> For there's many a man must whistle and ache
> And stretch and stitch till his callions break,
> And hark to the cock for the morning's sake
> And his cree cray crack craw crowing.

To, but perhaps not really, his surprise, the two toiling mariners joined in with a shanty burden:

> With a hey and a ho and the bo'sun's dead
> And his bed unmade in the morning.

Edgar found himself, without effort, trolling a second verse:

> The trisail's brayed on the mizzen trees,
> And sop up rum by the bottle,
> And the galley's alive with the reek of cheese,
> And the noontide lobscowse fails to please,
> And the cargo's eaten alive by fleas,
> And the donkey goes half-throttle.

The two rowers growled their refrain:

With a hoo and a hee and the first mate's oiled
And he's boiled with eggs in the morning.

To his, but he was no longer really capable of it, surprise, Edgar
found that he was being rowed towards a nice clean wooden pier,
and two little men in blue uniforms were dancing up and down on
it, as if with rage at the approach of the boat.

'What's that they're shouting?' Edgar asked.

Both rowers made faces, as if to say: it's always like this. The
one who was not Bob Eccles said: 'It's their dinner-hour, you see,
and they don't like to be disturbed at it.'

'*In it*,' the other said, 'or perhaps *during it* might be more of an
ecclesiastical polity.'

'No, more of an ecclesiastical sonnet, I'd say,' said the other, and
the tattooed face of Rhoda Fleming began to recite *I wandered
lonely as a cloud*. 'Not having that I'm not,' said her owner sadly,
looking down and giving himself three extra chins. 'It's the mention
of Wordsworth that does it,' he explained to Edgar. 'She met him
once, you see, when I was having a bath in Lake Windermere, if
you know where that is. Silly old man, I thought, with his top
hat on.'

'Look,' Edgar said, as the boat began to touch the steps of the
pier, 'why don't they get on with having their dinner instead of
jumping up and down like that in a rage?'

The other two shook their heads. 'See now,' said the one who
was not Bob Eccles, 'why don't I give my name so as you'll know
it? It happens to be Boniface, if you're at all by way of being the
least mite interested. Some say as it's really Bonny Face and others
as it's really Bony Face, but there's not one bone in my etchy omo
as you can see, save for the sniffer perhaps, so I plump for the other
meaning.'

'Your what?' asked Edgar.

'His sniffer,' answered Bob Eccles. 'Or his honk or hooter or else
his maundy thursday.'

'No, no, the other one.'

But by now the two little blue-clad men were jumping up and
down on the very edge of the pier and crying: 'The pancakes are

burnt and it's all your fault,' whereupon Boniface yelled:

'I don't believe you're having pancakes, today being Wednesday.' Surprisingly, or not so, this quietened them down a good deal, so that one of them said to Edgar:

'All right, let's be having you up then.' And they quite kindly helped Edgar as he came to the top of the pier-steps, one of them saying: 'You can come a nasty crack there when it's all slimy with the sea-slime and the outcroppings of the topmore gudgeons.' Boniface called up:

'Don't forget to tell them now where you want to go.'

'But I want to go where I've come from,' cried Edgar in some distress. 'I want to be in school for the end of the lesson and then be ready to go home to tea.'

'Tea,' and one of the blue-clad men shook his head, saying: 'You'll have to go a good way inland to see about tea. Where the Exhibition is, if the truth is to be told, and a good fair crack to the feet it is to get there. But let's be having you in the office.' And Edgar noticed that there was a little hut a hundred yards or so along the pier, from which loud screams were coming. The two sailors started to pull back towards the ship, which seemed to have travelled on a good number of sea-miles without waiting for them, singing:

> With a hoy and a haw and the skipper's fried
> And he's tied with springs in the morning.

'Now,' said one of the blue-clad men, 'let's have a look at you.' Edgar had a look at *them*. Their hair was very fine and very wild in the sea wind and their noses very red. They seemed, each of them, to be no more than about three feet in height, but they were so paunchy that their blue jackets were made to fit with a loop of string between button and buttonhole. 'Well, now,' said the one who was speaking, 'you seem to be a fair upstanding specimen of a recantation, and I'll thank you to know that I'm Mr Eckhart and this one is called Mr Eckermann.'

'You're Germans?' Edgar asked politely.

'No,' thundered back Mr Eckhart, 'we're brothers.'

'But I don't understand that,' said Edgar. 'I mean, you have different names. If you were brothers, you'd have the same name.'

They both roared with laughter. 'Ah,' cried Mr Eckermann, 'little you know of the great world, and that's a fact. Brothers have to have different names, otherwise you couldn't tell them apart. Suppose Cain and Abel had had the same name, eh? That would have made a pretty mess for everybody.' And they both chuckled. Mr Eckhart at last said:

'Not that this is the job our father would have chosen for either of us. I did a great thing once upon a time. I used to go around warning people about monsters, but they'd never listen.'

'Ah,' Edgar said, 'like the Blatant Beast and its mother?'

'Well, sometimes,' Mr Eckhart said doubtfully. 'But it was more what they call Venus, she being what was known as the goddess of love, whatever that is or was.'

'A lot of nonsense,' Mr Eckermann said. 'Me, I was a great one for the conversations, but that's all over now, aye aye, all over.' They both looked so sad, even though a seagull had landed on the head of Mr Eckhart and was crying 'Eclectic electric eccentric', that Edgar thought he had better remind them that there was work to be done in what they called the office, from which the screaming still came. He said:

'The trouble is I have no money.'

'Money money money,' Mr Eckhart grumbled. 'That's all anybody thinks about.' He looked at his wristwatch, from which a very subdued kind of singing seemed to be coming, and said: 'Well, as for money, the time's arrived. Come on, don't waste it. To the office.' And they hurried off, Edgar following, the seagull now on Mr Eckermann's head and calling 'Liddell and Scott, Liddell and Scott.' But when they came to the little hut it flew off, craaaarking, into the sea wind.

The hut was very small and very untidy. The screaming, Edgar now saw, was not coming from anybody being hurt but from a parrot with a little silver ring about its left leg, attached to a thin chain that was attached to a tall hatstand. The hatstand was crammed with every possible kind of headgear, from concertina-folding opera-hat to Sherlock Holmes deerstalker, and all were quite clearly too big for either Mr Eckhart or Mr Eckermann, and far far far too big for the little man who sat behind a desk in great gloom, eating some very sticky-looking and rubbery candy from a paper bag. He had a long nose like an empty ice-cream cone with a pencil attached to its apex, and this was all covered with candy, so that he had to keep wiping it with a very grubby handkerchief. 'It's a terrible burden to be sure,' he said, 'eating of this.' The parrot screamed very loudly from the crown of a bowler hat, but nobody took any notice. Mr Eckermann, or it might have been Mr Eckhart, said petulantly:

'Why didn't you make cocoa, as you were asked and as is your duty?'

'It's no good making cocoa, nor drinking it neither,' said the little man, 'since the spoon keeps getting into your eye.' And then he became very official, looking sternly at Edgar, putting the bag of candy into a desk drawer. Out of the drawer something invisible seemed to fly out for Edgar heard a tiny voice call:

'Aye aye. I. Eye.'

'Passport,' said the little man, 'and quick about it.'

'Titititit,' went the little voice. It was now near the parrot, and the parrot looked at it, its head on one side.

'You've let the echo out,' said Mr Eckermann or Mr Eckhart sternly. 'You've been warned about that often enough.'

'Nuff nuff nuff.'

'It does nobody any good, having it,' went the little man gloomily. He wore, under his blue jacket, a rainbow-striped jersey that Edgar rather liked the look of, though it would be much too small for himself to wear.

'The time's coming up for the race,' Mr Eckhart or Mr Eckermann said.

'Ace ace ace.'

'Now you have to place your bet,' Mr Eck said (it was easier this way, decided Edgar). 'Put your money in that letter-box there,' and he gestured with his nose towards a beautifully polished brass letter-box mouth in the wall.

'But I have no money,' Edgar said, 'as I told you.'

'I'll lend him a couple of hamadans,' said the other Mr Eck, taking some bright small coins from his jacket pocket. 'After all, it's what they call, or used to call in the days of my youth, a foregone conclusion.'

'Usion usion.'

So the money was put into the letter-box, and the other Mr Eck said to the parrot: 'Eclipse first and the rest nowhere.'

The parrot listened very carefully and, it seemed to Edgar, seriously to that, its head on one side, and it crooned to itself.

'What is this?' asked Edgar. 'Eclipse, I mean.'

The little man spoke. 'The most famous race-horse in the world it is, and running today in the Queen's Plate at Winchester. Born during an eclipse it was, and so hence, notwithstanding, and not to put too fine a point on it, its name.'

'Ame ame ame.'

'Quiet now,' said one of the Mr Ecks. 'Shut the echo up.'

'Up up up.'

Everybody was now quiet, and the Mr Ecks looked at each other in triumph, since the echo had, indeed, shut up. The parrot seemed to be listening to something intently. After about a minute it began to flap its wings and dance up and down. The little men, all three of them, looked gravely at each other.

'Won,' said one of the Mr Ecks. Echo agreed, three times.

'How do you know?' Edgar asked.

'It always wins,' said the little man. 'Never lost yet. Ah, here comes the money.' And out of the letter-box came the two coins, followed by the smallest coin that Edgar had ever seen. All three tinkled on to the floor.

'Can't win much, you see, it stands to reason,' said Mr Eck. 'It always comes in first, always has done, always will. Anyway, those two hamadans go back to us, and you can keep the vathek, not worth much but better than nothing.'

'Thing thing thing.'

'Thank you,' Edgar said, pocketing the tiny coin they called a vathek. The little man at the desk said:

'Anything to declare?'

'What do you mean?' asked Edgar.

'You answer the question. You're bringing things into the

country, and you have to say what they are. And some things you have to pay money on.'

'But you can see,' Edgar said, 'I have nothing.' And he held out his hands as if to show that there was nothing hidden in them.

'You're a bit of a liar,' said one of the Mr Ecks. 'You have that vathek in your pocket.'

'All right, then. I declare that.'

'Not enough,' said the other Mr Eck. He went over to a corner of the room, brushing the echo out of the way irritably as he did so. There was a load of old rubbish in the corner – bucolics and eclogues and barclays and sylviuses and economics and bagehots and darwins and ectors and kays and seneschals, all very dusty. He came out with a big dusty carpet-bag and began stuffing it with hats from the rack. The parrot danced and squawked, and echo squawked too, so that the parrot put his head on one side to listen, but by this time there was nothing to hear. Mr Eck gave the stuffed bag to Edgar and said: 'Now.'

'Ow ow ow.'

'Anything to declare?' asked the little man at the desk.

'Just this,' Edgar said.

'Confiscated. How dare you try to bring all those hats into the country.' And he began to throw the hats back on to the rack, missing several times to the great glee of the parrot. Very grimly, he said: 'I suppose you've no passport, either.' He began to rummage crossly in the drawer that the echo had flown out of. 'No good, no good,' he kept saying. 'There's nothing here that suits. This passport's for a young girl from the depths of Manchester, by the name of Edda de Maris, and this one's for an old man by the malory of Snorri Sturlason, from Trinitaria he is, so neither will do.'

'Do do do.' The echo was now right on top of the desk. The little man shot out his hand, closed it, and cried:

'Got it. In there with you, my lady.' And he put an invisibility into the drawer, then closed the drawer. 'So,' he said gloomily again. 'It looks as if we'll have to let you in without a passport.'

'Thank you,' Edgar said. 'And how do I get home in time for tea?'

Messrs Eckermann and Eckhart said together: 'We know nothing of tea here. It's cocoa we drink.' The parrot screamed and screamed at Edgar. 'What are you waiting for, boy?' said the little man behind the desk. 'We've done our duty by you as none can deny, so on your way to wherever you're going.'

'Sing him your song to cheer him on his way,' said one of the Mr Ecks.

'Oh, all right then,' grumbled the little man, and he sang grumpily, while the parrot screamed an accompaniment:

> Sir Arthur Stanley Eddington
> (1882 to 1944)
> was educated at Owens College, Manchester,
> And Trinity College, Cambridge,
> And was professor of astronomy at Cambridge
> And was a distinguished astronomer,
> Noted for his researches into the
> Stellar system and the internal
> Constitution of stars,
> Also for his contributions
> To the theory of relativity
> And the popularization of
> Modern physical theory.

As that seemed to be the end of the song, Edgar said: 'Thank you very much. That was delightful.'

'Delightful?' said Mr Eck. '*Delightful?* Stella Cistern was one of the most beautiful girls in the world.' They all now turned their backs on Edgar, including the parrot, so he left the office and went out into the sea wind. 'Christian Science. Christian Science,' cried the gulls.

2. *Eden*

Edgar walked towards the land. The pier led to a long street which stretched left and right as far as the eye could see, and it was full of pleasant-looking houses painted very richly – red and orange and yellow and even purple – and people were seated outside their front doors in little gardens, sunning themselves. They waved quite amicably to Edgar as he stood, his back to the sea, wondering which way to go. They were mostly quite small, and one little man had two dogs which were much bigger than himself. He kept hitting one of them with a feeble little hand, crying 'Naughty naughty', but the great beast, it was clear, did not even feel the blow. Looking up, Edgar saw a signpost which said 'TO EDEN'. There was no signpost giving other instructions, so it was to Eden he decided to go. As he started off, turning right to do so, a little old woman, fanning herself with a newspaper on a chair in her garden, called:

'Going to Eden, is that it, young man?'

'How far is it?' asked Edgar.

'It gets further every day,' she said. 'It's a question of the Expanding Universe, you know. But you should be there by nightfall if you don't dawdle.'

Edgar thanked her and began to walk. As the view of the sea on his right was rather monotonous, he crossed over, coming, as he walked on, to a number of little shops which sold canned gavestons, toy woolly lambs, strawberry isabellas, and other interesting things. And then he came to a baker's shop where a fat old woman was crying with pain because, as she told the whole world (though the whole world was not there to hear her, only a very thin man with a goatee, chewing and chewing) she had burned her hand in putting some loaves into the oven. The man said to her:

'It's not possible, right? There's no such thing as pain. It's all imagination, right?'

'But the pain's terrible, Mr Quimby. Look how red it's become. Oh oh, the pain's terrible.' Edgar stood, listening, fascinated, and they took absolutely no notice of him.

'See now, ma'am,' said Mr Quimby, 'and listen, right? There are two things in the world, right? One of them's matter – like that bread and that cat sitting by the oven and this hat I was wearing when I came in, right? That's matter. Pigs and dust and news-papers and pens and knives and pimples and boils and carbuncles and burns on the hand. Matter, right, *right*? And the other thing is mind, that is to say the thought I'm thinking now and the thought you're thinking, right? Well, matter doesn't really exist, did you know that? Well, you know it now, ma'am. When I see a pig or a pen-knife it's only a thought. It's something I think, right? There's nothing out there, that's true of that cat and that oven it's sitting by, it's all in here here *here*, inside the mind. Right, *right*?'

'I suppose you're going to say that this pain is inside too?' cried the baking-woman. 'That this burnt hand is inside the mind?'

'And it is too, ma'am,' said Mr Quimby. 'You think it's hurt and red and swollen. All you have to do now is to think it's *not* hurt and red and swollen. Right? Do that, ma'am.' He looked at a huge turnip watch he took out of his waistcoat pocket and said: 'Starting *now*.'

'But that's nonsense,' Edgar couldn't resist saying. 'I mean, if it was a toothache the tooth would have to come out, wouldn't it? It would still be a bad tooth even if you said it's only in the mind? Right?'

To his amazement, the baking-woman, whose hand really looked terribly red and painful, cried out: 'Spirit is immortal truth and matter is mortal error. Spirit is the real and eternal and matter is the unreal and temporal.'

'That's right, ma'am,' said Mr Quimby. 'You sure are learning fast.

'Learning?' she said indignantly. 'What do you mean – learning? I've always known it. It's me who am the teacher and you who are the learner. And *you're* going to learn fast. Now.' And she picked up a long bread-knife from the table and lunged at him with it. 'Right?' she said.

B.T.W.—B

'Ow,' cried Mr Quimby as he ran round the table, the knife after him, 'ow, ow, that got me in the elbow, ma'am, ow ow ow ow, you've ripped the cloth from the back of my portland jacket, ow, that was right in the main artery, ma'am.'

'All in the mind,' she cried.

Edgar got away very quickly, as he did not like either the big bread-knife or the look in the baker-woman's eye. So, hearing the cries of Mr Quimby and the shouts of 'All in the mind, right, *right?*' he walked on and on, and soon began to feel very thirsty. The sun was hot and he had had nothing to drink since lunchtime. A seagull flew up to him and, hovering in front of his eyes, scrawked: 'All in the mind, eh, sonny? Hahahaha.' Then it flew off.

It was not long before Edgar came to a lane to his left, full of shady trees, and, as he walked under them, grateful for the coolness, he saw a kind of arch woven out of what seemed to be paper leaves and flowers, and the sign EDEN in electric lights that were, sur-prisingly, since it was a bright summer afternoon, flashing feebly in and out like an advertisement for car-tyres or chewing gum. Some bulbs did not, however, seem to be working. He walked under the arch and there saw a cheerful little man picking himself up out of a huge pool of mud. The road ahead was also full of such pools, as if there had been very heavy rain quite recently, though there had been no such signs on the esplanade from which Edgar had just turned off. The little man, desperately covered in mud, spoke in a friendly and cheerful manner, shaking mud out of his ears, pouring out of a battered top hat which he then put back jauntily on his head not only mud but also frogs that croaked cheerfully.

'It's all in the mind,' said the man. 'Cheerful within means cheer-ful without, and don't' – laughing heartily – 'ask me without what.'

'Eden,' said Edgar. 'Eden's another name for paradise, isn't it?'

'All in the mind,' said the man. Coming towards Edgar he sud-denly slipped and went down into another mud-bath, from which he emerged as cheerful as before, if not more so. 'You'll get to like it if you keep cheerful. And there's no charge to go in. You don't have to give me not a penny, not a hiddekel (or tigris, if that's the name you prefer), not a euphrates or a pison or a gihon. In you go, and remember it's all, ha ha ha ha, in the mind.' Edgar thanked him and walked on, hearing the little man fall into yet another pool and chuckling heartily, but not, since he was now behind him, seeing him.

Edgar had never in his whole life seen so miserable a place. The sun was not shining; the sky was covered with rain-clouds, and there was a horrible smell of glue-factories. The houses he saw were black with soot and out of the chimneys of the big black buildings came black smoke that made him cough. There was a big banner stretching across the street, and it said: EDEN MEANS DELIGHT, AND DON'T FORGET IT. There were a lot of big black flies buzzing fretfully around, and Edgar said to himself: 'Whether it's all in the mind or not, I'll be glad when I can find someone to tell me where I have to go in order to get back to school and then home to tea.' There now appeared a very strange-looking lady, riding a white horse, wearing clothes of an earlier age, including a huge hat with a muslin veil (to keep off the flies, Edgar thought), and she carried a whip. With this whip she kept beating at a small Indian in a turban but not much else. He was running ahead of her, and, though he cried repeatedly: 'Oh, you stop that now, *missi-sahib*, oh my goodness, that is very provoking, indeed, on my word, yes, *missi-sahib*, you stop it now, please,' he did not seem to be hurt. Indeed, the whip never seemed to reach him. But the lady kept calling: '*Jildi, hitherao*, I'll tan your hide, by the Lord Harry, I'll thrash you within an inch of your life,' and she lifted up her whip, that whistled through the air, again. The turbaned Indian, catching sight of Edgar, ran behind him for protection, saying: 'She becoming very angry, oh my goodness, yes, but you are my father and mother, *sahib*, and you will keep off her anger from me, oh on my word, yes.' The lady said:

'Who are you, boy? What are you doing here?'

'I'm trying to get back home for tea.'

'Tea,' she said musingly, 'tea. Never touch it myself, bad for the liver, much prefer a whisky *pawnee*, a *chota peg*, do you understand? But if you really like tea, and there are some who do, do you understand, you'll have to go up country for it, ah yes.'

'You speak true, *missi-sahib*,' said the Indian from behind Edgar. 'Up country very good tea.'

'Well, he should know,' she said. 'Born here, drinks it himself. Now why was I beating the blue living daylights out of him? Can't think why for the moment. Must be a reason, though, do you understand?'

'Very good exercise for you, *missi-sahib*, ha ha. And for me too, oh goodness gracious, yes.'

'You see up there,' said the lady, pointing with her whip. 'That semi-detached house on the hill. Dreadful place, of course – only fit for a semi-attached couple – what, what?' She roared with laughter, and the Indian joined in, going:

'Oh, very funny, *missi-sahib*, you very funny lady, oh my goodness, yes. Ha ha ha.'

'Anyway,' said the lady, 'you go up there, boy, and ask. And now,' she said to the Indian, 'as for you, you lump of lazarooshian leather, you, I'm going to curry you and flay you, do you understand?'

'Aha, you very funny, *missi-sahib*.' And then: 'Ow, ow, you not do that, oh my goodness, please not,' as he ran ahead, though the whip always kept missing him.

Edgar obeyed her instruction, and climbed up a little hill at the top of which were two houses attached to each other – which raised the question of which door to knock at. Edgar chose the first one he came to at the top of the winding path up the hill. At once, to his terror, a very large snake opened it, apparently using its tail to manage the door handle. 'Yes?' it hissed. It wore an old-fashioned lady's bonnet. Edgar, trembling, wondered if this was the mother of the Blatant Beast, or perhaps the Blatant Beast itself. 'Yes? Yessssss?' it hissed again. 'Don't wassssste time, boy. Have you never ssseen a ssssssnake before?'

'Sorry, ma'am,' trembled Edgar. 'I was told that if I came here I would be told the way back to school and then home to tea, so I was told anyway.'

'All those tolds,' said the snake crossly. 'I know nothing about schools, boy. I never went to school. I didn't need to. I knew everything when I was born. And now I know more than everything, being older now than I was then.'

'Is it possible to know more than everything, ma'am?' Edgar asked boldly but politely.

'If it's possible to know less than nothing,' said the snake, frowning. 'And I should imagine you know less than nothing about, let me see, let me see, ah yes, about the gentleman who lives next door.'

'That's true, ma'am,' Edgar said, 'if nothing means the same as less than nothing.'

'No, it does not mean the ssssssame,' and the snake hissed angrily. 'Because, if you've been to school at all (and why aren't you at school now is what I could ask but won't), you'd know that minus one is less than nothing. And now, since we're on to numbers, give me the biggest number there is, because that would be about the same as everything.'

'It would take too long,' Edgar said. 'When I was a very little boy, I took a big exercise book to bed with me on a summer's evening, and I tried to write the last number of all. But I couldn't do it.'

'Of course you couldn't,' snapped the snake. 'Because even if you filled a million billion trillion quadrillion quintillion sextillion septillion octillion nonillion exercise books, you'd still be able to go on adding another digit. And I,' said the snake, 'I I I would be able to add one more. And one more. And one more. So, you see, I know more than everything. Good afternoon.' And she slammed the door shut with her head.

Edgar was not convinced by her argument, but he did not feel like banging on the door again to reopen it (the argument, that was, but it would also, of course, have meant the door as well), since he did not like the bad-tempered hissing and was a little put out by the idea of a big snake wearing a lady's bonnet and living in a house. What did it, or she, live *on*? He shuddered to think. He went to the house next door and banged there, and this time a rather pleasant-looking old gentleman opened up, dressed rather in the style of Shakespeare – doublet and hose and ruff – who said, smiling:

'Yes?'

'I was told to come here, sir,' Edgar said, 'to ask you how I can find my way home.'

'Come in, come in,' cried the old man, and he led the way along a dusty corridor full of maps and globes. 'I know all about getting to places.' Edgar followed him into a big room, just as dusty as the corridor, which, like the corridor, was full of maps and globes. 'It is my mission, so to speak, in life, so to say, and I'll soon, so to put it, put you right. I suppose,' he said, 'you've been next door?' He laughed loudly. 'They all go next door first, so to speak, and quite a shock it must be to meet Miss Lilith, as she calls herself. Eden Bower she calls her little house, a pretty name. I, for my part, so to express it, am called Richard Eden.'

'Is everything and everybody called Eden, then?' Edgar asked. 'Oh, my name is Edgar.'

'Edgar Edgar Edgar,' said the old man. 'Oh yes,' he said, 'so to say, everything is a bit edenified round here. Hence the name, you know, so to speak.' Then he began to fuss about among his ancient dusty maps, all of which looked to Edgar far too old to be of any use today, since they were all full of blank spaces called TERRA INCOGNITA, meaning *unknown land*, and this was true of a map of England even, which was all blank just north of London. There was a map of America on which it said HERE BE DRAGONS in the populous state of New Jersey.

'I want to get back to school and then home to tea,' Edgar said, looking for somewhere to sit down but finding only maps and globes, also still feeling very thirsty. Tea tea tea, he kept thinking. A nice cup of tea with milk and sugar. And some sweet biscuits. And a few buns. And thin bread and butter. And a pot of cherry jam.

'I should imagine you must be, so to speak, very thirsty. Perhaps very hungry also, so to express it,' said Mr Eden.

'I'd give anything, sir,' Edgar said. 'I'd even give more than anything' (thinking of the snake, Miss Lilith) 'for a nice cup of tea.'

'Tea?' almost screamed Mr Eden. 'Oh, you can't have tea. Far too expensive. Why, there can't be more than a half-ounce in the whole country, so to put it, and I should imagine that Her Majesty the Queen, may she live for ever, so to speak, has gotten hold of it. Eats it she does, mixed with a little salt, so to express it, and nobody is allowed to tell her that that's not the way.' He shook his head sadly and humorously and then let out a great shout, swivelling round to a square-shaped hole in the wall, about the size of a rather small picture. 'Maria!' he yelled. 'Maria, Maria, to express it briefly and sharply and punctiliously!' Then he winked at Edgar.

'Yes, sorr, yer honour,' came a little voice from the hole. 'What is it you'd be wanting at all at all, and me in the middle of me castle rackrent?'

'Fancies herself, you know, so to speak,' said Mr Eden. 'Been to America as a pioneer, as she termed it, and met up with Edgar Huntly.' He looked very closely at Edgar and said: 'You're not the gentleman by any chance now, are you? No, no, you're too young, so to express it, and you haven't pion ears. Well, it stands to reason she couldn't have been where she says she's been – California and the Wild West and so on – because those aren't marked on the map yet. See, so to speak.' And, indeed, beyond a bit of the north-east coast, there wasn't much of America on any of his maps.

'Maria!' called Mr Eden again. 'Fetch something to eat and drink for this young gentleman here, so to speak.'

'Oh sorr,' returned the voice, 'I'm right in the middle of me Frank and me Harry and Lucy. But I'll come right enough and I'll bring what's fitting to be brought for the likes of him, whoever he happens to be, bless us and save us.'

'Good, so to utter it,' called Mr Eden. 'Now then, I think your best way home, which, so to word it accurately, is your immediate and ultimate concern, is to go by way of Newfoundland and the West Indies. Yes yes yes.' And, totally absorbed, he began to measure distances on a big globe with a dusty pair of protractors. While he was doing this a very large mouse came out of the hole in the wall, saying:

'Ah sorr, the pity of it, but there's nothing in the house at all at all but maps and globes, which is well and good for a nibble for the likes of us, sorr, but not what would be giving the nourishment as a young spalpeen like himself now would be requiring at all at all.' The mouse had very busy whiskers and a little skirt on.

'Oh well then,' Mr Eden said, 'I can't oblige you so to speak except with a song, but perhaps a song will cure the thirst, so to put it, and Maria here will join in the chorus.'

'But I'm in the middle of me moral tales and me belindas, sorr,' said the mouse, in a voice that was not at all squeaky.

'You do as I say, Maria,' said Mr Eden in a gruff voice, 'and don't be giving yourself airs, so to speak, about your pioneering days in places that don't exist yet.' And then under his breath he muttered: 'Edgar Huntly, indeed, so to speak.' Then he raised his voice, which was already very high and wavery, and sang this song:

> You can drink the waters of all of the seas
> If you take out the saltiness first,
> For salt's very good with a piece of cheese
> Or to season celery, beans and peas,
> And anything else that your palate may please,
> But it will not slake your thirst.

There was a silence then, and Mr Eden said: 'Come on, Maria, join in the chorus,' but the mouse said:

'Ah, sure now, sorr, me heart gets near to breaking when I think of cheese.'

'Never mind about the cheese. The chorus, Maria, so to speak.' Then they both sang:

> Salt is nice to melt the ice
> But it will not melt your thirst.

Mr Eden sang again solo:

> I have drunk of the waters of all the seas,
> Till my stomach was fit to burst.
> I've been to the north where the oceans freeze
> And the south where the porpoise sits at his ease
> And the east where the spice-trees bless the breeze,
> But I've always found (and believe me, please)
> That it will not slake your thirst.

Then the chorus, while Edgar grew thirstier and thirstier:

> Salt is the thing of which I sing,
> And it will not cure your thirst.

Both Mr Eden and the mouse Maria seemed to expect applause, so Edgar gave it to them. Whereupon Mr Eden bowed in a very old-fashioned way and said: 'I think Edenborough is the place for him, don't you, Maria?'

'Oh sure now, sorr, and ye took the words straight out of me mouth. That's the place for him now, to be sure it is, don't be talking.'

'And how do I get there, sir?' asked Edgar.

Mr Eden seemed rather embarrassed at that. He said: 'Well, I've not been there myself, of course, so to express myself, not having the time with all the work here, so to speak, and to tell you the truth I can't find it on any of the maps. But Maria here says it exists, so to put it.'

'Oh sure, sorr, it does, and 'tis as foine a place as ever stood upon two legs.'

'Four legs you said, so to speak,' frowned Mr Eden.

'Two and four – sure they're the same thing,' said Maria.

'Ah, no, they're not, as I've repeatedly told you, so to say,' said Mr Eden, growing darker.

'Well now, sorr, that all depends which way you look at it.'

'Oh no, it doesn't if I may so express it.'

'You'll forgive the observation, sorr, but it does.'

Edgar could see that a boring argument was about to begin, so he took his leave, bowing politely first to both man and mouse and saying 'I am very grateful for all your help' – words which were ignored. Mr Eden and his maid were now throwing dusty maps at each other, and Maria, despite her comparative smallness, was doing very well. The room was full of dust.

Edgar climbed down the hill and saw, in a cloud of outdoor dust this time, a man on a horse in fine armour, a kingly crown on his head, leading a little army that was coughing with the dust. '*Avant, mes amis,*' cried the man on horseback, whom Edgar took to be a French king. '*Moi*, Henry the Fourth of France, am going to fight *lui*, Louis the Fourteenth of France. How dare he do what he's done. *Avant, à la victoire.*' Edgar, who was now down on the road, said to a very small soldier, who was coughing bitterly with the dust that was being raised:

'What's he done then?'

'*Moi,*' said the soldier, '*je ne parle pas français.*'

'But it was English I spoke,' Edgar said.

'Oh, so it was,' laugh-coughed the little soldier. 'I get so mixed up these days, what with fighting for the Germans one day and the Belgians the next, and the Spaniards, as it might be, over the week-end, that I don't know where I am. What was it you said?'

'What's the war all about?'

'*Ich verstehe kein deutsch.*'

'But it was English I was speaking.'

'So it was, so it was. Well, it doesn't do to know what a war's all about, for you might not be inclined to fight it, and if you don't fight wars, where's your bread and butter going to come from, eh? Not to mention a nice pint mug full of very milky tea with sugar in it.'

'I'd give anything for that,' said Edgar.

'I'm sure you would,' said the soldier, 'but where we're going it will most likely be wine.'

'Stop talking in the ranks there!' A sergeant with a great bristling moustache, his uniform all covered in dust, began pushing at the small soldier and then pushing at Edgar. 'You, boy, where's your drum? You should be out at the front there, just a few paces ahead of His Sacred Majesty's steed, beating away for dear life and keeping the men in step.'

'But I'm not in your army,' Edgar said. 'And I'll thank you not to push at me like that.'

'Shall I push you some other way, then?' barked the sergeant. 'Because I can, boy, oh yes, I can. Go on, then – out of it, if you've no stomach for fighting a just war. Sing,' he then cried. 'Sing, you underbred lumps of bone-idolatry, and keep your cowardly hearts up.' At once all the soldiers began to sing, His Sacred Majesty included, though some coughed too much with the dust to make a really musical effort of it all:

> Liberty of conscience,
> That's what we require:
> No banging us with truncheons
> And roasting on the fire.
>
> We'll go to church when we wish
> Or not, if we desire,
> And Friday's not for fish
> But steaks fried on the fire.

Edgar watched them march out of sight in a vast cloud of dust, and he himself took the road in the opposite direction, for he felt sure that they could not be marching to Edenborough. Edenborough, he was sure, was not ruled over by King Louis the Fourteenth of France. He was fairly sure, anyway.

3. *The Road to Edenborough*

It was a long long walk to Edenborough and Edgar saw very little
to admire on the way. On one side were fields with cows in them,
and on the other was a stream, parallel to the road, which was full
of jumping fish. The cows had been taught to sing. Edgar wondered
who had bothered to waste so much time in teaching them, especially as their songs were not very melodious. Their chief song was
one that is called *My Country 'Tis Of Thee* if you are American and
God Save The Queen (or *King*, if there happens to be a king on the
throne: we have, as I tell Edgar's story, a Queen – God bless her –
radiant in beauty and brilliant in brain: Her Majesty – God bless her
and save her – Edith the First, with – may she live for ever – a neck
so long and white – heaven preserve it – that she is called sometimes
– in total and seemly and loyal reverence – Edith Swan Neck) if you
are British. The cows could not, of course, manage the words of
either version, but they dealt with the tune by each taking one note
only. So one cow would bellow the first note, then repeat it (the
first and second notes being the same), then there would be a long
pause while another cow slowly came to the realization that it was
its turn to sing, and then it would bellow out the third note. It
would thus take about three minutes to cover 'My coun tree' (or
'God save our'), and this made the whole procedure very boring.
But it gave the cows something to do besides munch grass and make
milk, so perhaps it was not all really a waste of time. They had,
apparently, another song, much more difficult, and this was *Pop
Goes The Weasel*. They made it sound like a funeral march for
marchers without legs.

The fish in the stream on Edgar's right were much more lively.
They were jumping for flies, all of which they knew by name, but
they never succeeded in catching any. They were quite cheerful
about it, and Edgar heard them chirping: 'There goes Frank

Jeffrey – missed him again' and 'Harry Brougham always gives me the slip' and 'Sid Smith is too quick for me, bless him.' One old fish, whose jumping was rather painful and awkward, as though he had fishy rheumatics, kept grumbling: 'Bring the constable to them. Bash them with a truncheon,' but none of the other fishes took any notice. They were very pretty fish, silvery with gold-spotted heads, and some of them greeted Edgar with courtesy: 'Travelling with legs, I see, on dry land too. Get wise, my boy, to the truth of the matter. It's all in the water.' Edgar waved to them, smiling with a very dry mouth, but soon forgot them, and the cows too, when he came to a little stall by the side of the road which seemed to have bottled drinks for sale.

This stall, which was protected from the sun by a huge rainbow umbrella, had a flag flying from it which announced: 'SLAKE YOUR ARID THROTTLE WITH EDWIN'S BRISK AND BUBBLING BEVERAGES.' When Edgar came up to it, he found the drink-seller himself laid out at length on the counter of his stall, snoring away. He was, Edgar saw with interest, a large spotted dog with trousers of hideous cut, whose long snout twitched irritably in his sleep. Edgar took advantage of this unconsciousness not (heaven forbid!) to steal but to examine. None of the bottled drinks, which were very cold to the touch despite the hot sun and the lack of ice, were familiar to him. Bishopberry crush, absentee ale, rossettiade, jimandjack juice – he had never met any of them before. He was handling a delightfully chill bottle of Sir Walter Scott's Ineffable And In No Wise To Be Imitated Scotch Soda when he heard a growl: 'Caught you at it, have I, grrrrr?'

'I wasn't stealing, I was looking,' said Edgar. The dog still lay there, frowning and growling, presumably believing that the growl would be enough to frighten Edgar off. 'I'd like to drink something if I may. I'm terribly thirsty.'

'How much money have you got, grrrrr?'

Edgar took out his tiny coin, which he had difficulty in sorting out from the indiarubber and bits of chalk and string and bread-crumbs and ants' eggs in his pocket. 'This,' he said at last. 'One vathek.'

The dog let out a loud laughgrowl: 'Hahahagrrrrrrhahagrrrrrahaha. That won't take you very far with me, His Majesty King Edwin, grrrrr. In Northumberland, where I come from, we make very short work grrrrr of folk armed with grrrrr vatheks. So put it down on the counter near my left back paw grrrrr and help yourself to a tiny bottle of Edom O'Gordon's danishberry jumpjuice grrrrr. It has a face on the grrrrr label.' Edgar did as he was told with the coin and then searched for the bottle in question. He had great difficulty in finding it but, at last, from among the shining phalanx of strange drinks, a voice came, saying: 'Looking for me, is that it?' Edgar put out his hand, squinting for the source of the voice, while the voice said: 'You're hot, you're hot, now you're cold, now you're very cold, now you're freezing, now you're among the Eskimos, now you're on the North Pole, ah, better, better, ah, now you're on the equator, got me, got me, ah.'

The bottle was indeed a tiny one, and Edgar could hardly see the face on the label, which seemed to be of a jolly man with a black beard – much much smaller than the head of Queen Edith (God bless her) on a doll's house postage stamp. But the voice was fruity and clear. 'Get me down, boy. Go on. Do you the world of good, or bad, depending on how you are.' It seemed a very little portion of drink to cure a thirst, and Edgar did not like the use of the word *bad*. Nevertheless he pulled out the tiny cork between his teeth and promptly swallowed it (it was much too tiny to make him choke). Then he sucked in the tiny drop of drink. It was hard to say what it tasted like, but it was as if very very cold ice had been flavoured with currants, raisins, candied peel, chocolate, vanilla, nutmeg and a cut off an over-roasted joint of roast pork. At once Edgar felt a great deal less thirsty. The face on the label became still and silent, but the dog who called himself King Edwin of Northumberland and who had been watching all this time and growling gently to himself, suddenly let out a great bark.

'What's that for?' asked Edgar. 'Did I do something wrong?'

'Bow wow wow,' or something like it, went King Edwin. 'I said you were to help yourself to it, not to drink it.'

'But it means the same thing. If you ask somebody to help himself to slice of cake, it means eat it. Besides, you didn't tell me to stop when I started drinking.'

'That, bow wow, was to see the badness of you to the limit, which I knew was there. We'd make short work of you in Northumberland, I can tell you. Well now, helping yourself to a piece of cake means eating it, not drinking it. And you drank that stuff up, bow wow, grrrrr.'

'Wrong,' Edgar protested. 'Helping yourself to a book from a shelf doesn't mean eating it, either.'

'How do you know, boy, bow wow? In Northumberland where I was a king, they used to *devour* books. I know, because I devoured many myself, grrrrr. But all this is not the point.'

'You mean,' said Edgar, growing annoyed, 'I should have *eaten* that bottle, not drunk it? But that's ridiculous.'

'*I'll* tell you what's ridiculous and what isn't, me being grrrrr King Edwin. Now do what I say, boy, bow grrrrr wow.'

'You mean *eat* the bottle?' shouted Edgar.

'No no no no no, bow wow wow grrrrr. *Read it.*'

Edgar shrugged: this was certainly a *mad* dog. He was just going to say that there was nothing to read on the label except a tiny blackbearded face, but he saw that there was no point in arguing with a mad dog who thought he was King Edwin of Northumberland. So he looked down at the label and, not really to his surprise, found a poem there – written in beautifully clear handwriting and very easy to read. He read it aloud, and the dog gave a kind of purring growl, as though he had cats in his ancestry, which seemed to show that he liked to be read aloud to:

> Thomas Alva Edison,
> His blood a mix of Scotch and Dutch,
> Was dead in 1931,
> But he had lived both long and much.
>
> His years of life were 84
> And his inventions manifold.
> He knew what telephones were for
> Before the Graham Bell had tolled.
>
> When he was in his 30th year,
> Though many folk were prone to laugh,
> He startled many a serious ear
> By building the 1st phonograph.

> When he had just gone 32,
> He showed the true inventive stamp
> By making something brightly new –
> The electric incandescent lamp.

> When photographs had just come hither,
> Old T.A.E. went *Ha ha ha*,
> And made those stillies movies with a
> Kinetoscopic camera.

'An interesting man, that,' said King Edwin, 'grrrrrprrrrr. If we'd had him in Northumberland, there's no knowing what wonders he might have performed. So now then, boy, grrrr, go on your way to my great city of Edenborough.'

'Yours?' said Edgar.

'Yes, yes, grrrrr yes, they named if after me. It's Edwingrrrrr, really, though, but they made a mistake when they wrote it down. I didn't correct it, of course, for it was a very cold day, and everybody that came up up to me was saying, "Edwin, brrrrr," so that was all right.' The dog fell asleep again, snoring loudly, so Edgar, somewhat refreshed, continued his journey.

He still had several miles (or kilometres – more kilometres than miles, of course) to go before he got there. At one point he came to a big notice swinging high over the road, secured to two pillars that woodpeckers were happily pecking away at, which said: 'SEVERAL MILES TO EDENBOROUGH. SEVERAL X 1·609 KILOMETRES TO THE SAME. BUT IT WILL BE WORTH IT!' He was very lucky to be offered a lift by a sort of van that stopped just in front of him in a fog of dust, hooting away on horns that played a little tune. When the dust-fog cleared, Edgar was able to see that written all along the van was the legend THE EDENBOROUGH REVUE. He ran to it, the driver already had the door open, and he entered, saying thank you with real gratitude, to find that the interior part of the van was filled with little men who greeted him cheerfully. When Edgar had found a seat – he had to remove a wooden box labelled *Best Finnan Haddie* and a heavy tabby cat that was guarding it – these little men were very eager to explain who they were and what the Edenborough Revue was. They, they said, *were* the Edenborough Revue. They sang and danced and told jokes and acted sketches, and one of them, who said his name was Tommy Carlyle, did impersonations. He was a sad little man who rolled his r's a great deal and kept saying: 'Aye, aye, och, weel, that's the way o' it.'

'What kind of impersonations?' Edgar wanted to know.

'Och, weel, aye – here's one o' King Edward the First o' England.' (While he was saying that, Edgar thought: oh no, back to all those boring Anglo-Saxon kings, but then he remembered that Edward the First was *not* Anglo-Saxon.) Tommy Carlyle composed his sad face into a look of haughty majesty. Then he said: 'And the noo – King Edward the Second.' He made the same face as before. 'And the noo,' he said: '– King Edward the Third.' It was still the same haughtily majestic face.

Edgar said: 'Is that all you do – the King Edwards of England?'

'Och,' said Tommy Carlyle, 'there's an awfu' lot o' them. Nine to ma computation.'

'Eight, surely,' said Edgar. 'Edward the Eighth was the last one. He ruled less than a year. Since then it's been – oh, certainly no more Edwards.'

'Och, ye wee sleekit cowerin' beastie,' said Tommy Carlyle. 'There is unco' little ye ken aboot it and that's a fac'. Edward the Ninth – aye, there was a monarch for ye, Sassenach though he was.' And he composed his sad face into a look of haughty majesty. The rest of the troupe clapped vigorously, so Edgar joined in against his will, and Tommy Carlyle made a sad bow.

'Nobody like Tommy,' said a man who called himself Mr Gladstone and nursed a heavy bag on his knee. 'He always brings the house down in Edenborough.'

'What do *you* do, sir?' asked Edgar.

'Play the piano on the black notes, me,' winked Mr Gladstone. 'And old Tom Macaulay over there – he plays the piano on the white notes.'

The man referred to, who was smoking a big pipe that smelt of burning paper, nodded and nodded to show this was true.

'At the same time?' Edgar asked.

'Well, yes,' Mr Gladstone said. 'We get a bit tangled up, of course, sometimes. But if you've got all those black and white keys it stands to reason they all have to be played, otherwise there's no point in paying for them. That's right, Tom, isn't it?'

'Right, Bill, right.' And Mr Macaulay nodded. A piece of burning paper fell from his pipe on to the cat, which took no notice at all as it soon went out (the burning paper, not the cat).

'But it must sound – well, pretty awful,' said Edgar.

Mr Gladstone smiled. 'That's what they all say,' he said. 'Which shows they don't know much about it. Uneducated, that's their trouble. Right, Tom?'

'Right, Bill, right.'

'You have to be brought up to it,' said Mr Gladstone. Then he took a newspaper out of his pocket and began to read the front page with close and frowning attention. The newspaper seemed to be at least a hundred years old. A man who looked nearly as old and bent and stiff but who said he was a dancer (and that his name was Sir J. Stephen) now said:

'Not read it yet, Bill? You've been on that same page to my certain knowledge for the last fifty-five – no, I'm telling a lie – the last fifty-six point five five five recurring years.' Mr Gladstone said very sternly:

'There's almost more than meets the eye, that's why you have to read with very close attention. Right, Tom?'

'Right, Bill, right.'

'For instance, it says here: BANK ROBBERS GET AWAY WITH FIFTEEN THOUSAND POUNDS. Now I've been thinking of the true meaning of that for something like –'

'Fifty-six point five five five recurring years,' said Sir J. Stephen.

'Very well. And I think it really means that they got away with fifteen months – that being their prison sentence, you know.'

'You mean,' said Edgar,' that *thousand pounds* is a kind of code for *months*?'

'It could be,' said Mr Gladstone gravely. 'You have to look very deep into it. They always say that time is money. Right, Tom?'

'Right, Bill, right.'

'It would mean,' said Edgar, working it swiftly out in his head, 'five hundred pounds a day in September, April, June and November.'

'Well, there you are then,' said Mr Gladstone in triumph. 'And with twenty-five hours a day – which is what I want, and what I'm determined to get in the next parliament – that would mean – well, you work it out, boy.'

'Twenty pounds an hour,' said Edgar immediately.

'And not bad pay either,' said a man in clown's costume called Art Stanley. 'Better than what *we* get.' Then he looked sternly from his painted face out of the window, and Edgar looked too. There was a view of mountains and a beautiful big lake shining in the sun, and there seemed to be men dancing about on its nearest shore. 'There they are, then,' said Art Stanley. 'We'd better get out to 'em.' The rest of the troupe sighed and nodded. Mr Gladstone said to the driver:

'We'll have to get out, Matthew, and bang them about a bit.' The driver, a man with pencils and pens behind both ears, nodded sadly and braked the van by the side of the road. Edgar said:

'Who? Why?'

'Poets,' said Mr Macaulay, blowing burning paper from his pipe. 'Could never abide this lot. But you have to creep up on them slowly.'

Edgar sighed and asked no more questions. Instead, he got out with the others, who kept whispering 'Shhhhh' very loudly to each other and began to crawl feebly through the long grass. Tommy Carlyle started to sneeze.

'Shhhhhh. SHHHHHHHHHHHH!'

'Ah canna help it, mon. It's the hay feverrrr. Arch WHOOOOO!'

There were about a dozen of these men dancing about by the lake, all rather thin and tall except for one, who was fat and panted a lot and said:

'What's the summmmject or ommmmject of the exercise?'

'Listen now,' said a thin man with a mad look and a lot of teeth. 'It's to get the inspiration working. Inspiration means breathing, you see, and now we're all breathing really hard.' Then he began to recite:

> A daffodil's a little flower
> That gets its money by the hour.

> It blues the money, more or less,
> And buys itself a yellow dress.
>
> It flounces and is very vain
> But does not mind a drop of rain
> Or e'en when typhoons tear the county,
> Since it is all from Nature's bounty.

Tommy Carlyle, lying in the grass trying to control his sneezing, gave out a loud baying sound, like a dog that howls at the moon, and cried: 'Och, the blitherin' blatherskite. Och, the sheer horror o' it.' Mr Gladstone nodded resignedly at the others, and then called: 'Forward the Light Brigade!'

What Edgar saw then was not very edifying. The members of the Edenborough Revue leapt rather feebly on the poets and tried to throw them into the lake. But the fat poet who had talked of summmmjects and ommmmjects raised his hands into the air and said: 'Magic. Poetry is magic. Both the summmmject and the ommmmject.' And he recited, while the thinner poets were being put into the lake and then coming out again to put the Edenborough Revue into it:

> A weasel plonked a large guitar
> Upon the coast of Barbary
> Where all the deadly lemmings are
> And wisdom is a foul cigar
> Smoked by Sir Hubert Laurelee,
> And bayed her blessings to the sun
> And croaked a creaking malison
> Upon a sole belated star,
> And when the dreadful day was done
> She dove into the burning sea
> And there, for all I know of it,
> Her song, suffused with dreadful glee,
> May soothe the biter and the bit
> And lead the traveller home to tea.

Even Edgar, who thought the whole thing was nonsense, was affected by that last line, but the effect on Tommy Carlyle was quite remarkable. 'Och aye,' he said, nodding, 'ma bonny wee laddies, it's no' sae bad, ye ken. Aye, therrre's a cerrrtain quality aboot it, ye maun admit.' The poets took advantage of his momentary admiration to grab hold of him and throw him into the lake, but he still nodded sitting in the water with fish leaping out of his very loose collar, saying: 'Och aye, there's nae gainsayin' it the noo.' But the rest of the Edenborough Revue troupe grew very angry and began to grab the poets by the hair and throw them in to join Tommy Carlyle. The fat poet was the first to hit the water in this renewed assault, and he lay there crying:

'Now I understand. *His floating hair.* I always wondered what it meant when I wrote it, but now I know.'

Edgar, disgusted by the whole unseemly business, went back to the van, where the driver sat gloomily at the wheel. The cat was sleeping peacefully in the back but it woke rather angrily when Edgar appeared and said, cattily: 'If you've come to steal the finnan haddie you've another think coming, my boyo. I'll scratch you with vigour, also with my claws, so watch out.' Then it went to sleep again and the driver said:

'Always the same. Always always always. I've a good mind to get out of this job altogether and go back to what I was before.'

'And what was that?' asked Edgar politely.

'You see,' the driver said, ignoring the question, 'they've carried that case of finnan haddie about for longer than I can't remember. Now why they don't open it up and eat it is more than what I can't understand. I likes nothing better than some nice poached haddock with a couple of poached eggs on top. But it's my private opinion – and I'd ask you not to noise it abroad overmuch – that they keeps it there just to give the cat something to do. Protect it, you know. Ridiculous.'

'And what was the job you did before?' Edgar asked patiently.

'I used to go round the schools,' sighed the driver. 'Seeing that everybody was teaching proper and that the kids was being taught proper, as you might say. But they wouldn't take no notice of it when I put them right. You'd not hardly credit some of the things the kids was taught.'

'What, for instance?' asked Edgar.

'Well, that William Shakepaw did not write *The Dog of Venice*, for instance. Nor wrote *Mud, Simmer Knight's Cream.* Now this

Knight's Cream was very good, obtainable from the best of dairies, and it had to be simmered to taste proper, and Mud did it as well as any.'

'What sort of mud?' asked Edgar.

The driver sneered. 'There was only one Mud that I never knew of,' he said, 'and that was Albert Mud, a real good cook and the slowest simmerer ever you seen.'

'Look,' Edgar said. 'I think I'll get out and walk, if you don't mind.' For he was really growing very tired of all this stupidity. He would really even have preferred to be yawning in the classroom and hearing about the horrible Anglo-Saxon kings.

'Please yourself,' said the driver huffily. 'It's nearly done, all that flapdoodle out there by the waters. In here they'll be directly, spilling wet over everything. Then we can be on us way. Another thing they said he didn't write was *Hall's Well That End? – Swell*. That was a lovely thing. An American gentleman comes to this country looking for Sir Peregrine Hall, that being the man's name. When he gets near where he is they says to him that Hall's well's over there, and this American gentleman says that's fine and goes over to it.'

'Is that the whole story?' asked Edgar, fascinated despite his disgust.

'Why,' laughed the driver, as though amazed at Edgar's stupidity, 'would you want more? The whole story runs to near twelve hundred pages. There's what happens on the way, see, and what happens afterwards. But if you're like all the others, you'd best get out of my van and make your own way alone.'

'That's right,' said the cat from its sleep. 'I don't care much for thieves sitting around.'

So Edgar got out, just in time to see the Edenborough Revue troupe coming out of the water and the poets dancing about further away than they had been before. The troupe were all very wet, and Edgar did not much like the idea of having to sit with them. So he hurried off down the road, hoping he would reach Edenborough soon. He wanted to get home in time for tea.

4. Also the Road to Edenborough

Poor Edgar! It was taking him such a long time to get to Edenborough. Poor you too, for that matter: I'm sure your anxiety to get there must be quite as great as his. But if you only knew (and you will know all too soon) what was waiting for Edgar in Edenborough, you would be as happy as I am to put off his arrival there.

What happened to Edgar now was that he was intrigued by some curious-looking blue flowers growing in a cluster by the side of the road (the left side, if you want to know). These flowers seemed to be chattering at a great rate in very high-pitched English, and Edgar had to get very close in order to hear what they were saying. Also, of course, he wished to see where the sounds were coming from, for flowers, although they can sometimes look like faces, have no mouths. The sounds themselves didn't make a great deal of sense to Edgar, and he wondered why flowers should be so excited and talkative about this kind of thing:

'. . . It was King Nidhud told him to do it. He had to put the apple on his own poor son's head and then shoot an arrow at it. Egil – that was his name.'

'You're thinking of William Tell, stupid.'

'Egil. Egil. That was his name. He was the brother of Wayland Smith. You ask Mr Honeythunder. Or Mr Grewgious. They'll tell you all about it.'

Edgar moved closer and closer and then, to his shock and horror, found the ground giving way beneath him. What he had done, of course, was to tread on some grass that covered a deep ditch. Down into this ditch he went: it was a dry ditch, that was one blessing, but it was impossible for him to climb out. The sides of the ditch were of smooth clay, and he could not find a hand-hold anywhere. So he did the only thing he could do, and that was to shout for help. 'Help! Help!' he cried. The flowers did not seem to hear him.

'. . . The question is whether we have free will or it's all worked out ahead for us: You ought to read Jonathan Edwards, missionary to the Red Indians.'

'. . . Boxing is what I like, though we don't see enough of it here. The gentle art of pugilism is what it's called.'

'. . . Egil nothing. It's William Tell you're thinking of. A Swiss he was.'

Edgar was very irritated with the flowers. Luckily he was not hurt, only a little bruised, and the bottom of the ditch was mossy. But he did not want to stay there for ever, so he kept on calling 'Help! Help!'

'. . . You take Philip the Duke of Orleans, for example. Gave himself a new name – Equality, a silly sort of name – but he had his head chopped off just the same.'

'You ought to make a little poem of that. Equality – that was his name. But they cut his loaf off just the same.'

'I said nothing about a loaf, stupid.'

Edgar still went on calling for help and was still ignored by the flowers, but soon he found something heavy sitting on his chest. He could not see very clearly in the dim light of the deep ditch, but he felt sure that it was a big tortoise sitting there. He put up his hand to confirm this, and sure enough there was a great tough shell and a wrinkled lizard head peering from beneath it. The tortoise said:

'Would you like me to go for help?'

'Oh yes please,' Edgar said, but then he reflected that it would take a tortoise a very long time to go for anything. His doubt must have conveyed itself to the tortoise, which now said:

'Think I'll be too slow, is that it? Don't you believe it. From here to Edenborough is less than a mile, and I reckon I could easily be there and back by, say, the Christmas after next. That's not too bad for speed, the way I see it.'

Edgar groaned. He said: 'I don't have all that much time. I'd starve to death, lying here and waiting.'

'Ah, that's because you have a wrong sense of time. You don't live long enough, that's your trouble. Now we tortoises think nothing of living a hundred years. Like parrots, you know. Not that I think much of parrots. They can't really talk, they just imitate. *Pretty Polly* and all that nonsense. *Scratch Polly's head arrrrrrrgh.* Ridiculous.'

'Well,' Edgar sighed, 'if you're going for help perhaps you'd better go now.'

'No need to take that attitude. Plenty of a time for a bit of a chat and a few reminiscences of a long long life. Did I ever tell you about the second King of Rome — Numa his name was? His wife was a kind of a fountain called Egeria.'

'No,' Edgar said patiently, 'you never told me. We haven't met before. And I really do look forward to your telling me, but not now. Please, not now. What I want is to get out of here.'

Before the tortoise could say something offended in reply, Edgar to his joy heard human voices up there on the road. A lady spoke first:

'Oh, Willoughby, Willoughby, how clever those flowers are. Listen to them talking away.' Then a bored and haughty man's voice replied:

'Fiddlesticks, my dear Laetitia. What they're saying is hardly worth listening to. Not a single original thought in a cart-load of fallen petals.'

'Help? Help!' called Edgar. 'I've fallen into the ditch!'

'Now that,' said the man's voice, 'is just lying stupidity. Flowers don't fall into ditches. Or if they do they don't raise a big noise about it. It's a common hazard of flowers, I should say, to fall into ditches.'

The tortoise said: 'A fat lot he knows about anything,' and the lady said: 'Oh, dear Willoughby, you're *so* right.'

'I'm never wrong, my dear Laetitia,' replied the man, and Edgar called: 'Help! Help! It's a boy that's fallen in. My name is Edgar. Help, please help!'

'Ah,' came the man's voice, 'a boy, eh? I don't care much for boys. Not reverent enough. No appreciation of their betters. Best let him stew in his own juice.'

'Oh, Willoughby, no! That would be too cruel!'

'Think so, eh? Very well. Let's have young Crossjay over here.'

And he called: 'Crossjay, let us be having you.' Then he said: 'What I said was hardly apposite, my dear Laetitia. Stew in his own juice no, one can hardly say that. Rot in his own ditch – that's better, eh, eh?'

But now Edgar saw a jolly young round face peering down at him. This was Crossjay, Edgar supposed. 'Ah,' smiled Crossjay, as Edgar supposed him to be, 'got a tortoise on you. That's good, that's very good. Fond of tortoises I am meself. What's your name, old fellow?'

'Edgar,' Edgar replied.

'No, no, I meant the tortoise. Oh, offended, is it?' For the tortoise was now crawling away. It said to Edgar:

'Can't stand familiarity. I'm old enough to be that boy's great great grandfather. Well, I'll see you sometime, I suppose. Glad to have been of service.' And off it went.

'Give me your hands,' said Crossjay to Edgar. 'Old Durdles has got hold of my ankles.' And so Edgar was yanked up. He was very glad to see the light of day again and feel the road under his feet. The man called Durdles was very old and bald and seemed to be covered with stone-dust. He said to Edgar:

'Everyone to his taste, I suppose. But if it's lying in earth you wish to be, I have some very nice graves new-dug over in the church-yard, and I'll do you a lovely headstone for next to nothing. With cherubs on it too.'

The lady called Laetitia was tall and thin, but the man called Willoughby was even thinner and taller and he had what looked like a perpetual sneer on his face. 'Before we go any further,' he said haughtily to Edgar, 'I would have you know that I am to be addressed as *Sir* Willoughby.' He had a very tall grey hat on.

'Well,' Edgar said, 'grateful as I am for your help, I don't think the occasion for my calling you anything is likely to be much prolonged. For I must hurry on to Edenborough. Let me then reiterate my gratitude and take my leave.'

'Oh,' said Laetitia, 'he speaks so like a gentleman. You must try your poem out on him, Willoughby.' And it seemed to Edgar that she was rather proud of not having to call him *Sir* Willoughby. That she was not his wife Edgar had no doubt. Her clothes were very poor and full of mended tears, whereas he was dressed like a dandy. Sir Willoughby said, in a bored voice:

'Oh, very well. It is up to the already enlightened to spread the light, I suppose. Eh? I think that's rather good, eh, eh, what?' All this time Crossjay was peeling an apple he had taken from his pocket, using a very blunt knife and grumbling softly in a good-humoured way. 'Here it is, then,' said Sir Willoughby, and he struck a dignified posture like an actor:

> I used to know two Eliots,
>> Both good with words and stops and commas.
> They started writing in their cots:
>> The first was George, the other Thomas.
>
> Now one of them, despite the name,
>> A woman was, and not a man.
> But which was which? – A crying shame,
>> I do not know. For though I can
>
> Distinguish between types of wine
>> And playing-cards (all fifty-two)
> And weather foul and weather fine
>> And faces in a boat-race crew,
>
> Orang-utan and marmoset
>> And cherry pie and apple tart,
> Alas alack I never yet
>> Could tell the Eliots apart.

Before the lady called Laetitia could clap her hands and say how wonderful it was or Edgar could murmur something politely admiring, Sir Willoughby held up his right hand sternly and said:

'You must understand that I really do know which was which, but the sensible thing to do now and then is to pretend not to know everything. Otherwise people regard one as uppish. Hence,' he said, 'the poem.'

'Too many words,' grumbled Durdles. 'It'd be hard work getting all them words carved on a gravestone. Still, everyone to his taste, I suppose.'

'The point is,' repeated Sir Willoughby, 'that I really do know which was which. All that was poetic licence.'

'Done it at last!' cried little Crossjay, holding up his peeled

apple. 'Thought as how I should never get it done. Oh, well.' And
he threw the apple away into the long grass. He smiled at Edgar
and said: 'Can't stand the taste of 'em. It's the peeling of 'em I
really like.'

'Again thank you,' Edgar said. 'And now I really must be on my
way.' And he bowed in a very old-fashioned and courtly manner,
so that Laetitia giggled and said:

'Such a polite little boy.'

'I know which is which,' said Sir Willoughby loudly and crossly.

'So,' said Edgar, 'good day to one and all.'

'I've a little grave just right for you,' said Durdles. 'Won't be at
all right for you in six months' time, boys growing the way they
do, but now it would be fine. Come and see it.'

'I know, I do really know!'

'Of course you do, Willoughby dear.'

'Won't take a minute to view it,' Durdles said. Edgar began to
run. He ran and ran until he turned a corner. He could still hear
Sir Willoughby shouting crossly:

'I know, I know, I really do know!'

But soon he could hear nothing more, and all his attention was
taken up by the sight of the great city of Edenborough, which
stretched below him in the late afternoon sunlight. He stood on a
hill, and down there was a fine wooded valley with a silver river
running through it like a monstrous snake, and on the river, which
had many bridges, stood the city with its shining domes. 'Edenborough,' breathed Edgar to himself, and a little voice near him
repeated the name in tones of disgust. '*Edenborough*,' it said.
'Pah!' Edgar looked down to see a little grey man dressed all in
grey, leaning on a crooked stick. 'And what,' said the little man
frowning, 'might your name be, if, as seems more likely than not,
you have such? Come on, answer.'

'Edgar, and what's yours?'

'I'll give you three guesses,' said the little man. Edgar needed
only one. He said:

'Grey?'

'Depends on how you spell it. If you spell it with an *e*, no. With
and *a*, yes. Gray.'

'You seem,' said Edgar, 'to have a very low opinion of that great city spread all before us in the valley.'

'And so I have,' said Mr Gray. 'I wrote a poem about it once. Listen.'

Nearly everybody Edgar had met this day seemed to have a poem to recite; nevertheless, he hid his sigh and politely lent an ear. The little man recited, bitterly:

> On well-heeled feet and tartan-trousered legs,
>   They jeer and leer and sneer at all who come.
> They sift soft sugar over hard-boiled eggs,
>   They chew the crust and throw away the crumb.
> They season herrings with vanilla custard,
>   And groaningly they grind at ground-up gristle,
> They sup cold soup because they say they must. A d-
>   -ay goes hardly by without they whistle.

'Very difficult,' said Mr Gray, 'to find a rhyme for *custard*. Now here comes the important bit. Listen carefully –

> They hear loud music every time they feast,
>   They play a sort of game with bat and ball.
> They feed their children to the Blatant Beast
>   And to his dam, and do not care at all.'

'What is all that about a beast and a dam?' said Edgar, who could not hear very clearly, since Mr Gray had recited this last verse in a mumbling undertone.

'Dam? His mother, of course,' said Mr Gray. 'But you'll see soon enough. Now don't interrupt. I'm coming to the last verse, and that sums it all up. Listen –

> An old man's curse cast spavin on their hocks.
>   Soon they'll be glad to go into the dark.
> I'll find for each a cast-iron wooden box
>   And feed them to the turkeys in the park.'

He nodded direly and said: 'I don't think that's going too far at all. You'll see when you get there.' Then he hobbled off away from the town, leaning on his stick and muttering. Edgar, with joy and hope in his heart, made his way down the hill towards Edenborough. That poem was all a lot of nonsense.

ALAN BURNS

Alan Burns has written six novels: Buster *(1961)*, Europe After the Rain *(1965)*, Celebrations *(1967)*, Babel *(1969)*, Dreamerika *(1972)*, The Angry Brigade *(1973)*. *All were published by Calder & Boyars, except the last which was brought out simultaneously by Allison & Busby and Quartet. His play* Palach *was produced at the Open Space Theatre, directed by Charles Marowitz, and published in Penguin's in 'Open Space' plays. Alan Burns' non-fiction includes* To Deprave and Corrupt *(Davis-Poynter, 1972) and* The Imagination on Trial, *a study of the working methods of ten British novelists, scheduled for publication in December 1975. He held a writing fellowship at the University of East Anglia and was C. Day Lewis writing fellow at Woodberry Down School, London. Currently he is lecturer in creative writing at the Western Australian Institute of Technology.*

ESSAY

I cannot write a manifesto in the abstract, I can only define my ideas concretely in relation to my work.

I began writing short prose pieces in a rather pressured, affected style, trying to say something significant in each sentence. One piece was about digging a hole in the ground; one described a man rowing a boat. I started with something seen, then isolated and intensified it. The pieces were nearer to poetry than prose. Looking back I find them literary and a bit absurd. I remember writing in a lined exercise book in light blue Quink, a poem about a horse galloping across a stony beach. I'd seen the horse and the beach separately and put them together. I kept the poem for a long time. One verse described the horse like the sea 'breaking across the beach'.

I realized I could hang around for ever waiting for things to happen that would trigger off precious paragraphs. Then I saw a photograph in a shop window, of a man and woman kissing. It recalled the relationship between my mother and father and between them and me, which I had tried to define but had been defeated by its complexity. I solved the problem simply, by describing the photograph, the image. This was the key to my being able to write my first book, *Buster*. Using my memory intensely, I found I could review my life in pictures and describe them in sequence. At the same time I discovered I could lie. I had been held up by the need to tell the whole truth. Now I described the couple in the photo as if they were my parents although they weren't really. I could invent fiction.

The snapshot method worked best with the earliest memories when all I could see was a series of 'stills'. As I brought the story forward, nearer to the age I was, I remembered more and could tell a connected story. It was interesting the way the form changed, the narrative became more connected, as the boy in the book grew older.

The bit of *Buster* that led to my later work was a passage where the boy gets hold of an old typewriter and writes one word: Onion. He looks for the word most remote from 'onion' and hits on the word 'man'. Hoping to find total disconnection, he writes 'onion man'. The two words connect to make a phrase with meaning: a man who grows onions, or maybe sells or eats them. Thus at that early stage I was considering the question of connection and flirting with the notion of disconnection. In the next books I continued to see how far apart I could make succeeding images and yet connect them by ingenious or devious or extravagant or so-called surrealist means.

Disconnection fascinated me partly from an immature wish to shock, go to an extreme, make a break, an iconoclastic need to disrupt or cock a snook at the body of traditional literature. There was also the element of game, to set myself a puzzle, to stretch the two arms of a metaphor and still find a link between. The further I pushed the thing the more striking it became. I was also showing contempt for what I was doing, almost trying to write badly, from disgust with myself and with Literature which is not life but only marks on paper. Plus a political rejection of bourgeois art as a self-indulgence irrelevant to the struggle for social justice, which, by playing the bourgeois art game perpetuates a system based on exploitation and greed. Disconnection also expressed my own social estrangement, my distance from others, with the dual sense of superiority and yearning for closeness. Paradoxically, the act of wrenching images apart expressed a need to hold them close, like people. The couple kissing also made a connection in the sexual sense: I delighted in their closeness, envied it, wished to get away and leave them to it, desired to join in and be close to them.

My parents were separated by my mother's death. My elder brother and I were separated by his early death. The consuming nature of this experience showed itself not only in the disconnected form but also in the content of my work. *Europe After the Rain* is concerned with brutality and physical extremity but not with pain. Much physical damage is done but there is little emotional or psychological response to it. The characters seem numb. The climate of detachment reflected my own numbness in the face of two deaths. I had a particular delight and relief in writing that book, which derived from seeing that my most destructive fantasies could be transcended and used to make a book.

The story of *Europe After the Rain* was close to mine: a young man killed and a family broken, in a landscape of war and purposeless suffering. Yet I did not use introspective methods to gather the material. I came across it by chance. Three accidents happened: I saw the Max Ernst painting of the title, at the Tate. In a second-hand bookshop in Lyme Regis I found the verbatim record of the Nuremberg trials, and in another shop in Axminster I bought a journalist's report on life in Poland after the war. This last provided most of my background material. I had this badly written guidebook on my desk and I typed from it in a semi-trance. My eyes glazed and in the blur only the sharpest and strongest words, mainly nouns, emerged. I picked them out and wrote them down and made my own sense of them later. I dug up characters from that book though as a mere travelogue it hardly contained any. Perhaps some of *Europe After the Rain*'s 'numbness' derives from this distanced technique of writing from the unconscious. Painters often screw up their eyes when looking at a landscape so that in the blur they catch the essence.

In *Celebrations* I used other random methods, variations of the cut-up technique. Given this, I showed a strange consistency in my

B.T.W.—C

choice of characters. With no preconception or conscious decision I repeated my family pattern. Powerful father, absent mother, slaughtered son, surviving son, one woman: 'the woman about the house' as my mother was in our family of five. Whatever random techniques I used this pattern remained inescapable.

Celebrations grew from a mosaic of fragments written with no concern for ultimate plot connections. Delaying until the last minute any notion of what the book was about, I gradually assembled a series of heavy public rituals: marriages, funerals, wakes, steadily growing grander until they tipped over into absurdity. I got away from the bare, staccato style of war and found a full, baroque form to suit the content. I was disappointed that the book's reception was not what I had hoped, but pleased that my work was getting across to a slowly growing circle, notable among them John Calder, Bryan Johnson, Robert Nye and Angus Wilson.

After *Celebrations* I began again with fragments, so far apart as to make nonsense. In a succession of re-writes I pulled the pieces together. I could have re-written *Celebrations* to make it more coherent and acceptable but I stopped where I stopped. With *Babel* perhaps I stopped too soon. What defeated many readers of *Babel* yet gave it the quality I wanted, was that not only the narrative but also the sentences were fragmented. I used the cut-up method to join the subject from one sentence to the object from another, with the verb hovering uncertainly between:

General Westmoreland was seen at the Spring Show of the Royal Horticultural Society yesterday. Heavy bombers again pounded the open rock garden, the valley area, especially the primulas. A variety of weapons were on show, superbly flowering specimens, while troops were moving towards the Botanical Gardens . . .

If the form of *Babel* was obscure, the content was clear: it was about the power of the State. How in every street, every room, every shop, every workplace, every school, every institution, and particularly in every family, the essential pattern of power relations is dictated by the underlying rules, assumptions and moral principles of the State. *Babel* described not the obvious apparatus of dictatorship but the hints nudges nods assents implications agreements and conspiracies, the network of manipulations that envelops the citizens and makes them unaware accomplicies in the theft of their liberty. In *Babel* the crude despots of the earlier books, camp commander, factory manager, death, are re-constituted in the subtle dominance of the amorphous State.

My play *Palach* combined a number of themes explored in earlier work: the boy victim; the poignancy, bravery and senselessness of his sacrifice; state power. The 'numbness' of *Europe After the Rain* recurs as the trivial, indifferent chat of passers-by. From *Celebrations* came the use of rituals, like the boy's birthday and the drawing of lots, as substitutes for personal relating.

Babel had used press cuttings as raw material. Clearing my desk of these cuttings before starting a new book, I saw the possibility of reproducing the headlines themselves in a visual collage. Off-set litho printing enabled me to do this in *Dreamerika*. *Babel* had gone to unrepeatable extremes in the fragmentation of narrative, now I latched on to the story of the Kennedys whose characters and activities gave the reader easy reference points to help him through a sea of disparate images. I played hell with the documented facts, made crazy distortions of the alleged truth, in order to get some humour out of it, and also to raise questions about the nature of documentary realism. Screwing up the story made some very undocumentary truths emerge. Like when old Joe Kennedy buys the United States for 17 billion dollars . . . It was not until I had finished the novel that I realized the parallels between the Kennedy family pattern and my own: the same dominant father, the same martyred son.

After *Dreamerika* I gave up writing from the subconscious, making a mosaic of found pieces. I had written four books that way and the fun had gone out of it. But I was unable to sit at a typewriter and make up a story without raw material to work on. I was grounded in a method by which I found patterns and connections in a mass of indiscriminate stuff. I could no longer use journalistic material so I had to find something else. I hit on the idea of using a cassette recorder to record many hours of natural speech. I transcribed the cassettes and used the resulting material as previously I had used press-cuttings. I made a collage of voices. I carried over from *Dreamerika* the use of a well-known story and set of characters to create a framework and points of reference. The result was *The Angry Brigade*. Again I set out to free myself from my obsessions and again I was trapped. Same pattern: powerful State, youthful sacrifice. Like *Palach* the book was about physical action as opposed to mere discussion. From *Babel* came the anarchist ideology and its concept of the State.

In *Wonderland*, my contribution to this book, I have fused factory, hospital and work-camp into an all-purpose institution to represent the power of the State.

WONDERLAND

Ancient Roman mythology tells us that Venus, the original Goddess of Love, floated in from the ocean on a huge sea shell, fully grown and in possession of all that beauty of face and form which was to make her the darling of the gods and of all earthly males.

When I say working class, it's a good phrase, though it's a phrase I never use, to sum up people who live in three rooms because economically they have to live in three rooms. We use the social security and the health department to our advantage. The middle class do just as much damage to their children but they will not accept help or advice. When you say to them if you go to the children's department you can get a grant and you may get re-housed it doesn't mean a thing, they don't think it applies to them. They can spend £200 trying to undo their marriage or take another flat, they have quite a different set of problems.

My kid was snatched into care. After I got him back he never went for walks, for instance, in case he might get snatched from the crocodile.

I worked as a builder in those high rise flats where you can earn a tremendous amount of money. I brought home fifty, sixty, seventy pounds a week in notes. I gave my wife thirty straight off and the rest I drank, when I was drinking (I'm not at the moment). So there was no shortage of money, but we lived in three rooms of a rather run down house down the bottom end of Holland Road.

Hollywood mythology tells us that a modern Goddess of Love rode into Beverly Hills pedalling a lavender bicycle, dressed in tight-fitting lavender pedal pushers and a tight-fitting lavender sweater.

We were attached to Dr Garvin. He had a large practice mainly Irish, down the road there, and the trouble with the Irish and the main reason it was difficult to unwind his practice (because he was dealing in drugs) was they don't carry cards. When they return to Ireland the doctor might have five thousand patients on his books but there's no check. This all came out afterwards. He was pushing amphetamimes on his patients to keep them quiet. My wife was on these things for three years through no fault of her own. She became hooked doing what the doctor said. He got sent up the hill for two years. While he was in there he ran the practice through a system of locums! Then somebody local, one of those do-gooders, tried to get him out! He was transferred to the main block where he would be safe, but he continued to run the practice from there, taking the money through these locums. It took three years to get the practice taken over. A very good doctor, Dr Bell, runs it now. He said it was the tip of the ice-berg, he'd no idea how many people were using the things. After he'd got my wife off the pills she turned to drink because drink is very catching. If one member of the family does it the other usually joins in.

I'd got the older boy with me and was waiting to get the girl when she was old enough. They were well brought up children but very nervy, and yes, they'd been bruised. I daresay children don't mind physical violence, they prefer it to being ignored. That's why drugs are worse because parents cut off from their children completely, which tends to frighten the kids more.

The agent who discovered this Hollywood goddess, the myth continues' could see as well as any normally sexually oriented male that this luscious blonde was also fully grown and in possession of that provocative face and figure which would enable her in a few short years to become the darling of the cinematic gods and the earthly, but frequently wealthy mortal males.

I had this feeling that everything was going wrong. I was drunk, my wife was drunk, and when I went looking for her on Friday night I knew I should have got in touch with someone. This is one of the mistakes I made that sits on my mind. Over the weekend I knew there was going to be a bust up and I tried to contact someone but the switchboard closes at six o'clock and they don't publicize the night number which is only for emergencies. I rang again but they refused to give the emergency number. They said they would send a car round to my address but I said don't do that, it will precipitate a row that isn't necessarily going to blow up. My wife had left the kid with a neighbour when she knew I was coming looking for her. So the neighbour rang up too. Apparently – this came out at the meeting we had afterwards – the neighbour had been involved with Dr Garvin at one time and now she claimed she'd slept with me! She threw it in my wife's face, saying anyway your man's no good, I mean, I've had him, everyone's had him. And she had a boy friend in the office, though they tried to hush this up afterwards. They're very crooked up there, not all of them, but that lot, they're renowned. So I couldn't do anything, though I have the night number now. It's the main block, you ring the main block and they get hold of someone in your area. It's a long way round but they can't man every switchboard in the areas. They back you up legally too. When I said the child shouldn't be left at home with a drunk mother they said just sit there and lock the door on her and we'll be round. They can be very good. But the neighbour called them and said the child's grossly neglected, the mother hasn't been home all night and the father's gone after the mother blah blah blah. I said 'I'll be round in fifteen minutes, I only need to find a taxi.' They said, 'No, we're taking him into care.' Well they can't do that without a Mental Health Order. I don't know a lot about it but I know that. They shouldn't have done it without deciding whether the home was bad or not (the neighbour knew in fact it wasn't). But they took the boy away and put him in a Home so the two kids were in two different Homes in North London. Normally when this happens the kids stay with me, though it only happens about once a year. If it had been a weekday the boy would have been with me and I would have said no, you can't have him. I wouldn't allow any number of cars to take him away because I just don't let my children go into care.

The year was 1953, the place a Wonderland called Hollywood. A crisis had struck Columbia Studios. Rita Hayworth, the reigning love goddess, after an epic argument with studio president Harry Cohn over money, had flounced out on her contract, leaving the studio not only with a stack of expensive film properties which had been purchased for her, but no one to compete with Marilyn Monroe who was under contract to a rival studio.

Of course my wife came back. They found her. She was dead drunk. I went in and beat her up and broke her nose and blacked both her eyes and injured her spine and kicked her in the stomach. They'd phoned me that morning and said they didn't release children at the weekend. Once they're in the Home they're in the Home. God I was furious. Sunday morning I went round there and we had a general meeting about what we could do about it. When my wife walked in you've never seen anything like her face. It shook me rigid. I thought, that's the result of not making a phone call. It was chance. I didn't have the number I should have had. They didn't give it me when they should have done. They took the boy and I came back and found him gone and I took it out on the wife. I think it frightened me so much that they *could* take my kids away and they might not give them back. If one can point the finger at the villain it was that particular man on duty that night, the boy friend of the neighbour. They said it was something that will not happen again. They said they had reason to believe she had friends in high places, someone who said, 'I'll deal with this, I know this family.' He triggered off the situation, a man who didn't know enough to know he should not have done that. I don't think he was in the car that picked the boy up, I think that in the office he said, 'I know that lot, you go and pick up the kid,' under the Old Pals Act.

There were a number of things Cohn could do to get even with the uppity Miss Hayworth. He could black-list her. He could suspend her. He could tan her goddess-like fanny with the riding-crop he always carried.

In fact my wife looks forty-five, she's thirty-two, very hard-working. When we married she looked like a well-behaved little girl, always clean, turned out in a cotton frock with puffy sleeves, like a nanny child. That fits really. When we lost the kids she went to live with her sister. They both soon got what I call hatchet faced, with dyed hair. Other than that they didn't look the part. They never made much. They lived in a flat and two constitutes a brothel. The villain was the bloke in the office, he was running them, which was fair enough. They don't get the women usually, they're not out to harass the women, they want the man who makes the money out of them. If a man's running four or five girls he's going into the protection racket and he can build up quite a trade. You get him putting pressure on the shop round the corner. Those are the villains in those cases. The money gets siphoned off into big crime, that's where a lot of big crime comes from.

They didn't go after the real villain because he was one of them. They went after me. They were on the house for three weeks. I was livid. I don't like cars sitting outside, coming in late and finding cars outside. It was usually a disguised car but you know what they look like in their regulation flannels reading their regulation newspapers, you can tell them a mile off. You get the feeling, I've had it once or twice. I walked up to one and said, 'What you want today, mate?' 'Waiting.' 'You can't do that. I've got some stuff being delivered and you're bang in the middle of where I want the truck to come.' At first he was a bit shirty, then he said, 'It's not much of a job. I don't like sitting here any more than you like me sitting here.' He was all right, straightforward, short back and sides, only they all look neat and tidy whereas most people don't. After that they said they'd come and see me to sort it out. It was a time when I had a lot of trouble so I said call at tea-time when I thought I wouldn't be too busy. It nearly emptied the place! One guy who ran a strip joint couldn't get out the door fast enough, several went out the back, the most surprising people disappeared.

It was harassment to make me co-operate. They had to pick up someone, if not me. One of them asked me to help at least put the two women out of circulation. I said no. He said if we take her to court will you say she's not a suitable mother. I said indeed I will not. I never go into court. I do sometimes but not for you, that's the distinction. He wanted to know who my friends were, he asked to see my address book, but I wasn't having them go through the book saying 'Fancy him being here' with any name they knew. I think that's wrong. It's my right not to have them going through my friends. When I said so he was quite reasonable. I said, 'You don't do me any good coming round here.' He said, 'Why?' in injured tones, with his flannels and his white shirt sleeves rolled up

to here precisely. I said, 'You don't look like friends, let's face it.'
He laughed and said, 'I suppose you're right, we can't get away
from it.' He gave me the name of the man they wanted. I said, 'He
calls here sometimes, I'll let you know. But I don't like it. It stinks.'
He said, 'He's done seven years for grievous bodily harm, if it
interests you.' I said, 'Yes, it does.'

An ominous silence descended upon the Big Man's inner sanctum, a
silence broken only by the angry whoosh of the riding crop as bald,
beefy, powerful Harry Cohn, teeth clamped savagely on a cigar, strode
across the heavily carpeted office between rows of golden Oscars standing
at attention on his king-sized desk and the rows of nervously expectant
underlings standing before the desk.

When the man did turn up, the funny thing was he looked about
nineteen. He still had acne. I couldn't believe he'd done seven
years. I thought, what do you see in those two old bags, they can't
bring in much. I rang through and said I'll keep him talking but
you'll have to be here inside three minutes. We more or less did a
deal. I said if they left me alone I'd help them pick up their man.
Then they got into a traffic jam and didn't arrive on time. I was
pleased and I showed it because the whole scene stinks. I'd tried to
safeguard the children by offering them what they wanted. Otherwise they'd have broken up the flat in the middle of the night and
then I'd never get the kids back. A cut and dried decision over these
things is very hard, you do what you feel will cause least harm.

One thing was clear: something had to be done. When their car
arrived late nothing happened, they weren't put out. They said next
time you see him give us a ring, we must pick one of you up, so
make it soon.

When I phoned them I took care to phone from a call-box. I
wanted to ring up and say I would lead them to the guy if my kids
were left alone, but they traced the call and a car arrived. I said you
shit, you've radioed the cars, because he had promised over the
phone not to. He said, 'What?' I said these cars have arrived at the
phone box. He said, well there's plenty of cars. If I'd put the receiver
down I could have walked off, but the man was listening on his
little . . . Then they arrived and held me there. It was about eleven

thirty, I'd just been to the cinema. They held me until their boss arrived. They were quite rough. I don't blame them, they have their job to do, but they weren't gentle. I had to stand on the pavement with them punching me, until a big car came up and I was shoved in and driven off.

Suddenly Cohn stopped. He turned, his eyes gleaming with self-righteous anger. A triumphant smile twisted the corners of his mouth. He brought the riding-crop down in his desk with a resounding whack of decision.

We drove out of London on the M1 and I saw the work camp on the left, a factory with a tower like a giant Heinz baked beans can with horus sticking out.

'So we don't have another dame with big boobs on the lot,' he said. 'So what. We ain't got a star? We'll make one!'

Reception was a front hall, a waiting room with magazines. That's where visitors waited, well away from any peculiar sights or sounds. Then you walked down a long stone passage to the main building. The passage was beautifully done, with carpets and wallpaper and fireplaces in the alcoves. Apart from the telecommunications tower we'd seen from the road, the main building was divided into two: the main block which had got people for ever in it, and an oblong building with those who hadn't gone really wrong yet. The oblong building was about five thousand yards long and two thousand wide, covered by a series of pointed roofs, A-shapes placed side by side. In that were all the shop floors: machinery, toolsmiths, tinsmiths. Two levels, high level and low level (because the place was built on a slight hill), and a subterranean level where they did the plating.

Thus the decision was handed down from Mount Olympus by Jupiter, king of the gods. It had only to be carried out.

The oblong building was a bit like a school, you got the sort of freedom you get in school, yet you were not free. You had to do a certain amount of work but you didn't do a lot of work. There was no piece-work at this stage. It was guiding you and training and canalizing your mind in all senses: how to use a file, how to use a turret lathe and a centre lathe and a milling machine and all the other machines – bending machine – that one would use.

You had to do ludicrous things, like file down a block of metal into a two-inch cube. It was a very rough cast lump of metal, you had to cut it and file it and emery cloth it and then it was put – the best ones were put – in a glass case! Look what he's made! He's made this incredible two-inch block of metal! The best workers wore neat overalls, their hands were clean, always covered in that Swarfega stuff you put on your hands before you start work, it was very tacky and they'd be shaking their hands up and down to dry it out.

They gave me a job taking burrs off heavy frameworks, two-foot, three-foot frameworks. A burr is a piece of metal left behind when a high speed drill goes through it, it's the rough bit and it cuts really bad. There were many different kinds of scraping tools to get these burrs off and I learned to handle them. They were very heavy. I remember the incredible heaviness in my hands after doing that job all day.

We worked at benches, the tops of the benches were armour-plated eighth-inch thick. We worked angle-iron, H-iron, L-shaped iron. I went on to mark out control panels. A mark-out means getting a piece of iron and the drawing that goes with it. The drawing shows what size holes must be put in that bit of metal. You get whitewash and a whitewash brush and you whitewash the metal. You wait for it to dry. If it's not too rusty you mark it out. Then you centre-pop it with a centre-pop and a hammer, ready for the man with the drill.

The windows didn't open, or they opened a bit, so a man could not get through. All the windows were blacked out, the lighting was fluorescent strips and the strips flickered. After three days I got splitting headaches from the noise, the smells and the lighting.

Four times, three times I was shunted about. My job in the plating department was soul-destroying. The platers wore rubber aprons like mortuary attendants. There were three hundred men there that the manager, who was a sort of friend of mine, wanted to get back outside, but they couldn't. They had no families or their families had gone or they couldn't get proper work. They could have made it reasonably well if they'd had some support from a family.

As my father had a greengrocer's shop they said I'd do better in the time-office. I collected the clocking-in cards and entered them in a log. Managers' cards were orange, the rest were white. The work was peaceful but boring. I picked up the cards from the clocks in various places, took them back to the office and then redistributed them. So I made contact with all sorts of people, the people one was working with, which was useful. The time-office helped me back to life, I could begin to come out into life.

Max Arnow, Columbia's chief talent scout, spotted a young blonde at agent Louis Shurr's office. He arranged a screen test that had the blonde encased in one of Rita Hayworth's old gowns, standing in front of a prop fireplace, thrusting her ample bosom at the world, murmuring, 'I want love . . .'

The man who ran the time-office had been in the Air Force, in the battle, I don't know, he'd been brave, he'd known fear and failure. I'm a socialist and he was a fascist, but I don't believe in these labels: each of them I find I am. He was fed up with the work, he'd too much work on, he couldn't get it done. I only saw him about once a week. Well once a week isn't bad is it? Enough to keep in touch. I was absolutely rock bottom the last time I saw him, and he boosted me up, telling me what a great person I was, and I ought to do this and I ought to do that. Boosted up? Boosted up really on lies.

I went on to work on all the machines. By then I was on piece-work. You had to do Christ I don't know how many an hour. There was a flat rate. A rate-fixer fixed the rate. You had to do two hundred an hour to get 5 per cent bonus. You would get a batch of material, maybe a thousand items, and you would have to do a job on those items. The pressures of piece-work were enormous, it was impossible to make any of the jobs pay, that means make any bonus on them. That was the great crime because the whole point of using cheap labour, which is what we were, was to get as much out of us as humanly possible.

There was a very good fitter who used to take a pride in his work.

When he did a job the Inspector needn't go near it because it was always right. Unlike nearly everyone else who would bash a bolt through with a hammer, he would file the hole to make it fit tight. He was a proper fitter. This man was asked to work overtime. He never worked overtime, he had no need to. The pressure was on this particular job but he said no he wouldn't. The manager came down and had a word with him, and he still said no. That was all right. It happened a few more times and each time he said no. That man was taken off that job, he was forced out deliberately. They didn't want workmen, they wanted exploitation fodder, you had to do it their way or get forced out. Unfortunately that poor geezer was sent to the main block. All the ritual began. Someone appointed himself chief collector and all his possessions were collected up. The saddest thing of all was the raffling of his tools. It was like the end of the man, all these worn hammers, these dividers and rules and spanners, in a box, and raffled. He had a fairly expensive watch and that was raffled as well. The money went to his wife.

Meanwhile, the casting department placed the blonde in a quickie 'B' picture. A good amount of fan mail resulted. Gambling on the audience interest shown, they put her in another picture. The mail came in like a postal Niagara.

The job was not beyond me, it was that I had no interest in it. Had I knuckled down I could have done that side of it, the physical side, but the other side . . . Oh Christ I don't know how long I did that for, I think it went on for six months before I was shot across the road to the main block.

We went through the shot-blaster's hut, it was a large hut and inside was another hut with a big iron door. The bloke wore a mediaeval sort of helmet, with a little slit, huge gloves and a great iron pipe. It was the start of the horrors. It shook me in there. You go through two sets of doors, unlocked and locked behind you. You can't have any belongings because people just take them. I wanted to get out. I didn't belong in there. But you can't get out. They said to me, the new manager's on his way, when he comes don't annoy him, get undressed and have a bath, you're filthy, you've had a long day, you can talk to him, he'll ring up someone and get this sorted out. It all seemed very easy. I went and had my bath and I came back and everything had been taken, my clothes, everything, and there I was.

Harry Cohn thought again. He signed the new blonde to a $100 a week contract. But he continued to look around for a new love goddess to put on the vacant pedestal.

They kept my clothes as a punishment, like in school, I suppose any institution gets like a school. You're deprived of your rights like a child. Without clothes, coffined in a dressing-gown, it was humiliating.

Even the telephone didn't work, it was on a padlock and you had to ask for a key. When the manager came he just gave me a shirt and dungarees and put me on the line. There was nothing I could do. Everyone lined up and I had to line up with them. We'd had no breakfast, we all stood in a queue. Some of the young workers looked pretty frightened, they'd been told that when they got back they'd be all dopey and wouldn't remember anything. They hung on to each other and said they wouldn't go but when the charge-hand said 'Ready' they all climbed into the lorry. The ones who'd been before tried to cheer us up: 'Not to worry, it'll all be over tonight, you'll be back here having a pint, you'll be OK, you'll feel fine.' They don't reply, they repeat themselves, won't go, won't go, but there was a sense of powerlessness because you've got to go. The charge-hands can force you physically, they're chosen for their size. If people get bolshie they are held down and injected. Horrible thing. People screaming and shouting. Five minutes later you see them calm enough.

The skills required were not great. You only had the physical thing, the tactile thing, how to turn the lever. The human element was taken out. At five thousand an hour something would go wrong if the human element was allowed in.

If you've got a terrific noise and pain everywhere, all day long, in your hands and in your head, you're so furious with yourself you try to externalize it. That's very different from trying to kill yourself, odd cuts and stuff, which people seemed to spend their time doing.

The line makes you lose touch with any kind of reality, you're in this quagmire, you can't remember your past, your memory's gone. You can't remember your best friend's name, you can remember him but not his name. You don't know if he's married or whether he's got any children. He's just a space, though you know he is your friend.

Cohn paused to take another look at this blonde he had dismissed so lightly. He took a long, appraising look at her. She had a good, firm figure, and a pretty face – but there was more than that. In a town saturated with pretty girls there *had* to be more than that.

It's not self-hate it's self-love. If you don't reach their standards you break down. It turns to hate because you can't bear doing what you are doing.

I made slow progress. I used to copy the charge-hand in front of me. He was a huge, fair-haired, white-faced man, a clever man, I suppose he was, he must have been. I did whatever he did because I didn't understand the work at all, or rather I understood more when I started than when I'd been doing it for a week. In the break, seeing him sitting eating Spangles while I worked to catch up, it was so futile, I used to shit myself.

Like everyone else I waited for what would happen that night, I lived in anticipation of getting out through those doors. Several times I went out, I crept out, and got razor blades or something. I never thought of it as anything odd. It never disgusted me, when I tried to cut myself. When other people did it it was appalling.

One guy, Charlie, was only seventeen, he'd lived in orphanages and special schools all his life. Every time he'd got to like anyone in one place he was passed on somewhere else. He was very violent. They said he'd already put two men in hospital, and he had, with a broken jaw, and one had a broken arm I think. Suddenly, he used to work very tensely, staring at his machine, suddenly he got out of line, he went over and put his hands through the windows, then he broke a bottle and grabbed the glass. We were hours trying to get him to have his arms bandaged. Then he threw a cup and hit someone in the face. Three others put their hands through windows and broke bottles. There was all this glass. I can't explain it. It was mass hysteria. I wanted to do the same myself but I realized it would be crazy.

They put Charlie back on the line. After six weeks no one knows where the brain goes, or the mind. He did not speak for a month. If you lifted his arm or his leg, he sat or lay there, the leg would set in an impossible position, like a yogist. When he started speaking again he just quoted things. He said he was a friend of Henry Ford. His face, suddenly you would see him, he would be working and the whole thing would stop, his face would be rigid, and his hands, as if he had dropped out. Two minutes later he'd be back. I don't think he'll ever . . . He was seventeen. I don't think he'll ever . . . He was very intelligent. He had those eyes which are half shut but still crazily bright. He'd had a breakdown over his A-levels. I got to know him, began talking with him. He said, 'You don't think I'm mad do you? Don't think I'm mad just because Henry's my friend.' After four more months on the line he didn't know if he was French or English. If you asked him a question in English he would reply in French, and vice-versa. He had TB but he took up smoking French cigarettes. If you gave him a fag he'd take it and if you offered him another he would take that too, he'd have cigarettes between all ten fingers. I'd say, 'Want a fag?' I'd wait, and then I'd say, 'Voulez vous une Gauloise?' Then he burnt himself all over his hands and arms with cigarettes and he finally got out.

There was an indefinable sexiness about this one, coupled with a childlike innocence that intrigued as well as titillated the male gland. The hazel-green eyes were seductive, the full pouting lips were like welcoming beacons that murmured sensually, 'I want love . . .'

The works manager was female, she trained dogs and she treated us the same. If you weren't trained well she was bloody. Though she was a woman she was never shocked. If you told her you'd killed your mother and raped her when she was dead, she'd say yes, I must make a note of that. It was her job. When Charlie came back with his hands bandaged she just said, 'You stupid bastard, what the hell have you been doing to yourself? If you give me a tenner I'll cut your fucking arms off.'

She had a terrible job with the work-freaks. She said she had the opposite job to usual: people over-worked because it seemed the only thing to latch on to. She had the job of shaking them out of their work mania. They could be very funny, suddenly going from being depressed to being as high as kites. They acted like they were roaring drunk the whole time, working like maniacs, laughing, they'd do anything. One guy worked himself to exhaustion, he swore he'd never work again. Next free day he was digging in the garden, digging was the great thing, digging holes and filling them in. In the middle of the night-shift that guy had an epileptic fit and after it was over, horrible sight, what was so tragic, everyone laughed, you had to laugh, people did such crazy things.

For me the work pressures built up and up. I saw no point and no end to it. It builds up over a period and you shake it off. I fought it off by going wild. It was my last chance. When I felt the drop coming and I knew I was going to roll down the hill . . . I went high. I knew it was going to happen so nothing mattered.

In his forty years as a movie maker Harry Cohn had learned that what the public wanted was sex. If they thought this blonde had it, he wasn't going to argue with them. The girl's experience was slight but she had the diamond-in-the-rough qualities of a potential movie sex goddess, and Cohn was prepared to polish and shine her into a star until she radiated from movie screens the world over.

The point is I didn't want to run away, I didn't want to go any-where. At that time I didn't want to do anything, but I didn't want to go back on the line, that was it, that was what I ran away from. I walked near the wall when I was leaving work and slipped through and got on a bus. They ran after me but I'm a good runner. No, it sounds cunning, but I'd got a torch and in place of the batteries I'd slipped in a knife, a pen-knife, and they'd discovered it. So when they said they would put me back I ran down the corridor, out and over the wall, through the bushes, and got a lift from some old guy buying petrol.

After a day I wanted to go back. People don't want to leave, in the end. They come in fighting, drugged, deluded, against their will or because they can't get anything else, and in the end . . . it's such awful protection in there. If you want to go berserk you can. Anything goes. They need you so they watch you. You can have hysterics on the line but you're still valuable, you can be sent away and repaired, they can still use you, you are their property, so you'll always be taken care of.

He called her back into his office. 'Don't get involved with any of the guys at the studio,' he cautioned her. 'They can't help you like I can help you.'

I went back but I would not work. If you don't work you don't eat so I didn't eat, I only drank water. At first nobody tried to make me eat. Then they made me go in to meals. They dragged me in. I had five men carrying me, I was fighting and biting, very undignified, childish. So I got some broken glass. I broke a bottle and tried to cut myself and when someone came I threatened them with it. I would never have hurt them. But I sat there with this bottle.

They put me in a room on my own, bare room, completely bare, nothing to harm yourself on, nothing to climb on, nothing to break. No furniture except an iron bed. It's amazingly difficult to do anything with an iron bed bolted to the floor. The windows had nothing to hang anything on, no curtain rails, just unbreakable glass with bars outside. They didn't need bars with that glass. The room had unbreakable glass, everything unbreakable. The panic it instils in you, the fury. I banged on the door so hard, in the end I said I was sorry for disturbing everybody. They said it was natural to want to get out of a place you didn't want to be in.

The door had no handle, it was smooth and bare, it opened the wrong way, not inwards so you could bar it with a piano dragged across, but outwards into the corridor. They gave me plastic plates and cups and no knives. I slept because they gave me pills, pills all the time. You feel so hopeless in there, the idea is you'll be begging to get back on the line.

Someone stayed with me all the time, think how much it cost, and it didn't do any good, it wasn't getting to the root of the problem. It was protecting me from myself they said, but it was protecting their property for them. Whatever they did made it more of a challenge, because I was determined to do it. When you have someone following you they follow you everywhere, when you pee and when you shit, you leave the door open, they're with you every minute.

At last they gave in, made concessions, we struck a bargain. They would let me alone if I would go back on the line. As I seemed to get back to normal they put me in with the slow workers and the violent ones and the difficult ones like the guy who sat and masturbated all day and that was all he did. I was so frightened of doing something wrong that I did something wrong. One night they were playing the gramophone too loud and I wanted to sleep. They had a fixation about a certain record: WHAT HAVE THEY DONE TO MY HEAD MA? WHAT HAVE THEY DONE TO MY BRAIN? They played it again and again. I said if you don't turn it off I'll throw the gramophone through the window and I got up and I did throw it through the window. Next day they didn't remember anything, they didn't hold it against me, they just laughed.

So I tried to kill myself. Once I'd preconceived it and arranged it and I knew the time and how it would be I was tremendously peaceful because it didn't matter.

Then I was in bed, I don't know how long for because I was drugged. I'd cut myself. I'd lost pints of blood. I had to have transfusions, it went on and on, each bottle takes an hour. I had eight pints, you're only meant to have seven, but for some reason I had eight.

My kids were so shocked when they came to see me. They said I was never to talk about it, never say I'd been in such a place. When they came to collect me they brought their dog. They had to lock it up because it kept barking at people. Everyone seemed to have something wrong with them, I don't know, their bodies were a bit deformed, or they walked funny, and they laughed when the dog wouldn't stop barking at them.

Saying goodbye was agony. I didn't say goodbye. I said I'll come back and see you next week. I gave them presents. I was too sad to say goodbye. I'd got to know them. There'd been no conversation in the way people sit and talk about the weather, we'd none of that.

With his fatherly advice, Harry Cohn lifted the blonde to the pedestal left vacant by Rita Hayworth, and the publicity department began inform-ing the unsuspecting world that Kim Novak, Goddess of Love, had arrived in Wonderland.

People keep in touch tremendously with each other and with the camp. If you go down there they'll always tell you, someone's got a card from someone.

(Acknowledgements to *Kim Novak, Goddess of Love* by Charles E. Fritch, Monarch Books, 35c.)

ELSPETH
DAVIE

Elspeth Davie was born in Scotland, and after early years in England went to school in Edinburgh, trained at the College of Art and for some years taught painting. She lived for a while in Ireland before returning to Scotland. She is married, with one daughter.

She has published a collection of stories, The Spark *(1969) and two novels,* Providings *(1965) and* Creating a Scene *(1971), the latter winning a Scottish Arts Council award. All three books are published by Calder & Boyars. She has had stories published in various maga-zines, and in* Scottish Short Stories, *Vols 1 and 2, and in* The Penguin Book of Scottish Short Stories.

NOTE

It's good to hear someone describe his work, particularly if it is of a practical kind – that is if you can, at the same time, hear his machine going, examine the scalpel, knife or needle he uses, take a stir of his tub of dough or test the edge of a metal block. The difficulty with the artist, and particularly the writer, is that much of his work has its roots in the unconscious. There is little to show apart from the finished product. So, instead, he may start talking and answering questions and perhaps find himself giving hard-edged and conclusive statements about things he has not considered in that particular way. He is not always at ease in this, for part of his business as writer, in an age of form-filling and labelling, curt questions and short answers, is to see that the silent uniqueness of persons and situations, their essence if you like, doesn't get lost amongst the files. It's his job to recognize and preserve the more secret side of life. In the same way he'd better not put himself into a category, or bother about whether he is new or old, mainstream, avant-garde or what have you, or talk at length about influences. It's hard to write – very easy to trip up and come a cropper on the edge of a groove.

So how about books then? I don't feel too pessimistic about the fate of books. People are reading a lot. Some are even buying books.

But they are not always encouraged to read by the authorities. I once stood outside our main public library on a Saturday afternoon and was fascinated to see the number of people who came striding up, books under their arms, read the CLOSED notice several times with disbelief, and finally turned away looking incredibly gloomy. Some might say of course that these were only the morons who had not yet got it into their heads that the library of this particular capital city is always closed on Saturday afternoons. Nor are people always expected to be able to take their literature straight these days. Even first-rate actors reading Tolstoi or D. H. Lawrence on the TV screen must *be* Tolstoi or Lawrence and are made to hook on the appropriate whiskers or false beard for the job. Still, you could say it's on the positive side even though there's a lack of confidence somewhere.

The writers who chiefly interest me are those who strike in at an angle to experience rather than going along parallel to it. Amongst other things I would say the cinema has been a stimulus to them. On film there is this possibility of split-second shift from a close-up of, say, the human eyeball shining with glee or tears, to a rocket shot of the moon shining in space, with every other variation of light and dark, silence and uproar. There are of course science fiction writers who use such changes with supreme effect. But the field doesn't belong only to them. The desolating and the unfamiliar is happening continually between our getting up and our going to bed. It is of this day-to-day business of living, its mysteriousness and its absurdity, that I would like to write.

CONCERTO

About halfway through the concerto some of those sitting in the organ gallery, facing the rest of the audience and overlooking the orchestra, become aware of a disturbance in the body of the hall. The seats in this gallery face the conductor who for the last minutes has been leaning out over the rostrum whacking down a thicket of cellos with one hand and with the other cunningly lifting the uncertain horns higher and still higher up into a perilous place above the other instruments. Behind him the whole auditorium opens out, shell-shaped, its steep and shallow shelves, boxes and ledges neatly packed with people. The sloping ground floor and overhanging gallery have few empty seats and the place has a smooth appearance – a sober mosaic of browns and greys flicked here and there with scarlet.

At last the horns make it. But there is a quavering on the long-drawn-out top note which brings a momentary grimace to the conductor's mouth as though he had bitten through something sour. The horn-players lower their instruments and stare in front of them with expressionless faces. At any other time some eyes in this audience might have studied the faces closely to discover which man had produced the wavering note – whether there was a corresponding wavering in the eyes of one of them or a slight wryness about the lips. But not tonight. Tonight all eyes have been directed to another spot.

The disturbance comes from the middle stalls. Down there a man has got to his feet and is leaning over the row in front. He appears to be conducting on his own account. He too entreats, he exhorts. He too encourages something to rise. Now a small group of people are up on their feet, and just as the horns extricate themselves, this man who is conducting operations down in the stalls manages to persuade the group to lift something up out of the darkness between the narrow seats. It is a tricky business, but at last a man is pulled clear and comes into view in a horizontal position, his long legs and his shoulders supported by several persons who have started to shuffle sideways with their burden along the row. Everyone now seems anxious to support this thin figure. Each leg is held by at least three people and the arms are carried on either side by two men and two women. Someone cups his head. Another handles the feet. Even those who are too far away to be actually supporting any part of his body feel it their duty to stretch out a finger simply to touch him, as a sacred object might be touched in a procession. He moves, propelled by these reverent touches, bouncing a little in the anxious arms. It is almost as though he were bouncing in time to a great pounding of drums. For since the horn-players lowered their instruments the music has grown violent in tempo and volume.

But suddenly without warning the violent music stops. There is a second of stunning silence. Then the solo violinist who has stood patiently for some time letting the waves of sound crash over his bowed head, begins a series of scales which climb very quietly, one after the other, up onto a note so high that the silence can also be heard like a slight hiss directly above his head. This silence and the icy note of the single violin come as a shock to those whose eyes are riveted on the scene going on down below. For it is no longer merely a mimed scene floating in the middle distance. The silence has shifted it nearer as though a protective membrane which sealed it off had been abruptly ripped. Now there are sounds coming up — ordinary sounds which in the circumstances sound horrible. There is a dull bumping and dragging of feet, a rustling and breathing, low voices arguing. Obviously the thing is beginning to get the upper hand. It is attracting more and more interest. Heads are turning and the people in the organ gallery can see the round, blank, listening faces on either side change suddenly to keen, watchful profiles. There are even heads peering from the plush-covered front rows of the dress circle — the silver heads and craning necks of elderly ladies, long-trained never to peer or crane.

But there is one head which, shockingly, has not turned at all after the first quick glance behind. It is the man who is seated at the end of the row immediately in front of that from which the invalid has been lifted. Everyone else in his row is up ready to help. The man must have skin of leather and iron nerves. Eyes which might have scrutinized the horn-players now study his face to see whether he is going to relent, to find out if there is about him the slightest flicker of an uneasy conscience. But no. What kind of man is this? Is he the sort of man who might see his own mother carried past on a stretcher without shifting his legs out of the way? He does not turn his head even when the horizontal figure is moving directly behind his seat. At that very moment, however, the man and woman who are holding an arm, suddenly let it go – the better to support the fainting man's back while manoeuvring the awkward turn into the middle aisle of the hall. The arm swings down heavily and deals the man still seated in front a clout over the ear. It is an admonitory blow, as though from his deepest unconscious or perhaps from death itself, the invalid is aware there is still someone around who is not giving him the same tender attention all the others have shown.

There is now a fervent longing for the music to gather its forces again and crush the disturbance before it gets out of hand. But there is no hint of this happening. The violinist is still playing his icy scales, accompanied as though from remotest space by the strings and woodwinds. A man of fifty, he is tall and exceedingly thin with a bony hatchet face and fairish-grey hair brushed back from his brow. This brow gives the impression of being unnaturally exposed, as though his skull, and particularly the bone of his temples, had resisted a continual pressure of music which would have caused most other skulls to cave in. His eyes are deepset and give him a sightless look while he is playing. Strangely enough he is not unlike the man who is being carried out up the aisle. One is narrow and vertical with huge hands like an elongated Gothic cathedral figure – grotesque or splendid, depending on how the light might fall from a stained glass window. The other is stiff, horizontal and grey like the stretched-out figure on a tomb. The prostrate man has his own look of dedication, though in his case it is not to music, for by his collapse he has destroyed any possibility of listening.

These two figures, the vertical and the horizontal, in their terrifying absorption, their absolute disregard for everything else, seem somehow related. Both have their supporters, though now it seems that the horizontal has the greater following. The devoted, inner circle round him have made sure of that. Great, ever-widening rings of curiosity ripple out towards him, interlinking with the rings still concentrating on the violinist and causing even there a shimmer of awareness. The conductor of the devotees in the stalls is now walking backwards up the aisle on his tiptoes, well in front of the others. With his right hand he beckons reassuringly to the group coming up after him and with his powerful left he attempts to quell any sign of interference from those sitting on either side of the aisle. But those nearest the door, paralysed till now, suddenly spring to their feet and fight for first place to heave their weight against it. The doors crash outward and the heaped figures pitch through.

This crash has coincided to a split second with the quietest bars of the concerto – that point where not only the soloist but all other players have lowered their instruments – all, that is to say, except the flute. This flute has started up as though playing solely for the benefit of the group just outside the door, visible in the brilliant light of the vestibule. As though involved in a ritual dance they crouch, rise, bend and kneel beneath the hands of their leader who is now signalling to invisible figures further out. Someone carrying a jug and tumbler appears and kneels, and a chinking of glass comes from the centre of the group. It is a light sound but clear as a bell, and it combines with the flute in a duet which can be heard to the furthest corners of the hall.

At this point several people turn their eyes, in desperation, and stare at the unmoving man sitting now quite isolated at the end of his row. No one could say why it is imperative to turn to him. Isn't he a brute, after all – a stubborn, fat man with a crimson face, conspicuous only in being a figure of monumental unhelpfulness? Yet something about the man suggests that, like some squat, purple-cheeked Atlas, he is supporting the whole weight of the hall on his shoulders. The short, bulging neck holds up the over-hanging gallery. The legs are planted like pillars to the floor, and over his paunch the fingers come together in a massive lock. His bottom is sunk into the plush of his seat like a bulbous root into the deep earth. Nothing can budge him now. He is dedicated to absolute immobility, and the whole house knows it.

This man has never taken his eyes off the violinist. He stares ahead, unblinking – his blue, slightly protuberant eyes fixed. It is as though on him rather than on the conductor has now fallen the responsibility of holding audience and orchestra together – of pushing back the white heads in the dress circle, checking the obstreperous group outside the door, and by a superhuman effort of will turning the curious eye of the audience back into a listening ear. The soloist lifts his violin and for the first time throws a piercing glance down into the body of the hall. He exchanges one look with the immobile man sitting there. There is no recognizable emotion in this look, nothing that would ordinarily be called human warmth. Yet the man below glows and shines for an instant as though caught in a flare of brilliant light. The violinist raises his bow and begins to play.

In the meantime one of the group outside in the vestibule has at last remembered about the open doors. He pulls them to violently and the drama outside is shut away, at any rate from the ears – for figures can still be seen moving about behind the obscure glass. All the same there is a feeling of uneasiness – a feeling that the fellow lying behind that door will not allow himself to be shut away and forgotten after swaying the entire audience. This unease is justified. Scarcely have those around the door drawn their first breath of relief before it swings open again and the leader of the group strides in. His air is even more commanding than before. Now he looks like an ambassador from an important state. He walks along the empty row looking for something, before starting to tip up the seats and feel about on the floor. By this time the music has again gathered volume and nobody can hear the sound of the seats, though he is as skilful and rhythmical in the way he raps them back as the man behind the kettledrums. And now he is finished with that row and goes into the one in front where the stout man is sitting. He works his way along the seats, tipping, patting and groping till he reaches him. Now he is actually feeling around the other's feet. But the man – this rapt buddha of non-helpfulness – shifts neither his legs nor his eyes. He allows the other to squeeze past him, to glare at him, and even to push his foot aside.

At first there is mounting curiosity as to what the searcher will come up with. Yet the seated man has managed to concentrate most of this curiosity upon himself and then, by not moving a hair or allowing his attention to swerve for an instant, has redirected it up towards the orchestra. This is something which almost amounts to an athletic feat. The sheer effort of lifting the crowd on his eyeballs alone is appalling.

The swing doors again open and a woman appears and moves diffidently, apologetically, down the gangway, all the time looking towards the searcher and waiting for a sign. But the man is now working along a row further back and keeps shaking his head. Suddenly he disappears. He has pounced on something down there. It is a long handbag in imitation plum-coloured leather with a zip pocket at the back – useful but not elegant. An advertisement would describe it as a bag which could go anywhere. And it has been kicked around a lot. Already it has travelled back a couple of rows and sideways ten feet or so. The man and woman join up enthusiastically and are soon on their way out again, the woman peering meantime into the bag to assure herself that, in spite of the hideous confusion of the last ten minutes, everything is intact inside, right down to the fragile mirror in the lid of her compact.

Now some of those in the audience had imagined it might be a pair of spectacles the man was hunting for – spectacles belonging to the fainting man who, added to the horrors of coming to in a strange place, would find himself unable to focus on the strange faces looming over him. A few have never been able to shake off a suspicion that all this time these spectacles have been lying, ground to powder, under the stubborn heels of the man sitting at the end of the row. At sight of the handbag, however, some tie linking them to the group outside the door snaps for ever. As the man and woman finally push their way out there is a glimpse of a deserted vestibule. The group, as though sensing a defeat, have disappeared.

The music is sweeping to its climax. One by one each section of the orchestra is gathered up and whirled higher and higher in a struggle to reach the four, slow, separate chords which end the concerto. On this level plateau they at last emerge into safety, and the end is in sight. The fourth and final chord crashes down, submerging all doubts, and a great burst of clapping and stamping follows it. For a while the stout man refuses to join in the applause. One might even imagine he was receiving some of it for himself, along with the soloist, the conductor and the rest of the orchestra. But now for the first time he lowers the heavy lids of his eyes towards the ground and allows himself a discreet smile. Then he lifts his hands and begins to clap. His applauding heels shuffle the floor.

WAITING FOR THE SUN

'I don't know whether you've seen this one before,' Mr Shering would say, passing the photo round a company at his fireside. 'A fellow at my hotel took that — never seen the man in my life. He bobbed up in front of me one day — and that was it! Not so much as "by your leave".' Walking across to the lamp he would study another one for a long time, murmuring to himself: 'I haven't an idea where this one was taken. Wait a minute though. Wasn't I just stepping off the boat at Marseilles? It must have been the mother of that child who took such a fancy to me for some unknown reason. And here's another. Believe it or not, this time I simply haven't a clue. As likely as not some complete stranger took it when I wasn't looking. These things happen to me!' But his sideways glance as he passed between two handsome mirrors which hung on opposite walls clearly showed that he saw every reason why such things should happen to him. In these glasses he was reflected, diminished but shining, within an infinite number of gilded frames — a tall, heavily built man in his sixties who carried himself as though he had, in the past, held his chin up over a series of stiff collars and was now keeping it that way, no longer supported by the formal neckwear but simply by the memory of those people who had once turned to stare at him as he went by and wondered who he was. An actor, a visiting conductor, some distinguished man of letters? Once he had kept them guessing. Nowadays he thrived only on a few upturned faces staring at him from his own fireside, or the brief turning of heads as he laboriously boarded the trains and buses of out-of-the-way foreign towns. He had to make the most of these rarer and rarer occasions when he believed himself recognized for what he was.

This need was greater now. All the same he was hard put to know what he was himself. He occasionally referred to his 'full life', but somehow he had missed doing anything which gave him the right to display a label or put out a sign. Moreover since he was a young man there had grown up a much greater demand for exact self-description and the clear listing of virtues and vices in black and white. Confident 'yes' or 'no' answers to quick-firing questions were now expected as a matter of course. In the days when he had money it had been different. It was enough then to set out a tray of ornaments before his visitors and to keep a silk polishing cloth and a magnifying glass at hand for studying details and inscriptions. In no time he would find himself described by at least one of the company as an antiquarian. He had only to unhook one or two dark brown oil paintings from the walls and study them under the light, or thumb reverently through a worn leather-bound book – and he was unlucky if two or three did not refer to him as a connoisseur of painting or collector of rare books. It was a matter of picking the right company and keeping them at a certain distance so that there could be no question of disillusionment on either side. He respected other peoples' feelings and was extremely tender with his own. He deplored the growing tendency to probe and question. Born sceptics were nothing more nor less than boors to his way of thinking, and he had a particular dislike for those who, in season and out, were avid for the truth. He looked on them as selfish people, greedy for a special form of nourishment which had always been hard to procure, and was in any case a luxury which he himself had been able to do without for years on end.

Some loss in income made a difference to his way of living for a time. His health was affected, but only enough to keep him mooning about the convalescent wings of nursing-homes and from there to the back gardens and spare bedrooms of various acquaintances during the summer. When after a few years he took up his interests again, he discovered the world was changing out of all recognition. Speed and absolute efficiency were demanded, even to the forming of relationships. On every side there was a gathering in of facts and information, while the tools and mechanical devices for detecting flaws in machines and human beings were working overtime. He suspected that they were contained, when not in use, in the shiny plastic bags and steel-hinged cases which were everywhere being carried about in place of the crushable, bulging ones he had known.

B.T.W.—D

He began to move about in a world of his own, politely ignoring the people who asked him what he did, staring intently over the heads of those who tried to tell him what they did themselves. Long ago he had discovered it was not necessary to listen to every word spoken. Only a few words were needed in order to place the speaker. The rest had been a matter of patience – unending, unquestioning patience. But now, like it or not, he was moving into the sink-or-swim era of experts. Mr Shering realized he would sink without trace unless he found a new and effortless way to assert himself.

It was the necessity to combine being somebody with doing nothing which led him to his new interest. In no time it amounted to an obsession. In place of the prints and paintings and glittering trays of little knick-knacks, fat albums of photos began to pile up on top of his bookcase. When his finances improved and he began to move about again and see the world the interest came into full force. The time came when he could hand round photos dating back over years and point out the details which had a topical interest at the time.

'This was that town where there was all the rumpus – nine years ago – over the leading councillor. If you look closely I think you might just see his name chalked up in white on that wall there. The abuse was in red underneath – bigger letters in fact, but you'd have to have good eyes to see it. It's the red against the dark wall does it. And here's one in Sicily. It's supposed to be a photo of the volcano of course, but here's the tail-end of a bus come in the way. Incidentally that same bus was in the news a day or two later – overturned into a ravine with a load of tourists. It's rather a horror photo, I'm afraid – the more so when you remember the volcano started erupting six months or so later!'

People looking through these photos were more surprised, however, to see their extraordinary variety. There were all types here from small, blurred, amateur snaps to the studies whose light and clarity approached professional standard. Sometimes at first glance they made the mistake of imagining that Shering was himself the photographer. Nothing could be further from the truth and their mistake was quickly corrected on a closer inspection. While Mr Shering was pointing out the palm-trees, flags, ruins, and mountains which marked his travels, his guests were studying the figure, dignified and solitary, standing sometimes in the middle distance but more often in the foreground of each photo. Though his appearance in these pictures changed over the years, though his clothes varied with the summer or winter backgrounds against which he stood – like those animals whose brown coats turn white against the snow – yet he was always easy to spot. Shering never had to point himself out. He simply referred to the many friends he made as he went about, travellers like himself who'd taken him up on the spot as though they'd known him all their lives. He was lucky, he supposed, to have met the people who took him as they found him.

But the real reason was that though the world had changed he'd no intention of being left out of the picture. The desire to be photographed had grown from the need to be in contact again with persons who could admire him from a distance. This distance, lengthening with each disillusionment, gradually became the space between himself and the person with a camera. There was a fascination about such a contact. It was intimate yet impersonal. It was with people who, except for one sunlit encounter, would remain strangers to him for the rest of his life.

It was not others who took him as they found him. It was he who found and captured all those with cameras in their hands, recognizing them even from a great distance by their surroundings and gestures, as a birdwatcher spots his special birds. He would then come running heavily down some cliff path or down the worn steps of a cathedral, breathlessly descending to the beach or crowded square where someone was balancing their black box against a rock or the rim of a fountain. 'Hullo there!' he would shout while still some distance off. 'Wait a minute! Have you got that quite right? You're going to spoil a magnificent picture if you're not careful. Hold on. I'll be right with you!'

Occasionally he made mistakes in the people he approached. Any other man might have been struck to the ground by the looks certain photographers directed towards him as he came waving and running. He had withstood some terrible abuse in his time. But such incidents were rare. In any case the skin which appeared to be drawn so finely over Shering's well-cut features was surprisingly thick.

And years of practice had enabled him to spot the amateur almost without fail. When this happened it was no time till he'd struck up a conversation with someone behind an out-of-date camera, not long either before he was standing, his head turned away, his profile white as marble against some dingy ruin or black as basalt against a sun-whitened archway – waiting for the click which would release him from a casual, dreaming posture. 'Is that how you want me? Tell me when you've got it' he would murmur, scarcely opening his lips or lowering his eyelids. 'Well if you can really be bothered,' he would say in parting, drawing out a visiting card with his home address. 'It would be a memento of a very happy meeting, of a most interesting talk.' It was in this way that his collection of photos grew.

In great cities the poses Shering took up were sculpturesque. His look could be stern and sorrowful like the expression on statues in public squares. Occasionally his face, which showed the mildness of a sheltered life, could take on the look of a man of violent action – an expression he'd caught sight of on some nearby helmeted figure mounted on a bronze war-horse. On the other hand photos taken in the country showed him natural and pliable as his backgrounds. He was snapped leaning on gates or bending down to study a flower in the grass – always looking up at the right moment to flash a smile. He had no attractive wife to steal the picture, no restless children to smudge the effect in the foreground. He was suspicious of all tricks in photography – gadgets which made a raindrop on a cabbage leaf bulge like a crown jewel. People who used these devices tended to be more complicated than the others and might show less patience for taking straightforward pictures of himself. In spite of everything he maintained he had more friends all over the world than he could ever keep up with. The friends he spoke of were simply those people with whom he had sat and waited for the sun.

The hours he had sat waiting for the sun took up the greater part of Mr Shering's waking life. He had sat waiting with people amongst ruins, on the edge of piers, on mountains, in boats and in buses. Infinitely adaptable, he could wait as calmly with a solitary and tongue-tied tourist winding the first reel into his camera as with the seasoned traveller already halfway round the world. Long habits of posing had given him an expression of concentration which never wavered whether he was listening to the endless comparisons of hotel bedrooms or to the peculiar history of certain engraved stones set in a nearby arch. He was not attending. The brightening gleam in his eyes was not evidence of the climax to a thrilling tale but of the long-awaited appearance of the sun at the edge of a bank of black cloud.

It was the sun which held all things together in Mr Shering's disconnected life. His casual encounters were made only in its light, and faded when the light faded. Under heavy skies he lived from hour to hour, dulled and diminished in his own eyes, making few contacts, seeing and hearing little of what was going on around him. But he knew when the sun rose and when it set on every day of the year. Elusive as its shining was, the sun was the only dependable in a monstrously unreliable life.

One fine morning in summer, Shering, who was coming to the end of a fortnight's holiday near the south-west coast, decided that for his final outing he would climb as high as he could to get a last view of the sea and the surrounding country. The small hotel where he had been staying had become inexplicably crowded the evening before, and he'd decided to move on as soon as possible. Crowds were not for him. He needed a great deal of time and space for himself and he had resented this inrush of young men and women who overnight had transformed the quiet hotel into a place as busy and noisy as a city office. The irritation vanished however as soon as he'd left the village and taken the path which led up through a group of young birch trees onto the slope above. This was the only hill in the district and it counted as high. But the climb was easy. The air was clear. As he went up the blue spaces of the sky widened out and the mist rolled off the fields until at last he was able to look down at the sea sparkling in full sunshine below. He took the last part of the climb slowly, scarcely looking up till he reached the boulders which marked the top. When he did raise his head and stop for breath he saw a young man already seated there. Shering marked with approval the camera slung on his shoulder. But he also saw as he came closer that the man belonged to the party which had arrived at the hotel the evening before.

Shering remembered him all too clearly – this businesslike fellow packed with information of one kind or another who'd made it perfectly plain to the rest of the company, as he spread out maps and plans and diagrams, that he and his friends were not on holiday like the rest of them, but were involved in some project of the utmost interest to the entire world. Shering had got well out of earshot long before the nature of this research could be explained. Being on perpetual holiday himself, he had an instinctive suspicion of people who discussed work enthusiastically in public and a particular dislike of those who, groaning at the swift passing of time, insisted on counting up the few days of freedom left to them. Freedom lay heavily on Shering from one year's end to the next – limitless and all-enveloping. Long ago the word had lost its meaning. When he heard it discussed he felt as much resentment as if words from an unknown language had been suddenly thrust into the conversation. It had seemed to him possible, as he watched the earnest young men and women, that at any minute there might burst on his ears the question of time wasted and made up, a discussion of extra efforts to be made, of timetables, calendars and the hour-by-hour recording of important events. He had gone early to bed.

The young man on top of the hill however showed no particular emotion on seeing Shering. His face was thin and stern and his dark eyes stared confidently out from behind horn-rimmed spectacles. To the older man who was climbing laboriously up towards him he gave the impression, even though slight and rigid in build, that at this moment he owned the hill, the sky, the sea, and the whole surrounding countryside. He was absolute master of the situation, whatever it was, and this time Shering himself had not an inkling how the land lay. The young man gave no clue and threw out no communication line. But Shering, secretive himself, knew he was bursting with some purpose of his own. He was not here for the view. Not a muscle of his body was relaxed.

'We are far too early of course,' he remarked as Shering came up, and he gave a short laugh as though scorning himself – 'but I prefer to take up my position before the others arrive.' He seemed relieved that the necessity of speech was over and done with. He turned away at once and examined the sea with exaggerated curiosity. Shering sat down on the smoothest boulder and looked around him.

'It *is* early.' He spoke politely to the rigid shoulders. 'But not an unnatural time for me to be out and about, I can assure you. I think it's safe to say there won't be anyone else around for some time – unless of course you're expecting friends.'

The young man turned his head slightly to one side, but said nothing. It now became clear that the set of his face was due to extreme nervousness. He sat straight, his arms tightly folded across his chest as though rigidly controlling himself. Shering who prided himself on putting all kinds of people at their ease felt instinctively that this would be as hard a case as he had yet tackled.

'I somehow imagine – I may be quite out – I imagine from certain things you said last night that you are a teacher,' he began in the hesitating voice which overlaid an inexhaustable persistence.

'Science,' the young man muttered through his teeth.

'A teacher of Science,' said Shering with an edge of disapproval to his voice. 'Then in many ways I think I envy you. To be able to convey something of the mystery . . . something of the miracle . . .' But the young man was staring at the sky where a long strip of cloud was drifting across the sun. His face grew more than ever pinched and severe, and when at last the sun was completely covered he jumped to his feet with a groan. Shering saw what he could only describe as a tearing of hair, and he was amazed. Nothing in his opinion could account for such emotion, unless the relation between cloud and camera. But though he had stood by and watched the disappointment of hundreds of photographers – never had he witnessed a disappointment like this. By this time he also was on his feet and now stood with folded arms, his head flung back watching the sky. He had seen all this before. A whole continent of cloud might move across to blot out the sun. He could be patient.

'If I'm not mistaken it will all pass over in about twenty minutes or so,' he said quietly. 'You'll have your picture, if that's what's worrying you. Indeed, if I'm any judge of cameras, that one there will take a very fine picture in just this light.' But as he spoke these words he knew they were worse than useless – he even judged them downright dangerous. For the young man had turned abruptly. Shering found himself looking into a pair of glaring eyes, eyebrows raised in outrage above the horn-rims. It was a fanatic's face. At any minute he could be expected to raise his fists in the air and curse Shering for ever having set foot on the same hill as himself.

'I have as much right . . .' began Shering, taking a step back and glancing behind as he did so. But what he saw below him cut short all stating of rights.

A great crowd of people were slowly making their way up onto this hill where, in the last fortnight, not a soul had set foot. They came from all sides – men, women and children, winding their way purposefully along the grassy paths at the foot and looking up now and then with an air of expectancy towards the top where the two men stood. Further out in the lanes below Shering saw that cars were drawing up. Beyond that again and for as far as he could see, cars, vans and caravans were coming in, one behind the other, all along the criss-crossed roads of the surrounding district. Twisting through them and wobbling behind were long, glittering lines of bicycles, with the odd motor-bike coming up, jolting and bursting, from the rear. Every now and then those on foot who'd been pressed back into the hedges by passing traffic, widened out again in pairs or groups across the road and were passed in their turn by some solitary figure with a knapsack who had been plodding along since early morning. There was a continual movement going on – a knotting, a fanning out, a stepping back and forward. But there was no chaos on the roads. A single purpose drove them forward towards the foot of the hill where the first arrivals were climbing out of their cars and had started to move up behind the rest on to the lower slopes. In a few minutes solid ranks of people, close enough to hide the green, were climbing from all sides over rocks and through bushes, coming on with the silent determination of an army on the move. There was something strange to Shering in that determination. Were they converging on *him*? In one panic second his innocent life flashed by. For what crime was he to be punished on the hill? To placate what gods?

The panic passed. Looking closer he could make out specific groups among the crowd. Small family parties emerged with rugs and raincoats over their arms. Some carried thermos flasks, lemonade bottles and wads of sandwiches in brown paper. Shades of navy blue marked the circles of pupils from surrounding schools, accompanied by their teachers. Here and there official uniforms stood out. A driver and his conductor were coming up with a bus load of passengers. A couple of off-duty policewomen were going along with them, while down at the foot five nuns were paying off a taxi, chattering excitedly, their black habits blowing behind them as they turned to climb. Most prominent amongst the crowd was the large group of young men recognized by Shering as the group who had arrived at the hotel the evening before. It was at once clear to him that they, along with his companion in the hornrims, were the natural leaders of this gathering. They did not spread themselves like the others and their heavy, angular equipment had nothing to do with picnics. They were serious if not actually grim as they climbed up silently together to join the young man at the top.

Most of the crowd had now gathered on the highest part of the hill and soon the grass was patched with raincoats where the families were sitting down, already surreptitiously unscrewing thermos flasks. But there was something different here from the usual picnicking crowd. These people were focused outwards. It was more than a normal interest in the view. Their eyes remained mesmerically fixed even while they poured the tea and put their hands in and out of paper bags. Shering saw a few miss their mark and more than one stream of tea flowed down the side of a mug into the grass. Meanwhile those solitary persons who had come up to roam restlessly about on their own, now met and passed one another without a glance, only dropping their eyes from the distance once in a while to stare at watches.

Surrounded as he was on all sides, Shering felt increasingly ill at ease, like the solitary unbeliever in a crowd of visionaries. If he was conspicuous it was because he lacked the expectancy which marked all other faces, and feeling safer unobserved, he sat down cautiously on the ground. All the signs now persuaded him that he was part of a great open air organization – a political or religious sect grown strong and drawing followers from a vast area. At any moment an orator would spring to his feet. There would be answering shouts and chants and a raising of banners with secret slogans. Shering had watched such things before, but always from a distance. His spirits sank. It was too late to make his escape. There was now an unmistakable rounding-up going on. Teachers were gathering in the pupils who had strayed too far and here and there a parent was running after a child who'd broken away to other family groups. The bus driver had placed himself in front of his passengers in order to count them, his lips moving, his eyes going from face to face. The nuns stood quietly together, their tilted, white-bound brows towards the sky, arms on their skirts. While all around the groups drew closer and closer together, a hush had gradually fallen on the crowd. Shering noticed it first in the nearby families who had stopped talking and seemed to be taking care to fold up their paper with as little sound as possible. Nobody hurried. There was almost stealth in the movement about him and those who had got to their feet did it as though fearful of disturbing the earth they stood on. More and more people were staring at their watches and with an intentness uncanny to Mr Shering to whom time meant nothing. And now the silence which had deepened with every second was broken suddenly by a rustling whisper which swept over the crowd as they bent towards one another like reeds over which an unnatural wind had passed. Shering listened intently to the curious sound which came again and again from those nearest him. 'The sun!' It was this word he managed to sift from all the rest. It grew steadily in volume until it seemed his own secret sun-obsession was being declaimed from all sides.

'So that's it,' he said to calm himself, unaware that he was whispering like the rest. 'Well what of it?' He saw only a bright, mottled sky with one darker strip of cloud hiding the sun. He saw nothing strange. It was the same sky he had always stared at, the same cloud hiding the longed-for sun.

'Are you waiting for the sun to come out?' he said, throwing his words with enormous effort into a silence. No one answered, but several faces turned momentarily in his direction – shocked faces staring at a blasphemer. Swiftly they turned away again towards the sky.

Shering had gradually become aware that for the last few minutes a peculiar gloom had been falling through the air. He noticed it first upon his blanching hands. Then he saw the grass. It had faded as though a sudden blight had eaten up its green. Now sea and sky

turned grey. If a great storm was impending it was not from the few
clouds overhead – but rather from some black cloud rolling up to
cover the whole earth. Shering's only thought was for shelter. But
there was no shelter for him on the hill. He saw the sky change to
the north and the ground, as far as the eye could see, turned grey
as though sprinkled with ash. All over the hill as the darkness
deepened there was a soft surge of movement as people inside the
groups pressed closer and closer together while those on the outside
swung in nearer to the others. Shering felt more than unsheltered.
He was alone, unprepared for whatever disaster was about to break.
For suddenly a single gust of cold wind passed over him, pricking
up the hairs of his head. At the same instant, like a great net flung
rifling into the sky, a flock of starlings went up behind him and
took flight to the west. Shering raised both hands to his head and
in the silence heard his own voice whisper: 'No! Not yet . . . !' But
this time the sun was no longer a partner in the game. He knew that
in less than one minute he was to be witness to its eclipse.

The smoky yellow clouds covering the sun now turned dark red
changing as the darkness grew to a deep violet which Shering had
never seen before even in the most spectacular sunset. But the rest
of the earth darkened and withered rapidly. The faces around him
turned livid. Clothes, rocks, grass and blazing gorse bushes had
faded to ghosts of themselves. Shering, like the survivor of some
dying planet, was appalled to see a few stars shining in the clear
patches of the sky. The last light faded and he covered his eyes.
Stooping, his knees and shoulders limp as if even the red blood ran
grey, he gave himself up to the darkest moment of the eclipse.

Half a minute later Shering found himself on the ground staring
at the same landscape from which a heavy veil was being swiftly
lifted. Colour was coming back over ground and sky with such
speed that it seemed a thick membrane covering his eye had split to
let in this astounding light. But in seconds this brilliance had faded
again into the ordinary light of day. Over the whole hillside there
was now an air of recovery and relief and from all sides there came
a murmuring which grew gradually louder. Shouts and laughter
broke out, and amongst certain groups violent discussions started
up. The young men and women from the hotel were putting

instruments back into their cases and tucking wedges of smoked glass into the pockets of haversacks between maps and charts. The eclipse had not been perfect. Shering could see the earnest young man standing apart from the others still staring at the clouded sky, pale with disappointment. But the others had recovered from their frustration and were now rapidly making notes in small black exercise books. On all sides people were gathering themselves together, briskly brushing off the astounding along with the earth and grass from their coats.

Soon over the round top of the hill patches of green appeared again as groups started to move down the slopes — slowly at first, still dazed and chilled, then more quickly as they came further down where the grass was smooth. In a few minutes the whole hillside of people seemed taking part in a great race to see who could reach the level ground first. Where he sat Shering could feel the urgent beating of the earth under him. Flaps of coats and rugs brushed past his knees in a steady wind of movement, and once a swinging handbag tilted his hat over his eyes. Still he sat on, motionless, his eyes on the ground, feeling the racing current around him grow gradually less and less until it was no more than a gentle fanning of the air as the last and slowest on the hill went past. Far down below those who had reached the road were already starting up cars and pulling bicycles out of the hedges. The bus driver was in his seat patiently watching his passengers file in. The nuns, all folded and sober as birds after a flight, were waiting inside their taxi. The hikers were moving purposefully off down the lanes. Determined now to weld themselves to solid earth — nobody looked back and nobody looked up.

The last to leave the hill had been a group of schoolboys who'd waited for the lecture on what they had not, but might have seen. Their spirits were still high. As Shering had watched them race off he saw, halfway down, one of the group break away from the rest and come pounding up again towards the spot where he was sitting. As he came near the boy started to swing about in circles close to the ground. Now and then he pounced and raked the long grass with his toe. Nothing came of the search. His circles grew wider and dizzier, and he was already moving back downhill when there was a shout from above. 'I have it!' Shering was pointing to something red a few yards away in the grass. By the time he reached him the boy had fastened the red pen into his pocket and now flung himself, gasping, down beside Shering. 'A piece of luck!' he exclaimed when he could speak. 'I thought I'd never see it again!'

'It was lucky *I* saw it,' said Shering. He was not in the mood to speak of luck. Something about the boy's red face and the way he rolled himself exultantly on the ground reminded him that he himself had sat on the same spot, cold and motionless, for a very long time. His gloom and silence made itself felt.

'Why are you still here?' asked the boy, suddenly straightening up and staring at Shering with interest. 'Are you waiting for something more to happen? Because it won't. You've had it – probably for the rest of the century.'

Shering's eyes swept the horizon coldly. 'Nobody told me,' he said, speaking to the sky.

'We've known about it for months in our school,' said the boy. He took out a square of smoked glass, spat on it and polished it regretfully on his sleeve. 'A lot of use this was!' he said staring through it at the clouds. 'I could tell you all the eclipses for years back – totals and annulars. Of course you won't see a total till August 1999. Well honestly, I don't think you'll be around by that time, will you? But of course you might come in for a few lunars. By the way, did you ever hear of Bailey's Beads?'

'Never!' said Shering curtly. He took a quick look into the thick grass.

'Lots of people haven't,' said the boy with satisfaction. He was silent for some time, looking out over the countryside and relishing the widespread ignorance. Then he said: 'All the same I wouldn't have missed that blackout. Did you know that one of the kids from Lower School nearly fainted? Our Maths man, Baker, laid him on his back and produced a bottle of whisky. That would have been a botch-up for a start. Even beginners' First Aid know that. Anyway, you should have seen this infant's face! We thought he'd died. Imagine what a morning that would have been. Eclipse and corpse at one swoop! Well he wasn't dead, but he was terribly sick afterwards. All the rest of us looked grey and white at the time. But do you know what colour *his* face was? It was blue – pale blue with purple shadows. Of course we'll be getting an essay on this, and I shall put in someone lying dead in an eclipse – and no one looking at him. If you saw it in a newspaper you wouldn't believe it, would you? You could be lying dead right here in the grass where we are now, and no one taking any notice – just staring at the sky.'

'It's too cold to sit,' said Shering getting up from the ground. 'As a matter of fact I only came up for fifteen minutes, and I've been over an hour. I don't care to catch a chill on the last day of my holiday.'

'But the sun's coming out,' said the boy. He drew a small flat camera from his gaberdine pocket. 'I've got one photo to get before I go.'

'What kind of thing do you want?' asked Shering automatically taking his pose a few steps back.

'Well, as a matter of fact, I wouldn't mind a snap of myself,' said the boy. 'That is, if *you* don't mind. There's nothing else to take, is there? I'd like it right here on the spot where we saw it happen. It'll be unique. And maybe I won't have the same interest even if it does happen again. I mean you hadn't been all that interested yourself in eclipses, had you? It goes to show you can't go on and on feeling excited about things for ever.'

'And I thought boys of your age weren't all that excited about having their photos taken,' replied Shering sharply. 'Did you mean that *I* would take it?'

'Of course I would have asked one of the others,' said the boy. 'But they were all off like a shot. Anyway there's nothing in it. It's the simplest camera out. You simply press that – when I tell you. That's all there is to it. Wait a second!' He ran to a flat rock. 'What about this?' he called. 'Am I all right?' Shering didn't answer. He held the camera gingerly, bending his head only an inch or so as though over an unexploded bomb.

'Am I all right?' came the shout again. 'Can you see me?'

'Of course I can see you!' Shering lifted his head and glared before him. The boy was sitting on the rock with his knees drawn up, his hands clasped around them, and on his face the serious obliquely focused look of one born to be photographed. Shering experienced a sudden crippling spasm of jealousy.

'I'll send you a copy if it comes out!' called the boy. 'Press now!' His lips, Shering noted, scarcely moved.

'What are we waiting for?' called the boy again. 'The light's all right, isn't it. Have you got the sun behind you?'

Shering turned and stared in the direction of the sun. It was there where it should be, shining serenely over a quiet hillside. Except for the flattened squares of grass and a few empty paper bags there was no sign that anything unusual had taken place. But the face which Shering turned to the sun was utterly changed. It was no longer that of a trusting man, but rather of someone who can now believe anything of his accomplice – even that day might become night or night day before he can turn his head.

Amongst the photos which Shering showed to visitors there appeared, from time to time, one on which he made little or no comment. At first sight it was naturally supposed to be a rather dim photo of Shering himself, taken in his schoolboy days. He was, after all, there in every other photo they had seen, and there was even something reminiscent of him in this small figure who sat with averted profile and firmly posed hands and feet. But Shering was quick to correct the mistake. 'This – of the schoolboy – is the one I took myself,' he would say in a voice more restrained than usual, and in the silence which followed he would add in a low tone, still more sternly controlled: '. . . The sun disappeared for a time.' Nothing more was said, and no question ever asked, though during the swift appearance and disappearance of this photo it occasionally occured to imaginative visitors that the man might even be hiding the fact that he had a son. But Shering, putting it back carefully into the middle of a pack of photos like a man hiding an unlucky card, gave them to understand that this was one snapshot on which, dim as it was, he had no intention of throwing any further light.

EVA
FIGES

Eva Figes was born in Berlin but has lived in London nearly all her life, where she has worked in publishing houses, translated modern German writers, brought up two children and written five novels – Equinox, Winter Journey, Konek Landing, B *and* Days. *She has also written two non-fiction books,* Patriarchal Attitudes, *and a recently completed book on tragedy. All are published by Faber & Faber apart from the first novel (Secker & Warburg) and the book on tragedy. She is also active as a journalist.*

NOTE

I have written too many books to be dogmatic about writing any more. Once I would have told you about my aim to create a kind of poetry in novel form. Now I am less self-consciously concerned with the creation of a finished and, hopefully, beautiful artefact, than with finding some way of expressing the peculiarities, awfulness and seemingly ungraspable qualities of life itself. This inevitably involves me in constant literary innovation since familiar fictional modes deal with aspects of living that have long been grasped and have nothing unfamiliar or unexpressed about them. The old modes seem hopelessly inadequate; they also seem excrutiatingly boring, both to read and emulate.

I began with the realization that personal experience, unlike all the fiction I had ever read, did not tell a story. Now I would say that all fiction imposes a grid on reality, and that I am imposing a different grid. Experience is chaotic and each generation selects certain facets of reality from which to form a model of human experience which looks deceptively like a totality. It never is. This does not matter. What matters is that the writer should shock into awareness, startle, engage the attention: above all that he should not engage in the trade of reassurance.

Fiction, like all art, consists in making statements. Once a statement is repeated several times over people begin to forget that a statement is being made and really begin to believe that what they are being given is the whole and absolute truth. Most people prefer this, because it is so reassuring. But I do not wish people to be reassured in this way, not only because it is boring, not only because I know that the statements which are so reassuring are false or inadequate, but also because reassurance is dangerous. The price of survival is eternal vigilance. I am less concerned now with creating beautiful artefacts and more with the problem of going on, of survival, of grasping where I am and coming to terms with it. For me, now, each book is a life saving act on which my personal survival as a whole human being depends. If I succeed in fashioning structures which can contain the anxieties, the difficulties, the insights which beset me and which I regard as general rather than private to me I am not reassuring anybody, on the contrary, I am being highly subversive, painful, disturbing, but ultimately constructive.

Let us face it, the old reassurances have long lost their power to reassure. Nobody really believes in them any more. We need new statements. New models of reality. But above all people must be made aware that a statement is being made, and that they are not being offered the gospel according to Saint Anybody.

The artist provides messages about the nature of reality which, if he is successful, become internalized by one or more generation and become accepted as reality itself. It is amazing to me that the word 'realism' can be applied to generations of nineteenth-century novelists who never so much as mentioned the biological functions. Truth becomes a truism and then a cliché, after which it becomes impossible to test it any more. All one can do is drop it and turn to something else.

Having begun with an interest in the fragmentary nature of remembered experience I have found myself increasingly involved in making new connections, creating new networks which, if different in method from the traditional novel of the nineteenth century nevertheless do create a narrative of a kind and do impose a sort of order on chaos. I am using a different grid, which I first have to construct by a painful process of trial and error.

ON STAGE

Act I

At the beginning of the play Nelly and Arthur are young, and arrive separately on the empty stage which is initially unlit, bare and deserted. They have apparently come for some sort of amateur dramatic casting session, but nobody else apart from themselves turns up. Arthur frequently announces his intention of leaving but is always prevented from doing so by Nelly, who has come with high expectations and is determined to make something of the situation. Although she initially did not think much of Arthur he is, under the circumstances, better than nothing. He talks of death, the meaninglessness of life, while she nags him into finding some chairs on which to sit down. His efforts to leave are frustrated by regressive psychological fits, tears, tantrums, and her terror of being left alone – which arouses his pity. At one point he puts his jacket round her, whereupon she regards herself as in possession of his person. At the end of the act she sends him off to organize some tea while she starts dragging props in from the wings and thinking about colour schemes. The scene becomes a domestic kitchen.

Act 2

The scenery put on stage at the end of the last act has been elaborated on. It looks lived in and Arthur and Nelly, now middle-aged, are indeed living in it. He is reading a newspaper whilst she knits a pullover which Arthur declares he will refuse to wear. All conversation seems, to Nelly, to sound like a repetition of previous conversations – which it sometimes is. Nelly, once so sure about her future role, is now no longer sure of her own identity, and the past seems like a dream. But, being a lover of consistency, she believes in going on as they have begun. Life must be tidy, a well-made play, or one can be accused of having wasted it. She also considers it important to keep up appearances. Arthur, on the other hand, begins to show signs of restlessness again, and declares his intention of leaving, if only for a breath of fresh air. Nelly vacillates between grievance and studied indifference, and is finally triumphant when Arthur attempts to go through a merely painted door, bumps into the furniture, and admits that he has nowhere to go. She taunts him with his lack of initiative and changed appearance, which would make a new start impossible anyhow. Nelly, having gained the initiative, and much against Arthur's wishes, introduces her aged parents in wheelchairs. Their macabre and pathetic gabbling drives Arthur into a state of hopelessness and reduces even the stoic Nelly to tears. She goes to pieces in a monologue in which she declares that she cannot go on playing her part. Finally she turns to Arthur for comfort but Arthur does not answer . . .

Act 3

(The stage is still in total darkness)

YOUNG MAN'S VOICE: Sorry.

YOUNG WOMAN'S VOICE: Ouch. Who's that?

YOUNG MAN: I'll try and find the lights.

(After a pause the lights gradually come up. Scene as before, with NELLY, now an old woman, sitting in one of the wheelchairs. The other wheelchair is empty. She stares into space, sitting rigidly, her knitting in her lap. The YOUNG WOMAN stands up front, looking round)

YOUNG MAN *(entering, rubbing dust off his hands)*: What a dump. It's not what I expected.

YOUNG WOMAN: It looks as though it hadn't been used for years.

YOUNG MAN: The boards are pretty rotten. We'll have to tread carefully. Somebody could fall through.

YOUNG WOMAN: What a set!

YOUNG MAN: The lights are working. But I don't suppose the wiring is too safe.

YOUNG WOMAN: I'm leaving all that to somebody else anyhow. I don't understand about lighting. It looks so complicated.

YOUNG MAN: It's quite straightforward really. Nothing to it, when you know how.

YOUNG WOMAN: By the way, where is everybody? It must be getting late.

YOUNG MAN: Have you got a watch?

YOUNG WOMAN: No.

YOUNG MAN: Well, it doesn't matter. They'll be along. We could make a start by shifting this stuff.

YOUNG WOMAN: What a scene!

YOUNG MAN: Incredible, isn't it?

YOUNG WOMAN: I wonder what they used it for?

YOUNG MAN: I don't know. One of those old-fashioned family comedies, I suppose.

YOUNG WOMAN: I know. A kitchen sink farce.

YOUNG MAN: Something like that. Well, shall we make a start?

YOUNG WOMAN: I don't know . . . do you think we should? I mean, shouldn't we wait for the others?

YOUNG MAN: I see.

YOUNG WOMAN: I mean, suppose they don't turn up? It all looks very odd to me. Perhaps there's been a mistake. Then we'd have taken all that trouble for nothing, and got ourselves filthy into the bargain. Just look at the dust.

YOUNG MAN: It's no good if you're afraid of a bit of dirt. Somebody has to be prepared to get their hands dirty.

YOUNG WOMAN: I think we should wait. Suppose it's here for a reason? We'd get into trouble. Perhaps it's still being used.

YOUNG MAN: All right. We can wait a while. (*long pause*)

YOUNG WOMAN: Why did you come?

YOUNG MAN: I don't know. Something to do. (*pause*) And you?

YOUNG WOMAN: Same thing, I suppose. I hoped it would be a meaningful experience. I don't identify, so far. Do you?

YOUNG MAN: No.

YOUNG WOMAN: Do you think play-acting is the answer? I mean, to find an identity?

YOUNG MAN: Why ask me?

YOUNG WOMAN: I don't know. You seem so sure of yourself, as if you had made up your mind about all the answers. In such a hurry to get moving.

YOUNG MAN: We haven't got all day.

YOUNG WOMAN: I thought: if I have to get up there, in front of all those people, knowing I was being watched, having to remember my lines, I mean, you know, already written for me, makeup on my face, so that I looked like somebody. I thought, it would give some purpose to my life, a direction. I would have an identity, even if it was ready-made.

YOUNG MAN: I hadn't thought about it, and I'm not sure that it matters. Let's start moving some of this rubbish.

YOUNG WOMAN: All right. (*The young man starts roughly shifting props, pulling at the curtains, knocking things over. The young woman moves more slowly, cautiously, more interested in examining things*)

YOUNG WOMAN: Just look at these cups – aren't they curious?

YOUNG MAN: Just shift things, will you? We haven't got all night.

YOUNG WOMAN: I don't see the hurry. I think they're rather sweet. In a way.

YOUNG MAN: I'll try and shift this dresser. Move that stuff out of the way, will you.

YOUNG WOMAN: Wait a minute.

YOUNG MAN: What?

YOUNG WOMAN: The old woman – I think she's alive.

YOUNG MAN: She can't be. Don't be stupid.

YOUNG WOMAN: But she is. Come and look.

(*The young man comes over and they both stare at Nelly, one on each side of her wheelchair*)

YOUNG MAN: I think you're right.

YOUNG WOMAN: My god – what are we going to do with her?

YOUNG MAN: I don't know. I thought she was . . . well, you know . . . part of the furniture.

YOUNG WOMAN: So did I. She never moved. Not a muscle. But she's breathing.

YOUNG MAN: Funny old girl. Looks quite healthy.

YOUNG WOMAN: There – she blinked. I'm sure of it. What do we do?

YOUNG MAN: I know what I'm going to do – start shifting that dresser. You might give me a hand.

YOUNG WOMAN: But you can't – not now!

YOUNG MAN: Why can't I? Who says?

YOUNG WOMAN: Because . . . well, because of her.

YOUNG MAN: She looks all right to me, I wouldn't worry about her. If you want to, there's a telephone in the front entrance, you can make a call and have her taken away, but I'm staying here. There's work to do.

YOUNG WOMAN: But you can't move all this stuff . . . not now.

YOUNG MAN: Why not?

YOUNG WOMAN: Because it belongs to her, don't you see, it's her scene. She hasn't finished.

YOUNG MAN: You mean, we've interrupted her last act?

YOUNG WOMAN: Precisely.

YOUNG MAN: Christ, what do we do now? But we've booked the hall.

YOUNG WOMAN: I know. Obviously there's been some misunderstanding. Or the dates overlapped. Anyhow, we'd better not move anything, not yet.

YOUNG MAN: Are you sure? Are you sure she hasn't just forgotten to leave or something? She seems very quiet.

YOUNG WOMAN: Hasn't moved. I know.

YOUNG MAN: Perhaps she has forgotten her lines.

YOUNG WOMAN: I don't know. Perhaps that was the idea, you know, a wordless last act?

YOUNG MAN: I don't believe it – no words, no action either? I mean, how could she, stuck in a wheelchair?

YOUNG WOMAN: Hush. Her lips are moving. I think she's going to speak.

(There is a long pause, Nelly's lips move but no sound comes out. The young people look at each other and shrug)

YOUNG WOMAN: Perhaps you are right. We ought to have her taken away.

YOUNG MAN: Sure. What kind of a performance is that? You don't call that acting, do you? She just forgot to go. Went on sitting behind the curtains after everybody else went home. Or something. I don't know.

YOUNG WOMAN: Be quiet. She's going to say something.

(*They wait, but again only Nelly's facial muscles move, but no sound comes out*)

YOUNG MAN: Oh come on . . .

YOUNG WOMAN: No, don't you see, we've no right here, we've interrupted something. Anyway, I want to know what it's about, I want to hear what she's got to say.

YOUNG MAN: Are you out of your mind? What could she possibly say that we could possibly want to hear? It must have been boring as hell, this whole play. Look at her, she's bored herself half to death, sitting there.

YOUNG WOMAN: How do you know what happened? How do you know what goes on in her head?

YOUNG MAN: I know we've booked this theatre and we've got a perfect right to be here. We've got our own play to do and it's a darned sight more exciting than this could ever have been and I intend to get on with it.

YOUNG WOMAN: Oh, you're a fool.

YOUNG MAN: What did you say?

YOUNG WOMAN: I said you were a fool, an idiot, a loudmouthed idiot. Why don't you stop making so much noise for a change and listen, open your eyes and ears. You might actually learn something.

YOUNG MAN: From that old bag, I suppose.

YOUNG WOMAN: Could be.

YOUNG MAN: Don't make me laugh.

YOUNG WOMAN: I'm not trying to.

(*Long pause, both looking at the floor*)

YOUNG MAN: Well, if we're not going to do anything, I think I'll leave.

YOUNG WOMAN: Do.

YOUNG MAN: What about you?

YOUNG WOMAN: I'm staying.

YOUNG MAN: I see. Well, that's your business, I suppose.

YOUNG WOMAN: Yes. It is.

YOUNG MAN: Look, why does it have to be like this?

YOUNG WOMAN: Why does what have to be like what? I don't know what you're talking about.

YOUNG MAN: Yes you do. You know perfectly well.

YOUNG WOMAN: I know you wanted to leave. So why don't you go?

YOUNG MAN: I'm just going. (*He walks slowly towards the painted door at the back, looking at her, not where he is going. Knocks into a chair*) Ouch! Fucking chair! (*Young woman starts to laugh. Nelly joins in, in a high cackle*)

YOUNG WOMAN: That door is painted!

NELLY: It won't open! You can't get out!

YOUNG MAN: What do you mean? Of course I can get out. Just as soon as ever I want to.

YOUNG WOMAN: She spoke. (*the young couple stare at each other*)

NELLY: I said to him, you can't get out, I wouldn't go that way if I were you, he looked so bewildered, walked into a chair, he did, told me, I think I've made a mistake, there's been some sort of a mistake, I'm in the wrong play!! (*she bursts into a high, hysterical shriek of laughter which turns to choking noises*)

YOUNG WOMAN: What do you think she means?

YOUNG MAN: I don't know.

YOUNG WOMAN: Careful, she's choking. Better pat her on the back. (*The young man starts to slap Nelly between her shoulder blades while the young woman holds the chair steady. All this time they are still looking at each other*)

NELLY: So, I said, what are you going to do about it, it's a bit late in the day, I said, halfway through the second act. He just stared at me as though he were sleepwalking. I don't know, he said. (*she laughs*) So, I said, by all means go, I'll try and cover up for you, but what about you, where are you going to go, do you think there's another part waiting for you somewhere, that you can just walk on and take over? You'd like that, I said, wouldn't you, walking on, straight into the arms of a blonde plump lady. I know you!

YOUNG WOMAN: Do you know what she is talking about?

YOUNG MAN: No.

YOUNG WOMAN: I'm frightened. Don't leave me.

YOUNG MAN: I won't.

YOUNG WOMAN: She might die. That scares me more than anything.

NELLY: Where did I put my knitting, ah yes, here it is, getting on nicely. Hold out your arm, young man, and let me see.

YOUNG MAN: What is she talking about?

YOUNG WOMAN: Hold your arm out. (*He holds his arm out and Nelly measures the knitted sleeve*)

YOUNG MAN: She doesn't expect me to wear that thing, does she?

YOUNG WOMAN: Hush. Just go along with her. She'll never finish it now. She has obviously been working on it for years.

YOUNG MAN: Your eyes are strange.

YOUNG WOMAN: I know. So are yours.

YOUNG MAN: I could stare into them for ever.

YOUNG WOMAN: Yes, but meanwhile, what are we going to do? About her, this, everything?

YOUNG MAN: Don't worry. I'll think of something.

YOUNG WOMAN: It really scared me, finding her . . . alive. Gave me a shock, you know?

YOUNG MAN: Don't worry. We'll get rid of her somehow. Did you know you were beautiful?

YOUNG WOMAN: I don't know. I never thought about it. Don't be silly. It's cold here.

YOUNG MAN: Here, take my jacket.

YOUNG WOMAN: No thanks.

YOUNG MAN: Why are you so unfriendly – do you dislike me?

YOUNG WOMAN: No, of course I don't. Why should I? I don't even know you. It's just that . . .

YOUNG MAN: What?

YOUNG WOMAN: This place, it's creepy. Finding the old woman. Why doesn't somebody else turn up?

YOUNG MAN: Are you expecting anybody in particular?

YOUNG WOMAN: I didn't say that. But we can't hang about here, doing nothing. And you're not much help.

YOUNG MAN: Thanks. I know what I wanted to do – move the scenery and make love to you. It was you who didn't seem to think it a very good idea.

YOUNG WOMAN: I'm not sure that we should . . . I mean, touch anything. Not with her here. I wish she'd say something.

YOUNG MAN: Can't you forget her for a moment? She's not important.

YOUNG WOMAN: What an inhuman thing to say! You barge in here, start shifting her furniture off, and then you say she doesn't matter.

YOUNG MAN: Well, she doesn't.

YOUNG WOMAN: What did she mean, about this man thinking he was in the wrong play?

YOUNG MAN: I'm beginning to think I'm in the wrong play.

YOUNG WOMAN: Don't be silly. Anyhow, with the way things are going I don't think there is going to be any play.

YOUNG MAN: Why?

YOUNG WOMAN: Well, I mean, nobody has turned up. Surely somebody would have put in an appearance by now. I mean, there must be more than just us two. There has obviously been a misunderstanding of some sort. I don't know the exact time . . .

YOUNG MAN: Nor do I.

NELLY: Twenty past eight.

YOUNG WOMAN: Who said that?

YOUNG MAN: The old woman.

NELLY: Excuse me, I said, and I asked him the time. Twenty past eight, he answered, and I asked him if he thought we had come on the wrong day.

YOUNG WOMAN: This is uncanny. What did he say?

NELLY: Probably, he said. Or it was the wrong place, I suggested. Both, he said . . . probably.

YOUNG MAN: She's been listening, overhearing us.

YOUNG WOMAN (*to Nelly*): Then what happened?

NELLY: I asked him: were you expecting somebody, I mean, somebody in particular.

YOUNG WOMAN (*in a whisper*): Oh my God. What did he say?

NELLY: He said that he was. I shall never forget that moment as long as I live. It still hurts me to think about it.

YOUNG WOMAN: So it's true, what I feel.

NELLY: Nobody will come this evening. So why don't you leave?

YOUNG WOMAN: We might as well pack up and go.

YOUNG MAN: Why do you listen to the old bag? She's gaga, forgot her part long ago.

NELLY: Why don't you leave I screamed at him, not because of him but because there was a big black spider crawling up my leg and they always frightened me, even as a girl. Nelly, he said, you're getting yourself worked up over nothing, but I wasn't, I knew what I was talking about, it is me you want to get away from isn't it, I said, because it wasn't me you wanted in the first place, I was just a stand-in for somebody who never came. Year in, year out.

YOUNG MAN: I told you, she's round the bend.

YOUNG WOMAN: Perhaps you're right.

NELLY: Still, I gave a good performance. You'll be lucky if you do as well.

YOUNG MAN: Thanks. (*to young woman*) Come on, let's go.

YOUNG WOMAN: But we can't just leave her.

YOUNG MAN: Oh can't we! You can stay if you want to, I'm off.

YOUNG WOMAN: Goodbye then.

YOUNG MAN: Aren't you coming?

YOUNG WOMAN: No. Why don't you go? I'm not stopping you.

YOUNG MAN: But I can't leave you here, on your own, with the old girl.

YOUNG WOMAN: I don't see why not. You're a free agent.

YOUNG MAN: Anything might happen.

YOUNG WOMAN: It certainly might.

YOUNG MAN: It's a rough area. Girls sometimes get coshed, raped even.

YOUNG WOMAN: So I've heard.

YOUNG MAN: Okay, you win. I've obviously got to stay. (*pause*) In that case, what are we going to do?

YOUNG WOMAN: I don't know. I thought you were going to think of something.

YOUNG MAN (*after a pause*): I wish I knew what it was all about.

YOUNG WOMAN: I know. I was really excited before I came.

YOUNG MAN: We've been tricked, obviously. (*pointing to Nelly*) Do you think she's part of it?

YOUNG WOMAN: No. Well, maybe. But I don't suppose she has any more idea than we have. Sssh. I thought I heard something. Footsteps.

YOUNG MAN: No.

YOUNG WOMAN: I was sure . . .

YOUNG MAN: You're beginning to imagine things. It's this waiting.

YOUNG WOMAN: I have this funny feeling. As though somebody is watching us.

YOUNG MAN: In the wings, you mean?

YOUNG WOMAN: Yes.

YOUNG MAN: Some sort of joker perhaps. No, I don't think so. But I'll go and look if you like.

YOUNG WOMAN: No. Don't bother.

YOUNG MAN: It's your nerves.

YOUNG WOMAN: Yes. I don't like empty places. Particularly this one. It's not what I expected. (*The lights flicker*) What was that?

YOUNG MAN: What? I didn't see anything.

YOUNG WOMAN: I thought I saw the lights flicker.

YOUNG MAN: No. You're imagining things.

YOUNG WOMAN: Perhaps. Where is everybody?

YOUNG MAN: Look, I think we'd better find some way of passing the time, if we are going to stay. Take your mind off things.

YOUNG WOMAN: How much longer will it go on like this? I can't stand much more.

NELLY: Twenty past eight, he said, I make it twenty past eight.

YOUNG MAN: She's off again.

NELLY: That's what it was last time, I said. Either your watch has stopped or we've missed a day.

YOUNG WOMAN (*leaning over Nelly*): How long have you been here, do you know? (*Nelly stares at her but says nothing*)

YOUNG MAN: It's useless to ask her anything. She doesn't know.

YOUNG WOMAN: But she must have been here for ages. (*to Nelly*) Surely you know something?

NELLY: It's a very nice place, very nice.

YOUNG MAN: You see.

NELLY: A very nice place, very nice. Could do a lot worse. Mind you, needs a bit of work done on it. (*pause*) But then, a woman's touch, I always say.

YOUNG WOMAN: Let's go. I can't stand this.

YOUNG MAN: But what about her? I thought that was why you wanted to stay.

YOUNG WOMAN: Yes. No. Not really. I thought something important was going to happen here tonight. A new dimension. That's what theatre means to me. Because outside, everything is so meaningless. But I was obviously mistaken.

NELLY: Colour, lights, music from the orchestra pit, the women in their long dresses. A marvellous, magical evening. I was so looking forward to it.

YOUNG WOMAN: I don't believe her. Come on, let's go.

YOUNG MAN: What about her?

YOUNG WOMAN: I suppose we can take her with us.

YOUNG MAN: In that wheelchair? I'm not sure if I can manipulate it, how I get it out.

YOUNG WOMAN: Same way as it came in, I suppose. It must have got in somewhere. (*the lights flicker*) There it was again.

YOUNG MAN: I saw it that time.

YOUNG WOMAN: What's happening? What does it mean?

YOUNG MAN: Nothing, probably. A fault in the electric circuit. Something like that.

YOUNG WOMAN: I'm scared. Suppose somebody is playing a practical joke on us?

YOUNG MAN: The place is empty. I told you before.

(*The lights begin to fade, very gradually.*)

YOUNG WOMAN: It's getting darker. I'm sure of it.

YOUNG MAN: Your eyes are tired, that's all.

YOUNG WOMAN: I'm scared. We're going to get caught in the dark.

YOUNG MAN: Just let me get the brake off this wheelchair.

YOUNG WOMAN: Hurry up!

YOUNG MAN: It's so stiff.

YOUNG WOMAN: Leave her then. No, ask her who runs this place. Make her tell us.

YOUNG MAN: I think she's . . . unconscious.

YOUNG WOMAN: Oh god! Somebody must know. Somebody has got to be responsible.

YOUNG MAN: I'm never going to be able to get this chair out. It's too dark.

YOUNG WOMAN: I remember. There were some steps. We'll fall.

YOUNG MAN: I know. Stand still, that's the best. Here, I'm coming towards you. Give me your hand.

YOUNG WOMAN: I can't make you out any more.

YOUNG MAN: Never mind. I know where you are. There. Your fingers are cold.

YOUNG WOMAN: I feel like a little girl. I once got shut up in the coal hole. By mistake. This reminds me.

YOUNG MAN: Don't think about it. Just hold on to my hand.

YOUNG WOMAN: Do you think, if I scream, somebody will come to let us out?

YOUNG MAN: No.

YOUNG WOMAN: I thought not. My mother picked me up and held me in her arms. My poor lamb, she said, I wondered where you'd got to. She's dead now, I won't see her again. Odd, now that my eyes have got used to the dark I can see an ocean of faces, a dim sea of heads stretching out into the dark. They're so quiet, like the seashore on a calm night when it's dark and overcast. Did you know they were there?

YOUNG MAN: Yes.

YOUNG WOMAN: Why don't they make a sound? Will they speak to us?

YOUNG MAN: No. They belong to the past. They are already dead.

YOUNG WOMAN: We are still in the present.

YOUNG MAN: Yes.

YOUNG WOMAN: But it's going. I can feel it going, the light. Black water lapping round my feet. Almost . . .

YOUNG MAN: Yes.

YOUNG WOMAN: What a curious ending. I . . .

GILES GORDON

Giles Gordon has published three novels: The Umbrella Man, About a marriage *(both Allison & Busby) and* Girl with red hair *(Hutchinson and Wildwood), and two collections of stories,* Pictures from an exhibition *(Allison & Busby) and* Farewell, Fond Dreams *(Hutchinson). His stories have appeared in various magazines and anthologies including* Daily Telegraph Magazine, London Magazine, New Worlds, Paris Review, Penguin Modern Stories 3. *He co-edited (with Alex Hamilton)* Factions *(Michael Joseph) and is co-editing with Michael Bakewell* You always remember the first time *(Quartet), an anthology devised by B. S. Johnson, and being edited by him when he died. He has also published four slim pamphlets of poetry.*

He was born in Edinburgh in 1940, and brought up there. He worked in publishing for fourteen years, latterly as an editor at Penguin Books and as editorial director at Victor Gollancz Ltd. He makes his living now more from his activities as a literary agent (though he represents none of the contributors to this book) than from his own writings. He was a member of the Literature Panel of the Arts Council for four years, and is at present on the committee of management of the Society of Authors, and a member of the Writers' Action Group. He is married to Margaret Gordon, the children's book illustrator, and they have three children, Callum, Gareth and Harriet. They live in London.

PORTRAIT OF THE EDITOR
AS AUTHOR

In front of me, my desk. On it, the exercise book in which I am writing these words, the very words you are now reading. I sit in a chair, facing the desk, a ballpoint pen in my left hand. I am, as I say, writing. At the other side of the desk, beyond the exercise book, is my typewriter, an Adler Gabriele 25. Beyond the word machine, the window of my writing room. Beyond the window, the garden, green trees swishing in the wind against a faded denim blue sky. It is the longest day of the year. My hay fever makes it even more difficult than usual to write well.

There is a world out there, beyond the window. There is a world in my head. There is a world I try to pin down on paper. Three separate worlds that should bear some relation to one another.

I cross out, then tear up the above two paragraphs. But I cannot have done so because you're reading the words.

I start again.

In front of me, my desk. On its surface, the exercise book in which I am writing these words.

Going through a room, a whole house. People sitting there, in every room. Others wandering about. No one asking questions.

There is this blood, and it seeps out and goes on seeping out. And the body is left there, standing up, empty of liquid but the blood doesn't cease to pour slowly out.

Callum saying: Men are luckier than ladies. They've got penises. (Though he used the word winkle.)

Someone who talks so fast that the words come out as one single, endless note: a shriek.

Man kills someone. At first is horror struck because he thinks he should be. The body, the blood. Then: why should he be appalled? Why shouldn't an individual have as much right to kill as not to? (A case of where to draw the line?)

Gareth saying: You made a mistake, Daddy. If you'd put me in Mummy's tummy first I'd be older than Callum.

The above six paragraphs I have copied out, then typed, then they've been set in type, from a couple of exercise books in which I jot down ideas for stories, images, snatches of conversation heard or invented. They have nothing in common except that at the time when I wrote them they were of over-powering importance to me. Being lazy, it is far easier for me not to write than to write. Each one I thought at the time would make, could make, a wonderful story. None of them yet exists beyond the few words you have just read. Maybe they deserve to be consigned to oblivion.

I am (for what it's worth, and *that's* not for me to say; or shouldn't be) a writer of fiction. I am not an historian, geographer, biographer, sociologist, scientist, economist, educationalist, sports-

man, electrician, shopkeeper or emperor. Therefore my fictions –
novels, stories, poems – derive somehow from the grey matter (why
does the cliché always have it grey?) in my head.

I enjoy life, and find almost everything hilarious in one way or
another. I love people, and relish gossip, scandal and anecdotes
about them: *not*, I trust, for reasons of malice but because to me
any fact (or, rather, fiction) about people is endlessly intriguing.
I enjoy other people's books, but less than I once did. I enjoy opera,
much more than I once did. I aspire to a writing that combines and
mingles the sensuous, elusive beauty of music and the precision of
words wrought in good order.

It's a haphazard way to survive, being a writer of fiction. Emo-
tionally and intellectually I mean, but also (of course) financially.
I rarely know if I'll be able to make sense of the messages in my
head, criss-crossing behind my eyes. What is worse though is when
the messages aren't there, when I sit down at my desk on a Wednesday or a Friday at 9 am and the exercise book has no life, is dead.
It doesn't even stare back at me. It isn't interested. It takes no notice.

I may try a phrase, a sentence. Something may grow. Breath may
be imparted to someone. A character, or a scene. Two characters
against a particular background. I may think of somewhere to send
them, something to do with them. Some days I may get 2,000 words
down. It's usually as many as that, or none. And after six months
or a year I may have a novel.

I suppose it's all self-indulgence. But it is my job. It's a total com-
pulsion. I have to believe, and I do believe, that the next time I sit
down at my desk, pen in hand, paper in front of me, it'll all come
out right. That I'll be totally satisfied for the first time ever with
something I've written. And if I am, perhaps readers may be.

I'm grateful that practice doesn't make perfect. Each time I write
I try to do it better than the previous time. It's not *simple* escapism
(though maybe complex escapism) from the everyday world. But
to me, and I say this most earnestly, my fictional worlds are the true
reality, the mix of the three worlds I mentioned at the beginning.
I only exist through my fictions. I have no identity beyond me. They
make it possible for me to enjoy my reality.

ALPHA

The coffin was carried in. It moved forward. Even at the time, though it was held aloft, six feet or thereabouts from the ground, I wasn't aware of the four (or was it six?) men supporting it. Maybe it moved through the doors of the chapel, up the aisle between the rows of mourners to the front, of its own substantial volition. Yet had it not been held up by four (or six) stout men, surely I would have noticed.

I glanced at the box passing, to my left, then turned my head away immediately, at once, as if I had witnessed something I shouldn't have. The action was a reflex, not conscious, certainly not premeditated. I was standing at the end of the back row, next to the aisle. There were about twenty rows in front. Had there been a hole in the side of the wood, to allow the body to breathe, I was near enough to have bunged it with a finger without having to move, other than bend slightly towards the coffin. I gazed without seeing across the backs of the mourners, their heads turned in towards the aisle, to watch the wooden box pass. Faces on both sides observed partly recognized faces through and behind the coffin. There must have been two, even three hundred people. They were encaged by three windows, rectangular with arched tops. Later, I was surprised to recollect that they didn't contain stained glass. Outside light pushed in, almost unimpeded. Maybe the stains were elsewhere.

I realized what it was, swung like a censer my face back to look at the coffin. It was too small for the body. I was reminded (at the time? in retrospect? as I narrate these brief chronicles?) of the production of *Richard II* in which it was clear that Exton was presenting King Bolingbroke with either the head or the body of the recently departed monarch, not both; or was the dead Richard a couple of feet shorter than the living actor who had been playing the part?

'They lose a lot of blood, you know. And in his case, well, it would have been swilled away, down the plug hole. There'd be a lot of hand washing afterwards. Sickening, but they couldn't fill him up with it again, now could they?'

In *Richard*, the head or the body must have been placed in another box. A silver casket, perhaps. But it was all artifice, as the actor who had played the King took a curtain call. In fact, for longer than the applause merited. Half the audience had left the theatre and there he was, still scraping and smirking at the footlights.

It was possible that they had folded the body up. Unless his bath was unusually long (I had seen it, though not thought about it, and it hadn't struck me as an unnatural length), he wouldn't have lain out flat in it. People usually bend their legs, sit propped up with their knees above the water. Perhaps he slipped down into it. He'd have been heavy to remove, a big man. Like a knight in armour on a battlefield, fallen from his horse. Or a tortoise on its back.

The wooden box was carried slowly, slowly forward, up the aisle of the almost square chapel. The building was bare, no adornment, no fresh paint, bleak grey walls. A couple of vases of flowers. No, I think I imagine them: the altar, the table to receive the coffin, was naked. A slab. With a blue curtain behind.

The chapel was situated in a vast expanse of graveyard. To convey its size without recourse to comparison is hard, but it must have been, must be, five hundred acres. Or a thousand. There were, peppered about, other chapels of most or all denominations. Signposts everywhere, including a clutch at the main gates, fighting amongst themselves for recognition, supremacy. Like labels with numbers in the trench graves of pauper or unknown babies.

The two of us arrived together, ten minutes to go, ten minutes to three, having been driven from the city by an increasingly vituperative taxi driver. Maybe he didn't possess an *A–Z*, or the relevant pages were torn from his copy. Maybe the cemetery was so far out that it hadn't made the *A–Z*. Perhaps it would be in the next edition, if the boundaries of the city weren't contracting.

The meter clocked up £1. Anxiously, my companion tapped on the glass panel between driver and passengers. 'Don't do that, it's rude,' said the driver, half turning his head, and we apologized, giggling hopelessly as well. If we were going to be late, there was no point in continuing. After the event there would be, well, no event. Not, at any rate, of which we could partake. Bread was not being broken, nor wine spilt. We asked the driver, shouting so that he could hear, if we were going the right way. A foolish question to put to one set on a particular course but it is a fact that when we asked the question the taxi was speeding in the wrong direction. Directly so. 'Next time you people want to go to the fucking countryside, why don't you take a train?' Places known only as names near the end of Tube lines came and went. At ten to three we shook ourselves out of the taxi, at the main gates. All those signs, we could have been anywhere. I tipped the driver too much, feeling embarrassed.

'You better hurry,' said the woman in the gatehouse. On the wall was a plan of the cemetery but as the scale, if there was one, wasn't something that I noticed, the map was meaningless, wall covering rather than decoration, certainly not information to be memorized.

'You better hurry,' she said, craning her head round and up to look at the clock behind her. Nine minutes to three. We had told her whose funeral we had come to attend, and she gave us instructions as to how to reach the chapel. But we were inside the grave-yard, it couldn't be as complicated as she had indicated.

A November afternoon: sharp, bright as the Arctic. (I haven't seen it; in my mind I concentrate upon the intensity of light there was that afternoon, and my imagination suggests the metaphor. Tentatively.) There were a few people walking about, then more, moving in various directions, quite a few. Some looked real, some like spectres rising from behind tombstones, others like one-dimensional cardboard cutouts, figures on a children's stage. We began to walk more quickly. Cars passed us, silently as if without engines, but not people walking. We proceeded at a faster rate than anyone else.

(The coffin? Where was it? Already in the chapel? I looked at my watch. Five to three.)

We began to walk even more quickly. To left and to right, further than the eye could see, gravestones, a lot of space between them, then others huddled together as if to keep warm, as if to become anonymous. Some had suffered such wild weather that the inscriptions they had once carried were washed clean. There were flowers, splaying out of the ground, or showered upon it, apparently haphazard, and dew everywhere, sparkling like granite in the sun on grass and ground and stone. A sudden, tiny ravishment of colour glittered on the hard, cracked soil. Then bareness, and grass, and yet another path.

Cars passed us at infrequent intervals, and across the cemetery – a hundred yards away – I saw a hearse. It proceeded slowly (oh show me the speeding hearse!), then was lost behind trees and a building, no doubt one of the ubiquitous chapels. Before we had turned our eyes away, another hearse was driven along the same road, this one if not at breakneck speed at least at a rate that seemed incompatible both with the place and the vehicle's own dignity. Maybe it was going to be late for its own, as it were, funeral.

We walked on, occasionally – every few hundred yards – meeting a signpost, a crossroads. We selected, as in a game of chance, a particular direction, and sped along. It was too late to turn back, and futile to stop. Time wasted us, indeed. Now we were running, our coat tails billowing out behind us. We spoke to each other of everything but the present, not to mention our respective pasts with him whom we had come to see buried. No, not buried; but his last public appearance – his only public appearance in this guise. As we grew short of breath, we talked less, and less. A car passed us in the opposite direction. Solemn, pastry flat faces peered out, looking at us but not seeing anybody.

Ahead, a full poppy red sun prepared to sink, gorging itself, bleeding in the west. We caught its colours within the network of naked branches, which scratched its soft surface like silent needles. The ground on which we ran, across which we proceeded, must have sloped upwards quite steeply (though it didn't particularly seem so) because the sun dropped within a minute or two like a falling football caught in slow motion. We turned a corner, the sun in another direction, and immediately the afternoon was duller.

'Three o'clock,' I said. 'They'll have to begin late. Everyone'll be late.'

A car passed. I thought I recognized someone in it, from the side view and the back of the head.

'We must be going in the right direction,' I said.

Then a car stopped, twenty yards in front of us. In answer to the question, we said whose funeral we were going to. 'Jump in,' said the man at the wheel, not bothering to announce his destination. The woman beside him introduced herself, and the driver; and we gave our names. 'Oh, yes,' said the woman, and we were all silent. The car took us two or three hundred yards. The distance from the main gates to the chapel was, to be reasonably precise, nine-tenths of a mile, an obtuse sounding distance.

Another ceremony was concluding. A dignified space of time was allowed for the chapel to empty, then two hundred or so of us walked in solemnly, slowly, nodding and smiling stiffly at faces that may have been known. A man I knew well but couldn't at that moment place came up to me, thanked me for having told him the time and place. I was bewildered by his remark, but nodded and smiled. Had I known what he was referring to I would have remembered who he was. Then I remembered phoning him, but he was out, and speaking to his wife, or his daughter, and when I remembered that I remembered who he was. But he had walked away from me.

Inside the chapel, we waited ten minutes, even fifteen. Sitting there, rows of us, looking down and around. Thinking, or trying hard not to think. Concentrating on not concentrating. Memories, inventions. Interpretations, excuses. Apologies. Regrets. I'd seen him only the week before, and when he laid his head on his hands on the dining room table the elder boy said 'I want to whisper something to you, daddy' and the younger shrilled 'Why's that man gone to sleep at breakfast?' 'I expect he's tired,' I said quietly, hoping the situation would go away, that no more children's questions would be asked. Because he'd talked about it, I thought he wouldn't do it, and we had felt (wormwood, wormwood) a little pleased that we had helped to persuade him against it. Forty-eight hours later, his phone was off the hook, the doors barred.

Someone said, a disembodied voice, 'All stand,' and when they carried him in I felt ineffably lonely and dejected beyond my capacity to contain such disillusionment – not because he had done what he had done, but because he knew there was nothing more. No life after.

His widow left her place in the front row, moved forward to be with the coffin. They (the four men? the six?) placed the box at the head of the chapel, on the table, in the alcove beyond the mourners, and she walked forward to lay a wreath on the coffin. She seemed to stand there for ever, for ever, for ever – those assembled collectively held their breath – with her back to us all. Her body was impassive, gave no clue as to the movements of her face. Whether her face looked down at the wood or straight ahead it was impossible to say. If I knew, I would not choose to tell.

Outside, the graveyard devoured and consumed the city. It began as a gate, a lodge, a notice, a path, people standing about, walking, a car, headstones, flowers, dew, paths, more flowers, hundreds, thousands of headstones, tombs, urns, monuments, a hearse, a bus, cars, paths, a chapel, the sinking dying red sun. No music. No words.

The dew outside, evaporating in the afternoon air, on plants and stone, on hard paths and on earth, inside transformed itself into salt tears. A nose blown. Sniffling. But very little. She stood there (I had always, from the first time we met, thought her beautiful, had never felt guilty for desiring her; but now she was emasculated, unsexed, didn't think at all in those terms), her back to us all. In her own existence. Her own future. Her past, a common past.

A man put the clock back so that the funeral could begin again, could be done differently. Then life could restart. In the gatehouse, not in the chapel. The taxi driver, lost on his way back to the city, stopped for a second time to ask the route. They pointed and gesticulated but he wasn't able to hold in his mind the directions given. In the chapel, someone read words from a book but not a bible, then someone with a beard spoke of the man he had known. He told a joke that caused everyone to smile, to laugh. It released the tension. It was only funny in the context but in the context it was very funny. Then the lady, the widow, said something – a few words that were devastating, both in themselves and in her ability to utter them. The box had gone, it had slid through the curtains, the door behind. No, had been pushed there, gently, by hands that were not present, then were. The sliding coffin was another funeral, another crematorium. The mass produced one on the Northern line.

Jewish, because they'd all, except for me and I did not have one, kept their hats on during the ceremony. And a lot of them had beards. In the car, on the way back to the city afterwards, I told (why? I wasn't asked) how many funerals I'd been to that year, and that I knew, had known, three people who had died in similar but utterly dissimilar circumstances in the last nine months.

The doors were opened. The doors at the back, through which we had entered, and doors at the side that weren't opened before. Sun, no, light invaded the cold building, seeped in. The effect should have been to introduce life, to encourage breathing and oxygen, but it was dead air, dead light. The widow walked across the chapel, through the doors at the side. The mourners followed, into the afternoon, the early evening. The day was dying, still dying. Death takes time, a lifetime. Maybe the light had sought refuge in the chapel so as not to be utterly exterminated. But that sounds as if symbolism is intended, or significance, which is not the case.

We followed her. Some wearing black, more not. The black coats, black garments, even black glasses stood out. There were open necked shirts, frozen Adam's apples. Faces looked up at each other, etched recognition or desire to know. Occasionally, a nod, a slight rearrangement of features. Everyone had known him. That was what we all had in common. After you. No, after you. Please.

Outside, in the flowerbed which surrounded like a moat three sides of the chapel, were wreaths, flowers. I'd forgotten to send any, hadn't thought to do so. The earth proliferated with colour and blooms. I'd never known if flowers or wreaths were expected from those who attended funerals, or only from those who stayed at home, those who grew old. 'Oh, Christ, I forgot,' someone said. It hadn't been a religious ceremony, hadn't been a *ceremony* at all. Just the memory, in silence. And a few words to make his meaning. Then I realized, peering at the labels attached to the flowers, that mostly they weren't for him, to do with him that is, but for the ones before or after. Not that any of them could use them, but it is assumed that such remarks are in bad taste.

We stood around, two or three hundred of us, not quite communicating, not quite wanting to leave. I thought of the photographs of Solzhenitsyn at the funeral of his friend and editor Tvardovsky.

Someone nodded at me, smiled a little. I knew the face. We talked to each other, in the biting gloom. Our lips mouthed a dialogue but there was no soundtrack, not one word that was remembered even an hour afterwards. We moved around a bit, to keep warm, and I recognized with a cigar stuck between his lips someone whose face I knew from newspapers, and book jackets. I had met him once but the circumstances had been unexceptional. When I commented later on his presence, saying that I hadn't realized he and the dead man had known each other, I was told that they hadn't but that he'd sent the widow a cheque for £1,000 upon reading of his death. Two young children, no money.

Then she saw me. I'd been watching her, moving around everybody, into groups, talking to individuals and embracing them. I wanted to . . . say something to her. No, not even that, just let her know I was there. Her face smiled – lips, cheeks, eyes. The eyes especially. I should have approached her but was, like an idiot, pinned to the path. She walked quickly towards me, fell upon my shoulders in her heavy fur coat, held onto me, clung, hugged me. I couldn't respond, I'd lost my ability to react. I was shy, my mind disorganized. I was conscious that she wasn't letting go, that a few seconds were an understanding of years. I don't think we'd ever touched before. Then she broke away, saw someone else.

The man who gave me and three others a lift back to the city hadn't known how the death had happened. Nor had he known about the death of another mutual friend a few months before. He drove with extreme caution.

OMEGA

She lay there, legs splayed apart. Though exhausted, it wouldn't have been known; her body moved about at such a pace, with such energy and animality. It was strong, wild, the muscles, the skin, the flesh, the total power concentrated in the lower half, but the torso and above turning as well. She was on her own, the activity was hers, though other people were there also. They surrounded her, all above, nearly all above, looking down from a balcony that ran round three of the operating theatre's four walls. They wore green masks, smeared across their faces, their mouths. Their eyes concentrated upon the woman lying there, below them. Not lying there, moving about like a gladiator in the last throes, the death thrust having been administered; in her case, near to death before life.

On the floor, on her level, but standing up, erect, a doctor dressed all in green, wearing green rubber boots, coat, head covering and the smear across the mouth. And four, five nurses dressed in the same fashion. They moved so quickly, so efficiently it was hard to tell how many of them there were even though they were so few. Their faces were so largely hidden that there was no ready way of distinguishing between them, and they were all near enough the same build as one another, the same height.

Breathing heavily, the noise amplified. The sound knob on the radio turned up, up, up. She thrashed around, moved, turned over, turned back. Soaking, like basted meat. Her body naked, covered in places some of the time by a green sheet.

'Aaaaaah, aaah, aah' she screamed. A gut scream.

'Don't do that,' the doctor said firmly. More loudly than was necessary.

'Don't do that,' he said.

But she was doing nothing but screaming and moving her body. The men and women above, the students in the gallery, didn't react. They leant over the rail but didn't register to one another the exchange that had taken place below.

Another scream. A mask attached to a long piece of rubber piping attached to a cylinder was thrust at her face, smashed into it and held in front of her lips by one of the nurses, with the strength in her right arm of a girder. With her face, with the force of her body pushing upwards from the bare soles of her feet to her shoulders, through her neck, she couldn't dislodge the pressure of the rubber smothering her. It began to creep all over her, to absorb her body, the circles growing larger, magnified – hypnotizing her as well; and the circles were no longer claiming her mouth and face alone but her wet, heavy body also. The scream (did she remember it from a previous, different occasion; or was it happening in the present?) consumed her body, strangled it, echoed from it. Not from her stifled body.

'Breathe in, out. In, out. In – out. In ————— out. In ——————————— out.'

The voice said.

She could have strangled the voice, cheerfully sawn through the windpipe that caused it to utter, suffocated it; had she not herself been suffocating.

She opened her eyes. The faces were over her, above her, on top of her. She was standing, they were lying horizontal around her, hemming her in. She would walk on the waters, walk through them.

On the balcony, they looked down. Not moving. Observing. Two were taking notes.

'Push.'

She opened her mouth to say something but the mask rushed messily down her throat.

'Push.'

The hand was removed slowly, the mask taken away.

'Push.'

She let out a cry, but no sound.

'Push. Push.'

It shot out of her, wet and slippery like a twisting salmon. Red liquid hurtled beyond her, beyond it, onto the floor, a strong jet of blood and water. A nurse stepped quickly aside. It screamed, the wriggling miniature body between her legs. It was grasped in rubber gloved hands, lifted up, the cord cut, then hurried away out of the mother's sight, washed, fingers and toes and other parts counted and identified.

She lay there, quiet, still, after the act, sweating and filthy. Satisfied now, content. Smiling without knowing it.

'It's all over now.'

The students looked down, impassive still.

Then she remembered. It was happening again. It was happening. In the present. The mask was on her face. 'Push, push, push.' The supreme hurt. The child like an egg cracked out of its shell, dropped into the pan. The body kept coming as if it would never stop, that it would draw her after it, would never be complete. As if it was unrolling. Still spreading, coagulating. More and more of it, that she had been harbouring. 'Don't scream.' Between her legs – why did it happen there? – her body was most painful. The circles were destroying themselves, fading and contracting, feeding upon one another. Then it was beyond her, beyond her legs, but the soft, endlessly soft cavity between, where her legs almost joined one another, ached with an unremembered past.

She had given birth. To the placenta. But where was the baby? The after birth without its precursor? Yet the cries she could hear? Were they her own of twenty-nine years ago? Or had a tiny child crawled into the room, out of her, so small that it had slithered through a crack in a door?

A cry of a baby. Was it in her mind?

Opened her eyes. Like a moth, dazzled by the light above. Or a fighter on his back, caught in the floodlights after the count. Or an actor mouthing his lines at the audience, the curtain having failed to drop.

The ring of a telephone somewhere. Suddenly she knows it's the baby's father. Another ring. Another. She is more irritated than she can say that no one answers the phone. On the other hand, it doesn't occur to her to search with her eyes for the instrument. It rings again, at least in her head.

Pause. It should have rung another time, or been answered. She listens. There is low talking in the room, the theatre, but the people there talk to one another, not to a telephone voice. The students on the balcony look down, still silent.

The umbilical cord is cut. No more screaming, purring instead. The father holds the receiver in his hand. It gurgles. The phone has gone dead. There is no contact between him and her, and the baby cries. The cord holds the father, lover, male. He walks around the bedroom clutching the telephone receiver in his hand, the flex trailing after him. It doesn't occur to him that the hospital can't establish contact with him because the phone is off the hook. Indeed, it may be reported out of order. During the day, and now it is the evening, he has drunk a great deal.

The cord is cut, the baby released. It crawls away, is captured by strong hands encased in green rubber gloves. Is handled efficiently, briskly.

The mother's breathing is loud, amplified. She is tired, more tired than she has known, than she has thought it possible to be whilst remaining awake. She keeps trying to fall asleep, without trying, but they don't let her, they tell her how well she has done, clean and put away their instruments, tidy up, show her the baby. The students in the gallery above begin to move away, to disappear through white doors. Those who remain look down, don't speak.

She looks up at the baby held in the arms of a nurse in front of her. She doesn't associate it with what was released from her body.

'It's a boy,' someone says.

Did they say a girl? She can't remember. She can't remember if it was a girl they wanted, or a boy.

The remainder of the students leave the balcony.

The mother is lifted into a chair with large wheels.

The father looks at himself in the full-length mirror, standing close to it. He imagines, believes that he has an erection but when he looks down in the mirror he sees it is but a pimple. He feels elated, released, as if something has happened, or should have. His face hangs limp, loose, the whisky having slackened the usual tautness of his features. He walks through the glass, emerges transformed. He has donned minute, black wet look panties, his lady's long black wig, and pushed his feet and legs somehow into her knee-high lace up boots. His penis pushes out of the pants, above the elastic, and he folds the palm of his hand around it. He thinks only of her as he lies on the bed, holding himself, jerking himself.

His free hand holds the telephone receiver.

'Hallo?' says a voice.

'Boy or girl?' he asks. And the receiver emits incoherent noises, eventually ceasing to make any sound. 'Boy or girl?' he says to himself, over and over again.

In the hospital, she is asleep before him.

B.S.
JOHNSON

B. S. Johnson was born in 1933 at Hammersmith and (apart from the war, during which he was an evacuee) lived in London all his life. He read English at King's College, London, at the late age of 23, and was married with two children. He published six novels: Travelling People *(1963),* Albert Angelo *(1964) (both Constable),* Trawl *(1966),* The Unfortunates *(1969) (both Secker & Warburg),* House Mother Normal *(1971) and* Christie Malry's Own Double-Entry *(1973) (both Collins). In addition to novels, he published two volumes of poetry, and two collections of short fictions,* Statements Against Corpses *(with Zulfikar Ghose; Constable, 1964) and* Aren't You Rather Young to be Writing Your Memoirs? *(Hutchinson, 1973). He also edited various books, was poetry editor of the* Transatlantic Review *for ten years, and in 1970 was appointed the first Gregynog Arts Fellow in the University of Wales. He also worked as a playwright, and film and television director: his* You're Human Like the Rest of Them *won Grand Prix at two International Film Festivals in 1968.*

See the Old Lady Decently, *the first volume of a projected trilogy called* Matrix, *will be published by Hutchinson in 1975.*

NOTE

At the time of his death B. S. Johnson was working on a film commissioned by Harlech Television, Wales. The brief which Aled Vaughan, the Controller of Programmes, had given him was simply the idea of Bryan on a beach in North Wales for one day – no one and nothing else was to intrude on this privacy. The film in fact turned out to be a summary of many of the themes and ideas which had obsessed Bryan over a long period. The beach he selected was Porth Ceiriad bay near Abersoch in Lleyn. Lleyn always had a particular hold on Bryan. He described his first glimpse of it as like El Dorado and it became particularly associated with his fascination for the Mother Goddess, the theme of his last novel. Lleyn was also the setting for his first novel, *Travelling People*, which he wrote after spending three summers working in a country club outside Abersoch. These pages are a transcript of the film which was reconstructed as faithfully as possible from Bryan's notes and from our own discussions during filming.

MICHAEL BAKEWELL

from FAT MAN ON A BEACH

Part 1

Shot

Voice

1. Distant helicopter shot of Porth Ceiriad Bay showing Carn Fadrun in distance.

2. Helicopter closes in on beach revealing BSJ hurrying down cliff path carrying large hold-all.

3. Closer shot from helicopter as BSJ reaches bottom of path.

VOICE: This is a film about a fat man on a beach.

4. Mid shot BSJ slithering onto the beach.

VOICE: Did you hear what I said? – This is a film about a fat man on a beach.

BSJ starts to move across beach to Camera.

VOICE: Do you really want to sit there and watch it?

VOICE: Well don't say I didn't warn you.

BSJ walks steadily towards Camera. He stops and puts down his hold-all. He points Camera Left.

5. Beach and Headland.

6. BSJ points Camera Right.

7. Beach and headland in opposite directions.

Shot	*Voice*

8. BSJ points in air.

9. Passing seagull overhead.

10. BSJ points behind him Left.

11. Cliffs.

12. BSJ points behind him Right.

13. Cliffs.

14. BSJ points Left and Right, simultaneously.

15 & 16. Crash shots of headlands.

17. Crash zoom on bunch of bananas in seaweed.

18. Big close up of BSJ's mouth smiling with satisfaction.

19. BSJ reaches in hold-all and produces Polaroid Camera. He takes a shot of film camera.

VOICE: A man taking pictures of a man taking pictures – there must be something in that.

BSJ advances towards Camera and peers closely into lens, he pulls film from Polaroid Camera, replaces Camera in hold-all and times the exposure of film on his wristwatch. He waits and again consults his watch. He points Camera Left.

20. Medium close shot waves on rocks.

Shot	*Voice*
21. BSJ again consults his watch. Peels protective covering off Polaroid film and holds up to Camera a photograph of Camera and film crew.	
22. Close shot of photo and zoom out to close-up BSJ.	BSJ: So, let's be comfortable, shall we?
BSJ goes to hold-all and brings out folding canvas metal stool – he sits on it, it sinks considerably into the sand.	BSJ: Now then, why are we here? Ah, the old questions. You remember the old questions. Why are we here? Why are we here? The old, philosophical questions. I'll have to go and think about it.
23–25. Long shot BSJ pacing back and forwards with stratified cliffs in background. As he paces he wears a deep trench in sand – he falls into it.	
26. Crash zoom bunch of bananas in sand.	
27. BSJ sitting on stool talking to Camera – he is wearing a brown sweater.	BSJ: So, if we can't answer questions like: 'Why are we here?', can we answer any other sorts of questions? Well, like, say: 'Where are we?', 'Where are we?' Well, it is a

Shot

Voice

long story, actually, but I am going to tell it to you all the same. Round the coast from here, there was a tribe, an aboriginal tribe. This was several hundreds of thousands of years ago and very little is known about them, of course, except their name. They were called the 'Helawe'. They lived in a marshy district and this marshy district had enormous bullrushes, or sort of prehistoric reeds, which grew 6 ft tall. This was a bit tough on the Helawe because, unfortunately, they were only 5 ft 6 in. tall, so they spent most of their time going around saying: 'Where the hell are we?' 'Where the hell are we?'

BSJ jumps up and down in sand waving his arms from side to side.

28. High angle shot of Porth Ceiriad Bay from Cliff top.

WELSH VOICE: What do you know of Lleyn?

29. BSJ faces Camera in purple striped shirt. He holds a Red Ink marker.
The sky which up to this point has been bright blue is now grey and stormy.

BSJ: You'll notice the

Shot   *Voice*

weather changes a bit from
time to time. Where the hell
are we though? We still
haven't decided where we are.
(Can I start that again. . . .)
You'll notice the weather
changes quite a lot in this
picture. Where the hell are
we? Well, we are just about
here. Right on the end there.

BSJ rolls up right shirt sleeve
and holds his arm to Camera,
so that it forms the shape of
Lleyn. Camera zooms in to
close up hand.

BSJ: I used to chew my
nails, but I couldn't live off it
and I had 21 in any case only.
I only had 21 in any case.

BSJ marks his thumb with red
marker.

BSJ: We are just on the end
here. This is the Lleyn
peninsula in North Wales,
Caernarvonshire.

Camera zooms out to take in
BSJ's arm and shoulder.

BSJ: It sticks out like an arm
from North Wales and there's
Anglesey up here. Every
schoolgirl knows that it looks
like the head of a diver diving
into the Bristol Channel – the
Irish Sea. We are on a beach
called Port Ceiriad Bay, right

Shot	*Voice*
	on the end here. This almost lock-jaw like location – is called Hell's Mouth.
BSJ outlines shape of Hell's Mouth on his hand with Red marker. Camera zooms into hand.	
	BSJ: It was called Hell's Mouth because any sailing ship that got becalmed across here was driven ashore by the currents and inevitably wrecked. The locals used to be very savage at the time and used to cut rings off people's fingers – things like that – if they found them ashore.
BSJ marks position of Carn Fadrun on hand with Red marker.	BSJ: There's a mountain here called Carn Fadrun.
30. Helicopter shot of Bay with Carn Fadrun in distance.	BSJ: You can stand on top of that mountain and see all around the peninsula.
31. Close shot BSJ's hand.	BSJ: You can comprehend this peninsula as a place in a way that . . .
Light bulb explodes.	BSJ: (now one of the lights has gone, so probably you can't see very much at all now).
32. Long shot BSJ wearing	

Shot

Voice

brown anorak with hood up.

BSJ: Why all these explanations? Anyone would think we were making a film for the mass audience!

33. Wide-angle shot of Porth Ceiriad Bay with sun reflected strongly on waves.

WELSH VOICE: What can an Englishman know about Lleyn?

34. BSJ sitting on canvas stool with back to sea – he is wearing an anorak and there is a child's blue umbrella stuck into the sand by his side.

BSJ: How did I find this place in the first place. Well, I was hitch-hiking through North Wales. At the time I was rather an elderly student of 26 and I'd been reading English, which is a very bad thing for a writer to read – a quite stupid thing for a writer to read, actually, at University. And I'd been besotted by Irish writers like Sam Beckett, James Joyce and Flann O'Brien but I wanted to see the Dublin that they'd all written about. So I hitch-hiked from London on the Holyhead road through North Wales and was given a lift, not to say picked up, by a man who owned a country club at Abersoch and he, during the course of perhaps three-

Shot   *Voice*

quarters of an hour car journey
along the A5, offered me a job
as a barman; as I was a student
I was obviously going to be
cheap for him, at this country
club he ran in Abersoch. I
couldn't take the job then. I
went on to Dublin, but after
about a month my money ran
out there, naturally, so I rang
him up and said was the offer
of a job still open

Camera zooms into close-up
BSJ.   and I came here, and that's the
                                 way, one of those things . . . if
                                 I'd been sitting in a different
                                 place on that road, or if I'd in
                                 some way missed him by ten
                                 seconds, that man stopping at
                                 that point, the whole of my
                                 life would have been different
                                 subsequently. I shouldn't, for
                                 instance, have written the first
                                 novel I wrote, which was
                                 about the experiences of that
                                 summer, here in Lleyn. That
                                 was how I came to Lleyn. I
                                 remember leaving him on the
                                 junction of that road off the
                                 A5. He took me as far as, I
                                 think it is, Bettws-y-Coed,
                                 and he said: 'I am going down
                                 there' and I looked down there
                                 and it was a marvellously
                                 sunlit glacial valley. It

Shot

Voice

looked like Eldorado. It looked
absolutely marvellous. So
this was probably one of the
things which made me
remember his offer of a job,
made me want to go, because
it looked like Eldorado. It
looked like a very special
place. Lleyn is a very special
and a very curious and a very
strange place.

35. Heavily lyricized helicopter
shot of Porth Ceiriad Bay, a
slow tracking shot of cliffs and
shore at sea-level.

Girl's voice sings 'Young
Fellow from Lleyn' in Welsh
(English translation).

*YOUNG FELLOW FROM
LLEYN*
1. Young fellow from Lleyn,
    who's the girl of your heart,
   You who wander so late in the
     evening apart.
   My lover is young and she
     comes from the Sarn
   And neat is her cottage that's
     under the Garn.
        fa la la etc.

2. And what does she look like,
    the girl of your heart,
   You who wander so late in the
     evening apart
   Dark, dark is my lover and
     dark-haired is she
   And white shines her body
     like foam on the sea.

Helicopter stops at
water's edge. BSJ is sitting on

Shot	*Voice*
canvas stool as a speck in distance. Song breaks off abruptly.	
36. Mid-shot BSJ in stormy weather – he is wearing an anorak and black oilskin hat.	BSJ: That's enough of that. You're not meant to be enjoying this you know.
37. Crash zoom to close-up bunch of bananas in sand.	
38. BSJ jumping up and down pulling up sweater to show naked stomach.	
39. Wood fire (unlit) on pebbles by cliff edge. BSJ carrying hold-all and wearing red shirt walks into shot.	BSJ: Someone's laid a fire. Isn't that nice!
He takes a packet of fire-lighters and a box of matches from the hold-all and lights the fire.	
40. Camera zooms out from burning fire to mid-shot BSJ. He is sitting on the canvas stool. He reaches inside the hold-all and produces a woollen skull cap and a skull cup. BSJ pours wine into the skull cup and drinks.	BSJ: Skull cap. Skull cup. The man who produced my first film was called Bruce Beresford and he used this

Shot	*Voice*
	expression whenever we got in trouble on the film, which was often. He said: 'It will be all right, we can cut away to a bunch of bananas.' It was some time before I understood exactly what this meant. He'd worked for some film unit in Africa which belonged to the Government and the only films the Government, who happened to be in power at the time, wanted to make were films about their own speeches.
BSJ produces broken altar candle from hold-all. He lights it at the fire.	BSJ: So he used to have to put together these enormously long speeches by African politicians and try to make a film out of them, and of course, there are jumps, that is to say, the film only lasts for ten minutes in the camera normally, so every ten minutes you have a jump. You can demonstrate it very easily, like this . . .
41. Deliberate jump cut. BSJ's head and candle jump from frame Left to frame Right.	you see . . . If you take a bit out there, there's a big jump. My head appears to jump about. Now, if you slip in a

Shot

Voice

shot between those two things,
then the audience accepts it
more readily. They think while
the thing was on the screen,
then something else happened.
It is one of the little deceits
that film makers practise.
Bruce Beresford, in this African
situation, in the middle of these
politicians' speeches, just used
to cut away to a bunch of
bananas; hence the expression.

42. Bunch of bananas floats
through rock pool.

43. BSJ in purple striped shirt
sits against stratified cliffs.

BSJ: Now, the first time I
came down to this beach I was
brought here by a man who
ran the Club that I worked in a
Abersoch. He was a man who
was about 60 I suppose. He
was trying to pretend that he
was much younger. He had
young girl friends; he dressed
in a young manner and to me,
at the age of 26 – I was a very
young 26 – I was very much
of a prig, and it seemed to me
that one ought to be one's age
and one ought not to pretend
that the world was younger.
This man brought me to this
beach with a young girl of
about 20, whom he was, in

Shot	*Voice*
	those days and in those words, 'courting', and I was, in a sense, playing 'gooseberry' and was ashamed of it in a sense.
44. Panning shot of stratified cliffs.	He, as I say, was courting her, but was trying to impress me at the same time.
45. Mid-shot BSJ and cliffs.	So when we came down here, he showed me these stratified cliffs behind me and talked about them, and then went back to her. Later, I wrote a poem about this in which I tried to sort myself out. It is called 'Porth Ceiriad Bay'. It is quite short, so don't go away.

PORTH CEIRIAD BAY

46. Panning shot stratified cliffs Right to Left.	Descended to the shore, odd how we left the young girl with us to herself, and went straight to examine the stratified cliffs, forgot her entirely in our interest.
47. Camera pans down stratified cliffs very close.	You marvelled at the shapes the clockwork sea had worn the stone, talking keenly, until the pace of this random sculpture recalled
48. Panning shot stratified cliffs Left to Right.	your age to you, and then its anodynes.

Shot	*Voice*
49. Mid-shot BSJ reading against cliffs.	And so you turned, pretending youth, courting the girl as if you were a boy again, leaving the wry cliffs to their erosion and me to my observant solitude.
50. BSJ walks through rocks at foot of cliffs – he crosses a rock pool and goes out of shot. Bunch of bananas emerges from rock pool and crawls onto beach.	
51. Camera focuses up on rock formation, seagulls scream in background.	
52. Mid-shot beach. BSJ in brown sweater walks towards Camera. At the foot of the cliff he finds a dead sheep. Zoom in to close shot of its bloodied head.	
53. BSJ in pink shirt walks towards Camera along sea shore. The Camera moves with him, holding him in mid-shot.	BSJ: One of the things that happened to me down here is something that has stayed with me a very long time. The place is full of images; of metaphors; things happening. This one could, in fact, have

Shot

Voice

taken place anywhere, but it happened in Lleyn and I think that's significant.

I was driving from Pwllheli to Abersoch and I happened on a road accident shortly after it had happened. There had been a crash between, I think, two cars and a motor cycle, with a pillion passenger as well as a rider. The pillion passenger had gone straight through the windscreen of the car coming in the opposite direction, and the rider of the motor cycle had been thrown across the road and had hit a wire fence of the sort which has concrete posts with holes in them with single wires through them. He had been thrown against this wire fence and the wires had gone through him like a cheese cutter through cheese. They don't have many of them these days – wire cutters – a piece of wire on a board or a piece of marble – and the wire is simply pulled through the cheese. A very good way of cutting cheese. I expect the machines which package cheese use the same method, but we don't see that, we just see the

Shot	Voice

Voice

plastic packets – thank god. This – the way the motor cyclist had been cut up by these wires – I passed it only fleetingly. I just drove past and saw this man in a motor cyclist's helmet – and a fat lot of good that did him! – lying by the side of the road having been thrown against this wire fence, and it stayed with me – that image – that metaphor – wires going through a man like a cheese cutter through cheese – for a long while now. It's a metaphor for the way the human condition seems to treat human kind. The body as a soft machine, as William Burroughs said – a soft machine. Thrown against a wire fence, it just cut him to pieces. I passed that image just in that fleeting time with that man's life ebbing away. I learnt later, that he had been killed instantly, but there his life was, ebbing away. It happened in Lleyn.

54. Footprints in sand with tracks alongside. Pan up to BSJ walking towards sea in white shirt, he turns and notices bunch of bananas a few feet behind him.

Shot	*Voice*
55. Stratified cliffs. Pan up to show BSJ in white shirt reclining on ledge.	The word 'gull' comes from a Welsh word – 'Gwylan' – to wail. So, a 'seagull' in English is really a 'sea wailer'. I have got to use English when I talk to you. Wailer – W-A-I-L-E-R. It is a wonder we can talk at all! – communicate with each other, with these sort of words which have several meanings. It reminds me of a joke. Everything reminds me of a joke, if I am lucky! There was a girl being taken to the pictures – remember the pictures? – by a man and he said: 'We are going to see a film about Wales.' And she said: 'I am not terribly keen on Taffies as you know.' He said: 'No, no, no, no, no, no, not that kind of Wales.'
56. Mid-shot toy blue inflatable rubber whale at sea's edge. Along its side is written 'Having a whale of a time.'	BSJ: This is a film called *Moby Dick*.
57. Long shot BSJ.	and she said 'I don't like sex films either.'
58. Mid-shot two blue rubber inflatable toy whales playing together at water's edge.	

Shot	*Voice*

59. Long shot BSJ zoom in.

BSJ: But the seagull, the wailer, the sea wailer, is a word which has different meanings in different languages very closely connected with English. For instance, in old Dutch the word 'Gull' – G-U-L-L-E – means a great wench without wit. This is all genuine stuff, you know. That is why I've got the script here. (There is a bloody aeroplane now . . .) a folland gnat if I'm not . . . (drowned by aeroplane noise).

60. Crash zoom in to bunch of bananas on stratified rock.

61. Mid-shot BSJ.

BSJ: and in old High German, 'Gull' without an 'e' or rather Low German (you see, I am not making this up you know, it's all here in the script!). Gull is a 'Soft, mild, open-hearted, good-natured sort of person.' Is that your idea of a 'Gull'?

62. Seagulls fighting for food.

63. Mid-shot BSJ as before.

BSJ: The great Welsh poet – Dafydd ap Gwilim – wrote a poem about gulls called 'The Seagull'. I have tried to translate the first stanza of it; except 'translate' is the wrong

Shot

Voice

word. You cannot translate;
you lose everything, as
someone said, except the
poetry. I mean you can
translate everything except the
poetry. This is my attempt at
the first stanza of Dafydd ap
Gwilim's 'Seagull':

64–67. Seagull flying over sea.

BSJ:
Gull all grace on the flood tide.
Mailed hand of sea salt.
Moonlight white, reflected snow.
Perfect lily of the wave's valley.
Fish fattened, cork-like coaster,
shining sheet of paper.

68. Medium close-up BSJ.

Gull, Gwylan, Wailer,
Gull all grace.

69. Gull flies off.

70. Mid-shot BSJ.

BSJ: Oh, I have driven him
off. He cannot take my version
of Dafydd.

71. Bunch of bananas advances
steadily along seashore.

72. BSJ's feet edge away
from bananas which continue
to follow him.

73. Camera zooms out on rock
formation.

74. BSJ in pink shirt sits at
foot of cliffs throwing stones
at a stack of stones he has built
a few feet away.

BSJ: If I hit these stones,
will it be an accident do you
think? You cannot deny that
is what I am trying to do, and
I did it.

Shot

Voice

BSJ succeeds in knocking over stack of stones – he gets up and starts to pile them up again.

BSJ: Was it an accident? Why can't a film be a celebration of accidents? Why does it have to be neat and tidy and logical, because life is not neat and tidy and logical. Why can't the film be a celebration of the accidental? Do you have to be told a story every time? Do you have to have all the ends tied up so neatly? Telling stories, if you remember, is a child's euphemism for telling lies. Telling long stories is telling lies, because life does not tell you stories. Life is accidental.

BSJ goes back and starts to throw stones at stack.

BSJ: If you tidy life up, you have to admit that you are falsifying it.

BSJ hits the stack which falls over immediately.

BSJ: See, was that an accident? I think it was actually. The thing is, telling stories is tidying life up in a way that it may not be – I will tell you a poem:

BSJ:

Mary had a little lamb.
She put it in a bucket
And every time the lamb got out,
The bulldog tried to put it back again.

Shot	*Voice*
	You see, life doesn't tell you stories like that; that's tidied life up. It's really all chaos. It is chaos – I say it is. I cannot prove it is chaos any more than anyone else can prove there is a pattern, or there is some sort of deity, but even if it is all chaos, then let's celebrate the chaos. Let's celebrate the accidental. Does that make us any the worse off? Are we any the worse off? There is still love; there is still humour.
	Mary had another lamb. She also had a duck. She put it on the mantelpiece, To see if it would fall off.
	That is wrong actually.
	Mary had a little lamb She also had a duck. She put *them* on the mantelpiece, To see if they would fall off.
	Ho, ho, ho, ho.
75. BSJ stamps on bunch of bananas.	
76. BSJ in anorak with hood up sitting at water's edge with back to sea.	BSJ: And I think now you'd better go and look at something else while I take this coat off and change my shirt for sunny weather.

COMMERCIAL BREAK

Part 2

Shot	*Voice*
1. Camera pans off shadow of camera crew to BSJ who is sitting in a red shirt by the wood fire cooking a sausage.	BSJ: Ahh, so you're back. You still want to see a film about a fat man on a beach. Have a sausage as a foretaste of the good things to come.
2–4. In orange shirt BSJ walks along the water's edge examining various exotic shells, which are obviously planted – one of them, which he shows to Camera, still has a price tag. The last of these is a large piece of pink coral which he shows to the Camera.	BSJ VOICE OVER: One can learn lessons from anything. Anything!
5. BSJ in white shirt eating apple.	One can probably even learn lessons from eating apples. Learn lessons from anything. Cheers.
6. Panning shot of waves breaking on shore.	
7. BSJ in green sweater sits at the mouth of small cave – a firework is burning behind him.	I'm going to read some more poems now. It may be that if you want to go and have a cup of tea this would be a good time. I know that's what you masses are like. The mention

Shot	*Voice*
	of poetry and off you go. This's a Welsh one, of course. It is called 'Independence':
	Rhiain the Gas, the Welsh introduced her, a girl who so much looked like her on whom my life had foundered that I could not help but offer her a kind of love at sight.
	Rhiain once received me in her office at the Gas Co. opposite the college, to show the male her independent state and corner him on her own territory.
	The trouble was that just as she appeared so much like her, so she behaved the same. *Ah yes*, said Iolo, some weeks later, *We should really have told you about Rhiain.*
8–9. Waves breaking among rocks.	BSJ VOICE OVER: There is something primaeval about a beach isn't there? The first poem I ever wrote was about a beach. I am not going to recite that one though.

Shot	*Voice*
10. BSJ in white shirt lights firework at mouth of cave. Seagulls fly away screaming.	
11. BSJ in white shirt stands by mouth of cave.	BSJ: During the time I was Gregynog Fellow in the University of Wales, I wrote some Englinion, or I tried to write Welsh poems that were . . .
Fireworks go off within cave.	(World War III has broken out . . .). As I was saying before I was so rudely interrupted. I tried to write Englinion, Welsh poems which are very difficult to do in English. However, here are my poor attempts: This first one is called 'Fern':

Hookheaded hairy young fern,
　springy, curled,
coy greeny thruster set on
its own spread revelation

BROOM
Common broom confused with
　whin,
gorse, furse, finds its own-ness in
ternate leaves, coiled styles and jet
black seedpods: yet it is kin.

BEECH
Beech, from which *book*: like
　learning,
pellucid leaves' late turning
slows ending, adds adjourning.

Shot	Voice

Shot

12. BSJ in white shirt walks along beach to examine metal object in sand. He pulls it out – it is a large brass tack. He shows it to the camera. On its head is written the word 'TACK'.

13. BSJ sits by wood fire at foot of cliffs in red shirt drinking from skull cup. He brings out a packet of sausages from his hold-all and starts to fry them at the fire.

14. Helicopter shot of sea.

15. BSJ by fire as before holding out his hand to show shape of peninsula.

Voice

BSJ: The third summer I spent down here was the strangest of all three in many ways. I'd been asked to come down this time by a man I'd better call 'Henry', who believed that the treasure ship of the Spanish Armada was somewhere out there.

BSJ: You will remember in a peninsula like this, the treasure ship would be about there, off Abersoch. Now you'll remember the Spanish Armada – 1588 – it had a punch-up in the Channel and couldn't get back through the Channel to Spain, so it had to

Shot	*Voice*
	go all the way around Northern Scotland past Ireland.
Camera zooms in on sausage.	And this man, Henry's, idea was, or belief it was, a religious belief almost, one of them had come down through Ireland and had run for shelter in Abersoch here, and sunk in the bay and that this one was carrying
Camera wanders away to look at a telescope and then pans along pebbles.	all the treasure to pay the mercenaries in the Spanish fleet, the whole Spanish Army. So he got me here (can I have your attention please? Just a moment, come back please. This is an interesting story.)
Camera returns slowly to BSJ.	This man, Henry, got me here for the whole summer with the promise of skin-diving down off Abersoch, with the promise of untold millions of gold doubloons and pieces of eight, and all those romantic things.
Camera wanders away along beach.	BSJ: When I actually got here, I found that he hadn't got a boat; that he hadn't got any sort of skin-diving equipment. There was nothing we could do. It was a romantic

Shot

Voice

story . . . (Do you mind?
This is an interesting story I
am telling you – you keep
wandering off! Anyone would
think we were making a film
for the masses where they have
to be entertained every second!)

Camera reluctantly returns to
BSJ.

This man, Henry, had a
cottage, but it was very full
up with his wife and children
and things. So he put me in a
sort of caravan at a field
'called Dwylan'. Now Dwylan
is a very strange place. Dwylan
was a place where you had to
be very careful what you did
with your toenail cuttings. Now
I used to cut mine and keep
them in a little pile and
eventually I buried them in a
stone wall. That seemed the
safest thing to do. That
summer, that third summer,
seemed to mark some sort of
climacteric in my life, so I
wrote a poem about it.

16. Sun on sea through heavy
cloud.

*In the ember days of my last
free summer*

In the ember days of my last free
   summer,
here I lie, outside myself,
   watching
the gross body eating a poor curry:

Shot	*Voice*
	satisfied at what I have done, scared of what
	I have to do in my last free winter.
17. BSJ standing among rocks in green sweater.	Bit portentous, that. You can charge people to watch this – 25p a head; anyone with two heads 40p.
18. Sea sun and clouds as before.	
19. BSJ in green sweater as before.	Cut away to a bunch of bananas.
20. Bananas in waves.	
21. Big close-up BSJ mouth smiling in satisfaction.	
22. Long shot BSJ in white shirt on beach. Labrador dog bounds in and chases stones.	
23. Long shot BSJ in white shirt on beach beckoning Camera as if it were a dog.	BSJ: Come along. This way. Curious things to see. Curious things to see. Come along. Not so fast. Down boy. Down. Down. That's a good boy. Sit.
Camera 'sits'.	Now very gently come and see the curious things. Curious things, well worth seeing.
BSJ beckons Camera and shows it the remains of two sandals.	Look. One there and another

Shot	*Voice*
	one there. I think they've been making all these footprints. You see them all?
BSJ leads camera towards skull cup in sand. He taps the top of the skull.	And what's that there? Is anyone at home one wonders? Hello? Anyone at home? No.
Camera moves on towards thin part of the circle representing moon.	Ah, a sliver of the moon. A representation of the moon.
Camera moves on again towards electric light-bulb stuck in sand.	And here's a light. Another sort of light.
BSJ leads camera on towards two broken heels buried in the sand.	Isn't that good? Look and here are heels. Perhaps they help make the footprints. That one's been ground into the ground by another heel.
BSJ shows outsize paperclip to Camera.	Here – a paperclip. My favourite. Look a paperclip. Lovely paperclip.
BSJ points out Schweik doll buried in the sand.	And here's Schweik. Here's what you've all been waiting for. It's Schweik in his bunker. Good soldier Schweik.

Shot

Voice

Isn't he sweet. We all love
him.

BSJ beckons Camera towards
banana skin and waves it at
Camera.

BSJ: Over here. Careful not
to trip now. Don't trip on the
banana skin. There, did you
enjoy that? Did you enjoy
seeing the curious things.
Here's a little present for you
then. There. Good boy. Good
boy. Sit. Sit. Right. Off you
go and have a run round by
yourself. Off you go. Bye bye.

Camera rushes off through
rocks occasionally pausing to
'sniff' and 'lift its leg' and runs
off into the sea. A wave
dissolves into –

24. sand. BSJ hand comes
into frame Right and wipes
away sand to reveal mirror in
which are reflected BSJ and
Camera crew.

BSJ: Some things can only
be said indirectly. One can
only reflect the truth of what
they were. I am not quite sure
that I know the truth about
this particular thing I want to
talk about indirectly. There's
a mountain called Carn Fadrun
on Lleyn. It's the last
mountain towards the tip of
the peninsula which can be

called a mountain, that is its over 1,000 ft tall. I found myself one morning at dawn on top of that mountain, almost not of my own volition and stripping off all my clothes and making what I can only think of as religious gestures – worshipping some sort of female deity. Now I am not a religious person. I can't explain how that happened or why I felt the need to do it. That's the sort of place Lleyn is. I feel nowhere else on earth here, in Lleyn, doing that sort of thing, that Jung calls the archetype. Something that we do despite the last 2–3,000 years of civilization. There is a much longer period with archetypal patterns of behaviour inside us that we respond to sometimes in certain places, and Carn Fadrun must have been the same way for hundreds of thousands of years. Lleyn, in many ways, has been that sort of place for many hundreds of thousands of years.

25. BSJ in white shirt fights with bananas at sea edge. He finally subdues them and holds them over his head in triumph.

Shot	Voice
26. BSJ in green sweater standing among rocks.	BSJ: I think that'll probably be enough of that.
27. Helicopter shot of BSJ in brown sweater on beach. BSJ leads helicopter to him and motions it down. It sweeps over his head and we see its shadow. He runs towards sea and helicopter follows him. He tries to point out something in the rocks but we do not see what it is. Again helicopter sweeps over his head.	
28. BSJ wearing striped shirt with Assistant Cameraman and clapper board with back to sea.	BSJ: I think there have probably been at least two films trying to get out of this one film. If you feel that you don't really know much more about the Lleyn peninsula at the end of it, well that's probably because I don't know much more about the Lleyn peninsula either. One has to live here, and be born here, for a long while before one can begin to understand the strange sort of place it is. But at least we haven't pretended to be doing anything than making a film about it, about that problem and we have, at the

Shot	*Voice*
	same time, tried to be honest to the film itself.
29. Cut away of bunch of bananas in seaweed.	
30. BSJ as before.	So there are limits to that even. We have been down here something like 20 hours spread out over 3 days. But in the end, Lleyn ought to be left to the Welsh. To them. We ought to go. Off you go. Up, up, up, up, up, up.
BSJ gestures towards helicopter to take off and walks towards the sea.	
31. Helicopter shot. BSJ walks determinedly towards sea. Helicopter rising as he does so.	
He goes on walking until he is lost beneath the waves.	
Helicopter climbs to high shot of Porth Ceiriad Bay.	
32. Very high shot from helicopter flying along bay with Carn Fadrun in far distance. There is no sign of BSJ.	
33. Helicopter shot of Porth Ceiriad Bay from inland.	
34. Deserted beach – evening.	

GABRIEL
JOSIPOVICI

*Gabriel Josipovici was born in Nice in 1940. His maternal grand-
father was a Russian doctor who had settled in Egypt at the turn of the
century, while his maternal grandmother belonged to a long-established
Jewish family from Alexandria. On his father's side his grandfather
was Albert Josipovici, co-author of* Goha le Simple, *the book about
the Egyptian folk-tale hero which took Paris by storm in 1919. After
the war Gabriel Josipovici went to Egypt with his mother and lived
there till September 1956, when he came to England. After a year at
school in Cheltenham he went up to St Edmund Hall, Oxford, to read
English. He graduated in 1961 and since 1963 has been a lecturer in
the School of European Studies at the University of Sussex. He has
published two novels,* The Inventory *(Michael Joseph, 1968) and*
Words *(Gollancz, 1971), and a volume of plays and stories,* Mobius
the Stripper *(Gollancz, 1974), as well as a critical and theoretical
study of modern fiction and its precursors,* The World and the Book
*(Macmillan, 1971; Paladin, 1973). He has also written two radio
plays, and a number of stage plays, the most recent of which was commissioned by the Actors' Company and performed by them at the
Edinburgh Festival, on tour throughout the country, and for a successful season at the Shaw Theatre, London.*

LETTER TO THE EDITOR

Dear Giles,
   You ask for a short 'critical piece' to place alongside the fiction
I've just sent you and which, you say, will give readers some idea
of the way I think about writing and what lines I feel it should follow
in the immediate future. For many reasons, some obvious, some less
so, I find this an impossible request. Such a piece would be directed
at an anonymous public, but of its nature it is only the kind of thing
one might be able, hesitantly, to say in a letter to a friend. So in this
letter, for you, I am jotting down some thoughts and opinions which
you might find helpful. I hope they are connected, for they all

seem relevant to me, but I feel it would be a mistake to try and draw out the connections and so I have left them in the form of separate items. Most often I have started from the remarks of painters or composers because I find that they tend to put things far better than writers seem able to – perhaps because they use words less often.

1. Franz Kline: 'You don't paint the way someone, observing your life, thinks you *have* to paint. You paint the way you have to in order to give. Someone will look at it and say it is the product of knowing, but it has nothing to do with knowing. It has to do with giving.'

To talk about oneself and one's art as I am about to here is to talk from the standpoint of that 'someone else'. From one's own standpoint one never knows where one is going or why. That is probably why one writes: to find out. If I could say with certainty: 'This is what I am trying to do', or 'This is where I am going', I would cease to write.

2. From the beginning I have always wanted to make things, not tell stories. I have no capacity for invention, little interest in wrapping whatever I do invent in the required gestures of verisimilitude, and I have had no 'interesting' experiences. In short, I have nothing to tell and little desire to preach (why should my views on morality or politics be more interesting than anyone else's?). Yet I am fascinated by the impulse towards invention that wells up in all of us, and I am constantly filled with excitement at the world in which I live. (That it is a strange world may in part be due to the fact that I only came to this country at the age of fifteen, but I am sure this is not the only reason – think of Wordsworth and the Lakes or Wallace Stevens and New Haven or Florida.) Seeing people in trains or cafés I often feel an intense desire to grasp how they will feel at the moment of their deaths or when an irreparable loss hits them and knocks the breath out of their bodies. And in the middle of a town or an empty landscape I occasionally have the sense that I am seeing the world as a fly or a horse might see it. Then I want to make an object in words that will catch this sense without destroying or distorting it. Or perhaps it is just that I want

to live longer with this feeling and the only way I know how is to write.

3. Deleuze and Guattari: 'The proper name does not designate an individual; on the contrary, it is only when the individual opens himself up to the multiplicities which invade him, when he has passed through the most stringent test of depersonalization, that he acquires his veritable proper name. The proper name is the instantaneous apprehension of a multiplicity.'

In daily life we are, as it were, allowed one voice only, or at least only one voice at a time. But each one of us is constantly beset by hundreds of voices, all clamouring for attention. To give in to them in daily life would certainly be to go mad. But in art the possibility offers itself of giving them their head and not being torn apart by them.

There is a special problem with an art that uses words. A novel with many characters is still a novel with only one voice – the voice of the narrator, describing action and settings, moving the characters from place to place, directing the reader how to think and feel. A play with many subplots is still a play with only one voice – the voice which lies behind the convolutions of the plot, which determines how the thing starts and finishes, what gets left out and what included. How to escape from this dominant voice has been a central preoccupation for me from the start. I would almost be tempted to say that for me the test of quality of any work resides in the degree to which the artist has been able to free himself from submission to one central voice, without disintegrating into chaos either at the local level of the phrase or at the level of overall structure. That is why George Eliot and William Burroughs I find just about equally unreadable, the one holding back too much, the other giving in too much. That is why Rabelais and Sterne and Nabokov (especially in *Lolita*) are writers I admire and love and will keep on returning to.

4. From Proust I learnt to have confidence in my response to the world; from Stravinsky I learnt that coolness and clarity of outline can often lead to far more moving effects than those achieved by the expressive heat of a Mahler or a Lawrence. From him I learnt that

a work can be built in blocks, returned to again and again in the course of a composition, rather than in a purely linear, forward-moving direction. Stravinsky convinced me of the viability of my discovery, in the course of writing my first novel, that rhythm could be a central integrating factor even in a large-scale work, and from then on I have worked mainly in dialogue, dispensing with any narrative voice, using blocks of dialogue, sharply juxtaposed and frequently returned to, as the main structural element.

Stravinsky: 'Now [at 85] I feel like those old men Swift describes in Laputa, who wished to communicate no longer with words, but with objects themselves.'

These objects are of course not individual words or notes, but whole blocks of music, scenes or fragments of scenes. I have preferred to use dialogue in the making of such objects rather than description, like Robbe-Grillet, because I wanted the texture of my work to be alive from the beginning to the end. Here too Stravinsky has been vitally important. The sheer pleasure of listening to every sound he makes does not interfere with our sense of wonder at the intellectual rigour of his constructions. No division here into easy and difficult, high and low brow, radios one and three. Not since the Middle Ages has there been such an easy commerce of the pleasures of the mind and senses: this is a unified art.

5. John Russell on Henry Moore: 'The point is that the big late bronzes are adapted to a double perspective – that of the man who comes upon them from a distance, as he might glimpse a great ruin from the air, and that of the man who traverses them as a fly might traverse the Erechtheum.'

The object created always carries a fundamental ambiguity. This is in a sense the natural outcome of dispensing with the narrative voice. What John Russell says about the Moores catches very well my own desire to make things capable of being read in different ways, depending on the mood of the reader and the assumptions he brings to the reading. Thus in my second novel, and in some of the stories such as 'Seascape with Figures', the reader should feel that something of enormous, life-shattering significance has taken place – or again that *nothing* has taken place. Just as I would want the viewer of my two recent plays, *Dreams of Mrs Fraser* and *Flow*, to feel that he was being presented with a tiny, momentary gap in the continuum of everyday life, with the brief glimpse afforded by a dream, a reverie – but also that here was the absolute shape of entire lives, entire epochs even, unfolding in front of him as they might in front of a God or a particularly long-lived elephant.

6. Though the basic material for the making of my fictions has been the dialogue fragment, an important binding element is provided by the title. In two instances in particular, my first novel, *The Inventory*, and the story 'Mobius the Stripper', the title has been the starting-point for the work, establishing the limits I require before any work can get under way. In the novel the contradiction between the two elements in the title, *inventory* (the mere listing of random external objects) and *invent* (the organization imposed on the world by desire), was something that called for exploration in formal and existential terms *at the same time*. The formal exploration would itself be an exploration of the relation *in everyday life*, between these two – an exploration ultimately, I suppose, of the relation of the individual to the world into which he is born and in which he must die.

In 'Mobius the Stripper' the title is more playful. Reading Euler's famous essay on the bridges of Koenigsburg and the editor's comments on the nature of topology, Mobius strips, Klein bottles and the like, it came to me in a flash of what Freud would call wit, that one could write a piece in the form of a Mobius strip about a fat Austrian (?) stripper called Mobius. In the normal course of events I would never have written about strippers or bothered to create a work in the form of a Mobius strip (this is where I'd align myself with Pinget rather than Ricardou, with Bellow rather than Barth). But the happy conjunction of *a* form and *a* subject in fact led to a story which I was able to write with a kind of free-flowing pleasure I had never achieved in short pieces before.

7. In the making of fictions the primary need is to discover the rules, the limits. When one turns to the stage the limits are already there, ineluctably. The question then becomes: 'How to fill *this* space, *here*?' Or, more worryingly: '*Why* fill this space, here?' In

Dreams of Mrs Fraser the central question within the fiction – 'Why does Mrs Fraser exhibit herself naked in a cage for all to see?' – fed and was in turn fed by the question I asked myself – 'Why put an actor/actress on a stage for people to look at?' Mrs Fraser's own search for an answer is also mine, and mine hers (the second character, in his puzzlement as to her motives, mediates between the two of us, as he mediates in the play between Mrs Fraser and the real/imaginary audience). Once again the title directs us to two quite different possibilities: it could refer to anyone in the world dreaming of Mrs Fraser, and be an exploration of the nature and significance of such dreaming; or it could refer to the nightmares of the poor lady herself. Why should I be the one to say which it is?

8. The above remarks have been attempts to freeze the past and to draw a few generalizations from what I have done so far. There is no guarantee that what I have said really does apply, either to my own work or to that of other people. There is even less guarantee that it will continue to apply. Already 'Contiguities' seems to be moving in a rather different direction, though it has affinities with *Flow*. Perhaps it would be appropriate to end with a quotation from Henry Moore which struck me when I read it as describing very well the mood I was in when I wrote 'Contiguities'. Commenting on his strange Three-Part Object of 1960, Moore says: 'I don't know how a piece like that begins. I just begin in the morning with a bit of clay and form comes about. Either it has some interest, and keeps it, or it doesn't. If it has, I go on without having to know, or trying to know, exactly what it means. I wish in a way that I could be even freer than I am from the tie of having to know exactly what it means, so that I can take a form and develop it and carry it further without ever having to have an "explanation".'

Yrs,
    Gabriel

CONTIGUITIES

1. The room.
   You stand in the room.
   And a voice says: He climbs the stairs. With his coat tightly belted and his hat wedged down firmly on his head he climbs the stairs.

2. The other says: Go on.
   He waits.
   He says: Go on.
   You say: I – . . .
   He says: Go on. Don't stop. Go on.
   You say: I don't – . . . I can't – . . .
   He says: Go on.
   You say: I can't – . . . I – . . .
   He waits.
   He leans forward.
   He repeats: Go on. Don't stop. Just go on.

3. The other.
   His face: Fat cheeks; fat neck; and the hat on his head.
   And the woman says: I stand at the window. I turn from the window. I bring him his coffee. He smiles. I bring him his coffee.

4. The other.
   He sits at his breakfast.
   He says: I begin in the morning. My task begins in the morning.
   He says: When the alarm goes I stretch out my hand and silence it. Then I am awake. I bring my hand back under the bedclothes and wait, eyes closed, for a count of sixty seconds. Then I open my eyes. I am ready to begin.

5. The woman.

She says: I hold his face in my hands. I say: I hold your face in my hands. He doesn't smile. He looks into my face and doesn't smile. I hold his face, my hands on his face. My hands.

6. The other says: Go on. Don't stop. Go on.

You say: I – . . .

The other says: Go on.

He waits.

He repeats: Go on.

You say: I –

He says: Yes?

You say: I . . . I turn from the window. I see the door open. Her face in the doorway. The tray in her hands. I hear her say: Coffee.

– Go on.

– I – . . .

– Don't stop. Go on. Don't stop.

– I – . . . I don't – . . .

The other says: Talk. Just talk. Don't stop. Talk.

7. The woman.

She says: I walk by the river. I take out the sheaf of photos and tear them across and again across and scatter the fragments. Bits of paper blow into my face and settle on the water.

8. The room.

You stand at the window.

From the room only your back is visible.

And a voice says: Standing at the window. Looking out. Looking at the wall. At the brick. Sunlight on the brick. Peace.

Says: He climbs the stairs. With his coat tightly belted and his hat wedged down firmly on his head he climbs the stairs.

9. The other.

He says: My table is all set for breakfast. I light the fire under the water for the egg, switch on the toaster and the kettle. My egg boils for three minutes. I select the right hour-glass and watch the sand trickle through. I like my egg soft. Soft-boiled. Barely cooked. I like it like that.

10. The room.

You stand at the window.

And the woman says: Why don't you speak?

You say: I don't know.

She says: I like you when you are silent.

She says: It makes me uncertain of this room. This bed. This window.

You say: Yes.

She says: It makes me think of afternoons, walking by the river in the country.

You say: Why? Why a river?

She says: It does. It just does.

You say: We never walked. By a river. In the country.

She says: It just does. This room. With the sunlight on the brick.

She adds: On days like this.

You don't turn round. You say: We never walked. In the country. Never.

11. The other.

He pushes aside the breakfast things.

He leans across the table.

He says: I climb the stairs. At a certain moment I climb the stairs. A given moment. I climb.

He says: On the third floor the door opens. I enter the room. We begin to talk.

12. The room.

You turn in the room.

The other says: Go on.

You say: Turning.

He says: Go on.

– Turning from the window.

– Yes?

– Turning from the window.

– Yes? Go on. Yes?

– I – . . .

The other waits.

You say: I – . . .
– Speak, the other says. Speak.
You say: I don't – . . . I can't – . . .
He says, quietly: Just go on.
He waits.
He repeats, without insistence: Just go on. Just go on. Don't stop. Just go on.

13. The woman.
She says: At first it was easy. It always is. We walked along the bank by the river. Sometimes we lay under the trees and rested. Afterwards there was a silence.
She says: Afterwards there were silences.

14. The woman.
Her face.
She smiles.
And the other says: When I have breakfasted I shave. I pinch the right cheek with the left hand, left ear to left shoulder, caressing. The clock ticks on the mantelpiece. I examine my cheeks, my neck. The mirror comes between us.

15. The room.
You lie on the bed, one leg bent at the knee, the other stretched out across the sheets, the pit of your stomach in the pit of the bed.
You have the sense of many people hurrying about their tasks.
You have the sense of your body, still, on the bed, in the room.

16. The other.
He says: When I enter the room he turns from the window. I smile, taking off my coat and folding it, laying it on my arm with only the lining showing. He turns, smiling answer to my smile. There is a silence between us.

17. The woman.
She says: Later he admitted I might have been right. Not that he was not fond of the photos, he was, but that their presence might have proved a distraction, drawing our attention from what was important.

She says: I tried to explain that none of this had counted with me, feeling still the soft flakes as the wind blew the pieces over my face and scattered noses, smiles, legs, ears, over the water, but I saw he was not listening, or perhaps my voice did not emerge with enough power to carry across the intervening space.

18. The room.
   You stand in the room.
   You turn from the window.
   You look at the door.
   And a voice says: Listening to the footsteps on the stairs. Seeing her face. Lying on the bed, one foot on the floor, leg bent at the knee.
   Says: Turning from the window. Lying on the bed. Hearing her voice. Seeing her face.
   You stand in the room.
   You look at the door.

19. The other.
   He dresses: After the shirt, the trousers. After the trousers, the tie. After the tie, the jacket. After the jacket, the overcoat. After the overcoat, the scarf. After the scarf, the hat. He tightens the belt of the overcoat.
   In the face of the clock it is possible to see, as well as the hands, the numbers, a reflection of the chin, the neck, and so adjust the tie. By bending the knees a little the forehead comes into view, and, above it, the hat.
   He says: I adjust the hat. I am ready to emerge.

20. He says: Don't stop.
   You say: I don't – . . .
   He says: Go on.
   He waits.
   You say: Lying on the bed. One foot on the floor.
   He waits.
   He says: Yes?
   One leg bent at the knee.
   – Yes?

B.T.W.—G

– Sun on my face.
– Yes?
– Peace.
He waits.
He says: Go on.
– Peace.
– Go on.
– Peace.
He waits.
He sighs.
He says: Go on. Don't stop. Just go on.

21. The woman.
    She says: I walk by the river. I take the photos one by one and tear them across.
    She says: When I told him what I had done he took my face in his hands. He looked into my eyes, holding my face in his hands. I knew it was the end.

22. The room.
    You stand in the room.
    And a voice says: When she was there I fretted. When she had gone I felt the void. A common complaint. Lying on the bed, one foot on the floor, leg bent at the knee, the other stretched diagonally across the sheets, I thought of her walking along the bank of the river, tearing the photos across and across before delivering the fragments to the wind, and thought of the other, fat cheeks, fat neck, adjusting his tie, polishing his shoes, seeing his inclined face in the shining leather, placing the hat on his head, belting his over-coat, leaving the house, emerging into the street, walking towards the bus stop, smiling.

23. And again the other says: Don't stop. Go on.
    He waits.
    He says quietly: Don't stop. Just don't stop.
    He waits.
    He repeats: Just go on.
    You say: Standing.

He says: Yes?

– At the window. Looking at the wall. Brick wall. Mellow the brick. Mellowed by the evening sunlight.

– Go on.

– Standing by the window. Looking.

– Go on.

– The sense of many people going about their business. Peace.

– Go on.

– Silence.

– Go on.

– Silence.

He waits.

He repeats: Go on.

He waits, tapping the floor with his foot.

He says: Don't stop. Go on. Don't stop.

He leans forward smiling. He says: Speak. Don't stop. Speak. Just speak.

24. The room.

You stand in the room.

And a voice says: When he entered I claimed I did not know him. He smiled and removed his overcoat. He folded it carefully so that only the silk lining showed, and laid it over his left arm. I asked him what he wanted but he only smiled again and sat down on the bed. When I insisted on an answer his smile only broadened and he removed the hat. I noted that he lacked several teeth.

25. The woman.

She stands, leaning against a tree, smiling into the sunlight.

She says: Sometimes he talked about his past. He talked about his solitude, living in one room with nothing but a bed and a window giving onto a brick wall. He talked about his sense of peace in that room, with nothing to disturb him. Sometimes he would wake up screaming and talking about that peaceful room where he would lie and have the sense of the rest of the world hurrying about its business. He trembled as he talked, waking me with the terror in his voice as he talked of that time and of the peace of that time.

26. The river.

Bits of paper float upon it, carried gently downstream.

And a voice says: I asked her if she remembered but she would not be drawn. We looked at the photos, sitting on the soft bed side by side, but where I strained and questioned the printed images she was casual, almost off-hand. As she put them away I asked her what she intended to do with them, but she declined to answer.

27. The other.

He says: The bus arrives at 9.46. I find a seat at the top, no difficulty now that the morning rush is over. From the top the gardens are visible, a restful sigh on such a journey, so monotonously repetitive. At certain points, when the bus runs alongside a particularly high and uniform terrace of houses, it is possible to observe my reflection in the window. I take this opportunity to adjust my tie, my hat.

28. The room.

You stand in the room.

You stand at the window.

The woman says: There are things you don't tell me.

You say: Perhaps.

She says: When you turn from the window.

Sunlight on the brick. Mellow the brick.

She says: Do you know what I mean?

She waits.

She says: As though you had been listening. Waiting for me to enter. Listening.

You say: I don't know.

She says: That is what you always say.

You turn from the window.

She says quickly: Are you going out?

– Perhaps.

– Tell me, she says. If you are. Remember to tell me.

29. The room.

You lie on the bed.

And a voice says: Of course I recognized him when he entered. I must have seen him before. In a pub perhaps. Or in the park by the river. There are many people by the river. They sit with their backs against the trees, looking at the water.

30. The room.
    You stand in the room.
    You turn from the window.
    You lie on the bed.
    You turn from the window.
    The other says: Go on.
    He waits.
    He says: Go on.
    You say: Turning from the window.
    He waits.
    You say: Seeing her face.
    He says: Go on.
    – Hearing her voice.
    – Yes?
    – Lying on the bed. Turning from the window.
    – Go on.
    – Peace.
    – Yes?
    – Silence.
    – Yes? Go on. Yes?
    He waits, tapping on the floor with the tip of his shoe.
    He waits.
    He leans forward. He says: Don't stop. Just go on. Just go on.
Don't stop.

31. The woman.
    She says: I take his face in my hands.
    She says: I walk, scattering.

32. The room.
    You turn from the window.
    You cross the room.
    You open the door.

And the other says: After the bus there is always time for a drink. After that it is time for lunch. After lunch there are the stairs.

You close the door.

You turn in the room.

You turn, surveying the room.

You say: I turn.

You say: I lie.

You say: I stand.

Your words echo in the empty room.

33. The woman.

She leans against a tree, looking at the river.

She says, in the room: Do you want to go out?

You say: Out?

– To walk by the river. Lie under the trees.

You say: Is that what you would like to do?

She says: We could do that. Or we could stay here. If you prefer.

You say: No. I don't prefer.

34. You stand in the room.

And a voice says: I see her walking by the river. I see her scattering the fragments. Pieces fall into the water. Float away.

Says: The other sits under the trees, looking at the water, coat tightly belted, hat pressed down firmly on his head, motionless.

35. The other.

He says: Sometimes, if the weather permits, I have a little sit by the river, between lunch and the stairs. That's for my digestion.

36. The room.

You stand in the room.

You stand at the window.

And a voice says: Always he waits, pressing gently, not giving me time to think. He sits on the bed with his coat over his left arm only the lining showing, his hat in his hand, but he does not leave I wait for him to leave but he makes no move.

Says: I stand, leaning against the sill, nonchalantly, and we talk

Says: He stands, leaning against the sill, nonchalantly, and we talk.

Says: As he enters the room he lays down the coat on the bed and on the coat he lays his hat.

Says: He lays down the coat the hat I sit he stands. Lays down the coat keeps on the hat I sit he stands.

Says: The coat the hat I stand he sits.

Says: The coat I stand he sits the hat.

Says: Not this. Not this.

And you stand at the window, looking out at the wall.

And a voice says.

37. The woman.

She says: I walk by the river. It is the end.

38. The other.

He says: I climb the stairs. With my coat tightly belted and my hat wedged down firmly on my head I climb the stairs.

39. The room.

You stand in the room.

You turn, surveying the room.

You say: Not this. Not this.

You say: No wall. No window. No bed. No door. No stairs. No trees. No river.

You say: I say: No wall. No window. No bed. No door. No stairs. No trees. No river.

You say: Not this. Not here.

You say: I say: Not here. I say: Not. I say: I. I.

You stand in the room.

You open your mouth in the room.

40. You stand in the room.

And the woman says: I stand at the window. I turn from the window. I bring him his coffee. He smiles. I bring him his coffee. I bring it to him.

ROBERT
NYE

NOTE

I started to write stories to amuse myself between writing poems. There was once a longish gap between one poem and the next – seven years – during which I had time to write quite a number of stories, eventually published as *Tales I Told My Mother* (1969). These stories are intended to amuse others besides myself, although in effect I have noticed that it is mostly poets who tend to be amused by them. This might be because they are fundamental storytelling stuff, told tales, folk narrative, or because like the material in the old chapbooks they are composed upon certain principles of oral repetition and other verbal patterns not dissimilar to some of the rhythms governing poetic composition. I have also tried my hand at the same kind of telling for children, sometimes in direct transaltion or interpretation, as in *Beowulf* (1968), sometimes by reworking traditional material to make it new, as in *Wishing Gold* (1970). My task as a writer of stories I take to be the writing of a single story which might amuse children *and* poets.

At the same time my stories are intended as a relief from the truth-telling which poetry requires of its adherents. The connection between fiction and lying interests me. As a matter of fact I do not write short stories so much as tall stories, fibs, lies, whoppers. The matter is traditional, it comes from the parish pump not the well of personal experience. That is to say, my stories have their source in dreams which more than one person has dreamt, in ballads, jests, yarns, and in those folk tales which are as it were the dreams of the people coming to us without the interference of our own identity. I do not claim for them any importance on account of their origins. *A Bach fugue is an obsession overcome*, as Simone Weil says in a sentence which I have always meant one day to use as an epigraph to my fictions, *which is why the initial theme is not of so much importance*. The delight taken in *storying* in Chaucer, Nashe, Sterne, and for that matter the *Arabian Nights* interests me.

The other day I was reading Newman's *Grammar of Assent* (1870) and found certain implications of its title – a grammar of assent, written thus, in lower case – coming to mind as a metaphor of what modern writers try to provide for their readers. But then one must look with suspicion at that word 'modern'. Modern since when? And if one says, as some still do, as though dismissing the thing as a failure in a test-tube, 'the experimental novel', what is there to be spoken of? Its future? Everyone has been talking about 'the future' of 'the experimental novel' for as long as I can remember. Yet there's nothing new under the moon. A grammar of assent might be worth attention, might be worth being grounded *in*, if only because the grammar of negation offered us by so much contemporary writing is by definition futile, and declines towards nothing more final than incoherence. The pity is that few critics talk about the *past* of the experimental novel. (Gabriel Josipovici in *The World and the Book*, 1971, is an honourable exception.) Taking the English language alone, how many of those who refer glibly to this or that pronouncement of the (I think) over-rated Robbe-Grillet have read Blake's *An Island in the Moon* (1784–85)? How many of them know their Peacock, their Swift, their Nashe, their Sterne? The truth is that we have a *tradition* of 'experimental' writing in English, but this commonly being referred to only as a series of isolated eccentric works the continuity of that tradition is lost. English criticism has not yet caught up with the English imagination. The best book on Sterne, for instance, is by a Frenchman, Henri Fluchère, whose *Laurence Sterne: de l'homme à l'œuvre* (1961) comes right out and demonstrates how Sterne's narrative method, far from being crazy, is sensitively at one with what it intends to convey.

To be blunt, could I suggest that there is in effect only writing that is alive, and writing that is half-alive? Writing that is alive is what we call eccentric (if in English) or experimental (if in French). Perhaps my naïvety will be forgiven. It springs from having perpetrated two prose works – *Doubtfire* (1967) and *Tales* (1969) – which technically and otherwise are indebted to Sidney's *Arcadia* (1590) and Nashe's *The Unfortunate Traveller* (1594), both declensions within a grammar of assent in their day. English critics however saw fit to discuss them largely in terms of their own preferences in recent foreign literatures. There are even gentlemen amongst whom Joyce is spoken of as a kind of Irish disease which briefly infected the pure blood-stream of the novel in English, and who will accuse any young writer who cannot emulate C. P. Snow of aping the latest French manners. But that is another anti-story. Let me make the positive suggestion that someone devotes a critical book to what the *English* have done on the edge (or is it at the root?) of fiction. Such a study could even find its fashionable epigraph in Michel Butor, who has admitted more than once that experimentation on the other side of the Channel owes more than a pound to the Reverend Mr Sterne.

Yet I will admit finally that they order this matter better in France, so long as you travel far enough – beyond even Charles Sorel's *L'Anti-roman* (1633) – back, in fact, to Rabelais, who is for me the master storyteller, the master of form at one with content. Rabelais likes it here. He tells his tales and he laughs. The laughing is the telling, the tales those that make themselves known to any pedantic peasant. They are good tales, tales of giants and philosophers, and if not the best at least sufficient to sustain his awareness of meaning as a property most likely to turn up in a persistent state of possibility, tasting as you might say of Now for ever after – which is to speak of an immediateness difficult to maintain in prose bound by a system of tenses to some acknowledgement of the passage of time. I would like to be found to write with a little of his spirit, celebrating *lalme et grand mère la terre* as he calls it in the Third Book. A habit of taking whatever comes to hand – a dry summer in 1532, a cask or two of wine, all that he had heard or read which seemed to rhyme or chime – this habit allowed Rabelais to give fictitiousness its head. If you take a few related details and look at them hard enough you are likely to end up with a myth; if you concentrate on the local and domestic it is possible that you will find the world and his wife without trying; we have been shown how bread and wine can be veils, but perhaps there is a sense in which the whole world is a sacrament, a sense approached romantically by Charles Williams, who is said to have thought of the Incarnation whenever he lit a match, a sense approached materialistically at many points by Rabelais, who was at least as well aware of the need to concentrate on what was under his nose, in Lyons, in 1532, as Sterne was, in Sutton-in-the-Forest, in 1759, and as Joyce was when he began to cook the soup of a day in Dublin in 1904. That sense may be academically patronized as eccentric, on account of its energy in pursuit of digression and irrelevance, but it is arguable that it presents a more recognizable paradigm of things as they are than do the tame tricks of those writers who never digress for fear that the act might involve them in some truth which they do not want to know, or even perhaps evoke a coherence beyond the irrelevant.

ADAM KADMON

For instance, Adam Kadmon. Tell you all about him. All about Adam. Adam Kadmon. Start at the beginning. For instance, crickets. What do you know about crickets, when it comes down to it? Not grasshoppers, fanciful things, drowning in dew. Crickets. A simple question. You hear these crickets making their noise in the fields at evening, you standing on the stone step by your door which is also green. Nothing more ordinary in the wide world. But you don't understand them. Crickets, they say. Crickets, your ears tell you. That noise speaks what is making it. It's dull. It's brown. It has nothing to do with you.

Adam Kadmon was born in a certain town on a certain day in a year before the years your author knows. His father was a shoemaker. His father's name was Isaak. Isaak Kadmon said the sign over the door of his shop, *Isaak Kadmon Shoemaker.* It was in a steep little street, indifferently cobbled, you wouldn't have looked twice. Then there was Adam's mother. Well was she his mother? More of that later. The leaves are still falling in the lamplight, look, falling still on the wet cobbles in the lamplight, but that will be in Tempelhof, not where the Parade Ground is. Important to get one or two things clear from the start. The miller's thumb, for instance. The art is in the stone. It looks crude, it looks easy, two girt stones grinding together, what could be simpler. But in the cut and clarity of that furrow, the way the miller marks his stone, or the miller's man, his amanuensis, there you have it, the whole art. When he opens the gate the stream runs straight. If he opened it full it would bring the mill down. So he opens it half, the water flows through, the green water, and round and round the wheel goes, and the chalky walls shake and you can smell the flour fly, the oatmeal in the air, in the low gloom, though it's a while now since they bore sacks up the thin stair, spread corn to warm on the worn stones, lit the fire under, and let the wind spin the cowl as it would. When you look up it moves slightly, that cowl, then the whole twisted roof moves, and you're lost. Also the miller has bad breath.

Enough of millers. The place closed, of course, for a lack not of corn but of men who knew how to grind it, in the old ways, to the ancient specifications, with water and stones, furrows and thumbs. The miller's taste was in his thumb. We know too little about the miller.

Isaak Kadmon loved the miller's daughter. She was a fine creature. Her name was Angelica. They did not marry because their fathers spoilt it. How did they spoil it? By plotting marriage. Listen Isaak, said his father to him, I want you to marry the miller's daughter. Angelica listen, her father said to her, I want you to make a good catch for yourself, that Isaak Kadmon, for instance. Speak nicely to her, said Kadmon père. Be sweet to him, said the miller. Next day the would-be lovers met. Isaak, said Angelica, my father has told me to marry you. Is that so? said Isaak, in that case I think we should sleep together first to find out if we're suited. Angelica agreed. That night they lay together in her bed above the mill wheel. The air was salty with flour. His eyes pricked. She did not know what to say. Isaak, she whispered at last. Yes, said Isaak. Did you come round the mill pond by the blue dovecots? says she. Yes, says Isaak. And did you notice a big heap of dung under the wall? she asks. I did, says Isaak, somewhat surprised. Well, says Angelica, that's mine. Yours, says Isaak. I did it, says Angelica, every bit. She was a lovely lovely creature, but she did have the one shortcoming – she lacked conversation.

So Isaak married Sara. More about Sara in a minute – this is not Sara's story, this is the story of Adam Kadmon. Some say Isaak was not his father. It happened, you see, that Isaak and Sara were living in a wild place, long away from everywhere, where maps stopped and strangers seldom came. Sara was as sweet as a bee and a good wife to boot, but Isaak loved her so jealously that he couldn't bear another man to be looking at the ground where her shadow had passed. One night there was a howling storm. Standing at the window at the turn of the stair, Sara calls to Isaak to come and look out to sea. There's a ship there, blown like a feather before the wind and being driven into their bay for shelter. Soon enough after there's a knock at the door. Rattattat. Isaak opens it. It's a tall red-haired man in a black coat asking for food and a bed for the night. He's a gentleman down to his bootlaces, you can see that, and as he sits there warming his hands by the fire and looking at the lady of the house as she carries in the dishes one by one, it comes into Isaak's head that anybody glancing in at the window just now would think what a fine married pair they make, and himself only an interloper thrown up by the storm on a shore where he doesn't belong. As Isaak rubs his temples with this line of thinking, the stranger throws back his head and yawns. He has an uncommonly pretty mouth and a most artistic manner of yawning. At the same moment, almost as part of the same gesture, Sara yawns too. It's a sign, Isaak thinks to himself, it's a sign between them; she must have known him before I married her, when she was only Sara Mundi. He sits furiously beside the fire, still and passionate, nursing his grief. If he had met a former lover of his wife's on the road or in the tavern, he could have knocked him down and killed him. But this pretty fellow with the red hair and pink mouth has come to him cunningly, in search of sanctuary from a storm, and is now a guest within his house. You can't throttle guests. They eat their meat pie, the three of them, with gravy, by the hissing fire, with little speech, and none of it from Isaak, who sits sullen and sunken in his skin. When the stranger has disappeared upstairs with his candle, Isaak goes to the Bombay tea-chest and takes from it a hank of hempen rope. His wife he gathers by the wrist. Come, he says, and leads her out into the storming dark. What's the matter, Sara cries, what are you wanting with me? Love, says injured Isaak, and the truth. You have them both, answers Sara, oh you've always had them. And I mean to keep them, promises her Isaak. I mean to keep you true, he explains, by way of elaboration, and not have you opening your legs for that old flame of yours who's in the house. His wife holds up her hand. I swear to you, she says, by my own dear hope of heaven, I am innocent of this sin which you say is mine. I never saw that man before in my life, she adds. In that case, says Isaak, you were quick to be making the signs of lust between the two of you, watching and smiling, yawning when he yawned and the rest of it.

He's in a fury now, our Isaak Kadmon, and his fingers fly and burn as he fashions a noose in the end of the hempen rope and drops the noose about his wife's young neck. He leads her through the dark towards the wood. The wind is dropping but it still blows hard enough, every third gust or so, and they have to struggle to reach the ragged trees. As they go, Isaak and Sara, a noise of wings goes with them, it's a flock of small birds, fluttering against the ends of the storm. The moon rides out and there's a pool of moonlight for them to move through, like people underwater, as they reach the first tree of the wood and Isaak throws his rope over the lowest bough. Up goes the rope, and it crosses the branch, but it does not lodge there. The birds are there first, you see, hopping and dancing, and the rope slides down over their beating wings, and skids away, and falls to the ground. Isaak tries again. Up goes the rope, the birds' wings beat, down it falls without purchase. We will go, says Isaak grandly, to the next tree; it's an oak, in any case, if memory serves me right, which will be more apt. With a tug or two at the hempen rope, he leads Sara on by the neck. But when they reach the great oak the same thing happens, the birds are there before them and the rope slips down over their beating wings. Isaak stamps his foot. He drags his wife from tree to tree. But it's the same at every one. The birds are there before them, through the storm, flying in the dark. At last, Isaak says: I know one tree where your birds can't save you. It's the gallows he means, the gallows standing on the far side of the wood, where the road curls round before it falls into the sea. Sara's weeping, Sara's white and shaking, she knows he means the gallows. But Isaak's got a heart like a rock in him now, and her tears won't change that. He's choked with jealousy. He drags her through the black wood to the gallows. When they're there he throws the end of the hempen rope up and across the bar – but even as the rope is snaking through the air, the air is full of wings and the moon spills on them, and on the gallows, and on the man hanging there, and Isaak sees the flock of birds fly down again and settle on the bar, so that his rope won't rest. And there are more birds than ever this time, the air's all birds, all over the dead man too, sitting on his head and his shoulders, swallows mostly, but martens and fieldfares as well, blue and black in the swing of the moon, falling off and hanging in the air, fighting for places, perched on every upright and horizontal, their wings a-flicker, so that it might as well be water the rope is trying to hold. Isaak was a simple man and he knew a miracle when he saw one. He unloosed the rope from round about Sara's neck, and he fell on his knees before her and the gallows in the rain that was beginning. Forgive me, he said. Nine months later, to that night, Adam was born.

This is the story of Adam Kadmon. When April was unpicking the blossoms on the whitethorn, when expert April was unlocking the earliest blossoms on the whitethorn, when April with shy smiles was unclenching the first fists of whitethorn blossom, Adam Kadmon, our hero, son of Isaak, was born at Zinnowitz in Usedom. The midwife, whose name was Rachel, and who hailed from the neighbouring island of Wollin, could find no swaddling clothes, so she wrapped the babe in an old petticoat of her own. Looking at his head, she pointed to a caul on it. Born under a lucky star, she noted. Then she saw the black spot, no bigger than a sixpence, on his left shoulder. Alas, she wept, signed also with the devil's fingerprint. Usedom is a perfectly flat island, 31 miles long, separated from Wollin by the Swine, the two of them dividing the Stettiner Haff from the sea. Adam Kadmon first drew the breath of life in this sausage-shaped Prussian province, though some say that it was not at Zinno-witz, but Swinemünde, and not in April, most suitable of months for pilgrimages, but that it was on the 12th day of the month of March, the feast day of St Gregory the Great, Servant of the Servants of God, Bishop of the Apostolic See, Apostle of England, our father who sent us baptism. Such opinion has it yet that his father was Isaak Kadmon, an honourable man, who used to relax by playing his musical boxes backwards, and coming of a family sufficiently genteel, whose care, according to the affection implanted by nature, towards his own son, as well as his being a lad of great hope and good disposition, was chiefly bestowed in informing his mind with Greek and Latin literature. Holding that classicism deals with reality in terms of the ordering and clarifying functions of the mind, while romanticism prefers to work in terms of overwhelming personal experience, whether its mood be one of rapture or outrage, it was Isaak's wish that his boy would be able to tell a dactyl from a spondee. On the other hand, there are those who claim that the rascal Adam was born in the morning of the 23rd day of September, St Adamnan's Day, and that he was named at noon, and went in the evening to swim across the Swine with the midwife Rachel on his back, bearing her home to Wollin. This same Rachel was a small woman, plain and eager, an intense little mouse living in hope that a big tomcat would one day jump on her. Blissfully shy, tremulously silent except when telling stories, suffering from a chronic liver deficiency and an equally chronic need to be loved, she quivered through what passed for life in Prussia wearing a barège dress with a pattern of faint green moss, her hair en bandeaux, mittens on her paws, the eyes behind her spectacles on sharp look-out for symptoms of insincerity, moral facetiousness, or otherwise offensive brilliance in those she met. She was serious and fussy, this Rachel, liking sunsets and waterfalls, the kind of person afflicted with aphorisms in the presence of either – and that is all your author intends to say about her. Arrived in Wollin, Rachel placed salt in Adam's cradle and sewed a speck of iron into the seams of his blouse. The child was sained then. Fir candles were lighted and whirled round the bed in which mother and infant lay. This whirling was done three times and in the direction in which the sun moved round the house. Usedom is only 13 miles wide at its broadest part. Sara's labours had lasted seven days and seven nights. Her women were about her but the menfolk stood afar off in the fields, terrified by these prodigies in nature. As they watched they saw the house catch fire and burn in flames that spired skyhigh. They ran for water. But Rachel came to the door and said, Be still, the child is born. The house was not burned, neither had a single flame harmed the inmates. The men were dumbfounded, until Isaak took thought and remembered how Moses saw the burning bush – the flames that burned yet consumed nothing. (Exodus iii. 2–4.)

This is the story of a certain man called Adam Kadmon but take cauls. They used to think they stopped you drowning, they used to advertise them in the papers and sailors would buy them. Haly how, sely how, a lucky cap, a holy hood, which midwives like

Rachel called a howdy or a howdy-wife. According to some, and not all of them fools, the keeper of a caul would know the health of the person who was born in it: if firm and crisp the caul, then he (or she) alive and well; if wet or loose or slack, then dead or ill. The colour of the caul was important also – black caul, ill luck; red caul, all that is good. Diadumenus was born with a caul. He became emperor.

Adam Kadmon came veiled into this world, for his head, his face, and the foreparts of his body, were covered over with such a thin kell, or skin. His father, seeing this, convinced himself that a renegade Franciscan who used to haunt the house was the real father – it was so like a friar's cowl – and up he jumps and threatens to kill the fellow. Warlock! Jansenist! Protestant! shouts Isaak. I'll kill you! I'll puncture your testicles! Not at all, says Friar Goat, I am an innocent man, I shall offer a novena for you.

Friar Goat, oh yes, Friar Goat, for the best grin through a horse collar, Friar Goat always won first prize. A lapsed Catholic of the Latin rite, he was the founder, reformer, and sole member of the Autonomous Pan-Sophic Prussian Order of Illuminated Friars Minor Conventual of St Francis. His eyes were the colour you see in a mountain lake, an intelligent clear colour, given to winking not blinking, strong on charity, hard on heresy. His hair was very dark brown, so dark as to appear almost black. In his youth he had been anxious to distinguish himself by committing new sins. He had sat brooding on the Baltic coast, trying to work out exactly what the sin against the Holy Ghost might be, so that he could commit it, never be forgiven, and become immortal in the memory of men as a saint-in-reverse. (Unless the sin against the Holy Ghost is clichés, then your author doubts if even he had committed it.) On the occasion of his first visit to Swinemünde, this free-lance friar did not address a single word to Sara, and when at Isaak's request he dined there two days later the only notice he took of the lady of the house was to command her to sit at the same table. His condescension in allowing them to share the dinner they had cooked for him was a source of joy to the humble-hearted Kadmons, although his habit of rejecting his meal from his stomach and chewing it over again, as a cow the cud, some twenty minutes after its original ingestion, caused them no little wonder. It was Friar Goat's pleasure to continue this second chewing for no more than an hour, after which he smoked a sweet tobacco. Visits followed upon each other, the turning point being reached one Saturday morning when the shoemaker, in the act of handing a glass a kümmel to his guest, regretted that his apprentice had run away. Then I will help you, Friar Goat said, with every assumption of impulsiveness. I know something of cobbling, he added, and at the worst I can do as well as one of your adolescent labourers. Isaak thought that the little schismatic was joking so he did not reply, but later when he saw him attaching insoles to the bottom of a pair of wooden lasts and fastening the leather down with lasting tacks, speech proved beyond him. He watched as Friar Goat pierced round the insoles with a bent awl, and it was only when he realized that this was not play-acting and that the friar was hard at it, that he ran to him, and begged him to desist. It's not right that your reverence should so demean himself, he said, forgetting the correct churchly mode of address in his admiration. There's nothing demeaning about it, purred Friar Goat, placing the uppers on the lasts and drawing their edges tightly round the edges of the insoles. Cobbling is the only secular work in which a mendicant priest may profitably interest himself, he lied. He fastened the uppers in position with lasting tacks. Without prejudice to his immortal soul, he added. Lasting is a crucial operation, as Isaak knew too well, for unless the upper is drawn neat and tight upon the last, without a crease, without a frown or wrinkle, the shape of the shoe will be spoiled. Friar Goat did not falter. He inseamed as if he had been born with an awl in his fist. Then he pared off the rough edges and levelled the bottoms with a piece of tarred felt. It was the hobby of many of the patriarchs, he explained. That night he shared the supper of the Kadmons yet again, and for many a night thereafter, so that soon it was common knowledge in Swinemünde and Heringsdorf that the ecclesiastical eccentric was in partnership with Isaak Kadmon, the cobbler. It was not so commonly known that he had also taken the education of the Kadmons in hand – slipping frogs, worms, and mice into the marital bed, teaching them to play with non-poisonous snakes, measures to ensure that they developed an attitude of honest indifference to those things which might otherwise engender wasteful impulses of fastidiousness or fear.

But did Friar Goat share in Isaak's bed? Had that whited se-
pulchre known Sara? Not to the cobbler's knowledge, and still less
with his approval, but there was a story that travelled about the
island at the time of Adam's conception, and the story went thus.
Isaak one day having to journey to Ahlbeck, he says to his wife:
Listen, while I'm gone you're to say No to that Friar Goat. Nothing
but No? says Sara. No, no, no, no, no, all the time, says Isaak,
always answer No, whatever he says to you, and never add another
word to it. Do you understand? Sara understood. Isaak went away.
Friar Goat's in through the back door in five minutes. Good
morning, my dear, he says to her, wringing his white hands and
then studying the palms of them as one would refer to an index of
human vanity; you'll be missing your husband, I expect? No, says
Sara. Oho, wonders Friar Goat, what does this mean. Sara answers
no to all the questions which he puts to her. The friar does not
despair. Persistence is his strongest suit. Well, he says, if I put my
hand on your knee, you won't mind then? No, says Sara. And if I
lift up your dress, says the happy friar, his cheeks dimpling, you
won't be complaining and telling your husband? No, says Sara. So
Friar Goat puts his hand on Sara Kadmon's knee, and he lifts up her
dress, and he takes down her knickers. His mind is smelling like a
rich man's funeral. His eyes roll. Tell me, he says politely, would
you object if I was to futter you? No, says Sara. So the false friar
futters her, and when he has finished he says, There, my dear, you'll
be satisfied now. No, says Sara. Alleluia, says Friar Goat. He
futters her again, concentrating the while in order to delay the
moment of ejaculation upon certain psycho-philosophical anxieties
of David Hume's concerning the nature of the process of human
consciousness. Will that do? he enquires solicitously at the end. No,
says Sara. Friar Goat leaps out of bed and wolfs a dozen oysters
and a loaf of cockelty bread. Then he's back at it again. This time
he confines himself to fantasies of pure solipsism while she claws his
back and observes a fly on the ceiling. Is that, he pants, enough?
No, says Sara. Confused, exhausted and contrite, the friar creeps
away. Adam was born nine months, nine days, and nine hours later.

Adam Kadmon, Adam Kadmon – your author thought everyone

had heard of the man, the mighty Kadmon? Sirs, you must know now, if you didn't before, that there was a man, called Adam Kadmon, a certain man who was a fine man, greater than Tubal Cain or Roger Bacon, an upright downright honest man, subtler than Avicenna, wiser than Paracelsus, knowing as much as Cornelius Agrippa himself of the doctrine of sympathy and antipathy in the mineral kingdom, and of the mystery which is fire – whose faithful secretary he was – a man who lived in the old days, not so long ago, and who will live still, if you'll hear me out, for as long as this lasts, at least.

Adam Kadmon was the son of Isaak. During a feast, when many guests were seated round his father's table, Adam, being then but seven years old, was seized by a griffin and carried away. Over land and over sea the griffin flew, until it came to its stinking nest on top of a cliff in the Bosphorus, where it deposited the lad. One of the griffin's brood, wishing to reserve such a delicate morsel for its own delectation, caught up our Adam in its talons and flapped away to a neighbouring tree. But the branch on which this junior monster perched was too weak to support a double load. It broke. The startled griffin dropped its Kadmon in a thicket. Undismayed by thorns, young Adam crept from the griffin's reach, taking refuge in a cave. A great surprise awaited him there, for he found within the cave three girls who had escaped from the griffin in the same way . . .

Your author doesn't think that is going to do. Try again. Writing makes history possible. Least among lies is that told in jest (*mendacium iocosum*). These fictions are jocose, and not officious. These fictions are fantastic, and not pernicious. These fictions are a comedy, and not malicious. These fictions form a story of beginnings. Your author tells of Adam Kadmon, your author gives an account of his origins and originals, to feed a need for stories, but no attempt is being made at a biography. Here are no legends, sagas, myths, or mysteries. Your author tells you stories. This is the story of Adam Kadmon. It is a story neither cosmogonic, theogonic, anthropogonic, nor eschatological. It is inspired neither by hope nor fear, but a pure desire to tell lies. It must not be thought of as a fable or an old wives' tale. Being jocose, it might even be said to be not incompatible with a taste for truth. It offers no information about the world as a whole. On the question of the meaning and end of life it has nothing to say. This is the story of Adam Kadmon. It is a pack of lies.

Let us consider then the time when Adam Kadmon rose up in the night, while his mother and his father slept. He went down to the sea. In the morning he came back. One night later his mother Sara dreamt of fire, and woke. She saw her son go and she followed him to see what he was doing. Adam went towards the shore and then along the sands. He walked into the sea until he was up to his neck in water. There he stood. There he stayed. He did not move. He did not speak. The dark hours passed. The black waves leapt. Sara watched. Adam Kadmon did not come from the sea till daybreak. Then he walked up the sand, knelt down upon it, and prayed. And, behind him, two otters came, bounding from the foam, slippery through the gloom, and they stretched themselves in his shadow, warming his feet with their breath and drying him on their fur.

Isaak suffered badly from indigestion. Are you aware, said Friar Goat, that the acid in your stomach would burn a hole in a carpet? Go on, said Isaak. I tell you true, the wee excommunicate promised. Only recently, he went on, the acid present in an average stomach during an attack of indigestion was poured onto a Soumak carpet in Coserow. Do you know what happened? A hole, Isaak suggested. As big as a saucer, says Friar Goat. Can you wonder ulcers form, serious stomach troubles develop? he demanded. Read this Prussian officer's story of how he mopped up the acid inside him. Isaak took the folded holograph manuscript which the plump friar handed him. He read as follows: I have been a martyr to gastric ulcers for five years, went through numerous operations, gained no benefit. I tried everything, but was unable to take solid food. My wife advised Digestif Goaties. After using them, I improved, and was able to take solid food and to consume a mutton chop this weekend, the first meat for three years. Now I carry half a dozen Goaties in my pocket when I go into battle, and take two after each meal. They have been a godsend to me. (Signed) Landsturm Ersatz, Konigsberg. That's remarkable, says Isaak when he's read it through, can I ask you one thing though – do you take them

yourself? Each and every one blessed by his holiness the Archiman-
drite of the Pre-Nicene Gnostic Orthodox Church, says Friar
Goat neutrally. You suck them like sweets, he explains, they
dissolve in your mouth, flow down in the natural saliva, reaching
your stomach full-strength. Pain ceases. You can eat anything.
Anything? Isaak asks slyly. Suck two Goaties after each confes-
sion but before making your communion, advises the discreet
Pelagian.

When our Adam Kadmon came of sufficient age, his father Isaak
determined that he should have a pair of trousers. Kadmon trousers
were no ordinary trews. They were, rather, a species of breeches
with the vest growing as it were naturally out of them, like branches
and leaves out of the solidness of the trunk of a great oak. Further-
more, to ensure goodness, the trousers had to be made in a church.
This could not be done by day, for the parish priest did not approve
of tailoring on God's premises. Isaak called Jimp the tailor to him,
and told him that if he would make the trews by night in the
church he would pay him treble wages. Jimp agreed. It was not so
much the glamour of the money that attracted him, but the knowledge that the church was haunted and the imputation – which he
resented – that a tailor would not be brave enough to spend the night
there. For Jimp was well acquainted with what is said of tailors:
that it takes nine of them to make a man, that a tailor's sword is
only a needle, etc., etc. So night comes, and Jimp comes to the
church. It's cold and dark inside, the air dewy with recent burials in
the crypt, the stonework seething and the mice rustling among the
smooth pews gleaming in sudden shafts of stained moonlight that
fall through the high windows as the moon rides fast. Jimp sits down
crosslegged on the tomb of a knight and his lady. The tomb is
comfortable enough, the effigy of the lady having been removed by
order of the Reichshofrat, with a result that there is plenty of room
for a tailor on that side of the bed. Jimp lights his candle and puts
on his thimble. He threads the thread in his silver needle and he sets
to work at the trews. Jimp worked well. The seams grew. The
stitches flew. Loop, double chain, tambour, lock – he's throwing in
the lot for luck, and to celebrate the dexterity of his fingers, his
mastery of his trade, for this Jimp's no amateur. Then all at once he

notices that his candleflame, his candleflame is shivering. It shivers. He watches it. It shakes. He watches it. Then the shivering and the shaking stop. The flame burns bold again. Perhaps, thinks Jimp, it was just a breath of wind, a draught in this draughty church, a crack in the old cracked floor. It was not. The candle shakes again. The flame spills. The pavement splits from side to side. Looking wide-eyed down the nave in a bolt of moonlight, Jimp sees a head thrust up through the floor. It is an ugly head, like a fist upraised, the hair black and matted, the eyes staring. The mouth of the head is deep and red, the voice a dull whisper. The voice says: Do you see this head of mine? I see that, but I'll sew this, says Jimp. And he stitches away at the Kadmon trews. Then the head comes up higher through the breaking floor. Its neck comes into view, and terrible it is to see, the veins thick and hanging out, with a beard on the Adam's apple. The voice speaks again through the red red mouth: Do you see this neck of mine? I see that, but I'll sew this, says Jimp. And he stitches away, tambour, tambour, at the Kadmon trews. Head and neck rise higher yet. Now our little tailor can see the shoulders and chest of a vast thing thrusting up through the floor of the nave. It's like a tombstone with flesh on it. Again the voice speaks: Do you see this great chest of mine? And again Jimp answers, I see that, but I'll sew this, and he keeps on sewing, sewing at the trews. It kept on rising through the pavement, whatever it was, until it shook a pair of arms with the bones poking through in poor Jimp's face. Then it cries: Do you see these horrible arms of mine? I see those, but I'll sew this, answers Jimp, wailing, yet ever mindful of his grammar. And he stitches and stitches the harder at the trews, for he knows there's not much left in the way of time now. Jimp is nipping off threads and taking the long stitches when the thing brings a leg up through the floor and stamps with it upon the pavement. Do you see this leg of mine? it cries, and its voice doesn't whisper now. I do, I do, answers Jimp. I see that, but I'll sew this! His fingers burn to be done. His needle flashes in the candleflame. His stitches loop longer and longer as his hands gallop over the cloth to complete the task. He is just coming to the end of the trousers when the thing pulls up its other leg out of the rotting darkness under the floor of the church. Jumping up, Jimp huffs out his candle and springs down from the tombstone. He hares from the church with the trews tucked under his arm. Out of the church he was safe, the thing could not follow him. But Jimp heard it ramping and stamping up and down the nave for hours after, and peeping in through a stained-glass window he saw it sitting in the font and eating corpse, both hands full and its red mouth dribbling black. The sight was such that the little tailor turned and ran for Isaak Kadmon's house. The trousers were delivered and Adam wore them.

Well then, now then, Adam Kadmon, the matter of his mother, his real mother and was she Sara. She was not. Was she Angelica then? Not likely. Adam's mother's name was Helena. She was the daughter of a petty prince, Tewdrig, who loved her dearly until it looked as though she had the plague. Then he called her to him and he said, I am uneasy, girl, lest your health should succumb to this disorder which presently lays waste all Prussia. Go, therefore, my chick, to Usedom, and God grant that you may stay there in safety. Helena was a lively piece. She wore a girdle made of kidskin. She prepared to go. Prince Tewdrig gave her an escort worthy of his condition. (He was the sort of prince who judges the truth of meta physical principles by their moral consequences; in short, a rat.) Twelve maids of honour accompanied Helena through Pomerania and three hundred Einjährig-Freiwilligen. Having seen her safely despatched, Tewdrig, with his principal catamites, retired to his castle at Württemberg, where, isolated from the rest of the people, he remained until the plague had passed. Helena, meanwhile. The incidents of her journey were not encouraging. On the first night in Hinterpommern, she was so cold that no less than a century of the Einjährig-Freiwilligen perished. This might be thought appalling, but if your author uses that word then what is he to say of the completion of her second day's journey, when another hundred men went under? Two hundred defaulters through death, however did not prevent Helena from continuing her travels, and she struggled on through Vorpommern, shedding men all the way until at last she set sail for Usedom, and landed in safety, but with only one male attendant left. This gentleman soon perished and the Lady Helena, the prince's daughter, being left to wander without

escort through the fens and sandhills of old Usedom, meets up with
Isaak Kadmon. Now Isaak, your author would have you know, was
a bit of a man in his own right. By one blow of his fist he'd flattened
a thunderbolt once, which he kept in his waistcoat pocket, in the
shape of a folded pancake, rolled up, to show to his enemies, if they
felt like a fight. When he sees Helena wandering, her hair so long,
her breasts so high, he marches straight up to her in the sandhills
and offers her the hilt of his sword. The prince's daughter looks him
up and down. She likes what she sees. I will take you on, she says,
and you'll be well rewarded on one condition. Aha thinks Isaak, but
it isn't aha at all, for the Lady Helena adds: The condition is that
you must never use any dirty words. I can't abide a dirty word, she
explains. True enough, it suits her character, you will admit, for
isn't she the great ice-maiden, the winter doxy, with snowflakes on
it and the north wind blowing hailstones down her slot. Do not
forget the three hundred Einjährig-Freiwilligen. Fallen. Not to
speak of the twelve maids of honour skewered on that excep-
tional clitoris. However, Isaak is nothing if not adventurous, and
there are few adventures he prefers to those which test his verbal
resourcefulness – and the Lady Helena's person, as your author has
presented it, would seem to offer hope of those few too. So he
agrees to her condition, and is made her man. They travel on
through Usedom. As they come out of the forest above Zinnowitz
what should they see but an old white sow, with a boar aboard
grunting away so vehemently that the foam is flying out of his
mouth and hanging on the wind like spindrift. The Lady Helena
turns to Isaak. She lays her hand upon his sleeve. Isaak, she says,
Isaak, what do you make of that? Isaak thinks for a bit, and he thinks
how she has forbidden him to use dirty words and how her grotto is
said to be so particularly icy, and in the end he says, What do I make
of that, lady? Well, it's staring you in the face isn't it? The one
underneath is a kind relation of the one on top, some sort of aunt I
should imagine, and her nephew isn't feeling well, and she's carrying
him home. The Lady Helena looks at Isaak sharpish. Then a laugh
begins to tickle in her throat. Yes, she says, that must be it. They
journey on. And as they come out of the fens above Ahlbeck what
should they see but a herd of cattle, and the bull just making himself

at home on one of his favourites. The Lady Helena touches Isaak's wrist. Well, she says, what's that then? Isaak doesn't have to think so much this time, he's getting the hang of it. I'll tell you exactly what it is, he answers, the poor old cow is pathetically shortsighted, and she's eaten all the grass in sight, so the bull, who looks after the cows, is just giving her a gentle shove on her way towards some new grass. The Lady Helena laughs again. You must be right, says she. They journey on some more. And as they're coming over the moor to Swinemünde, what should they see but a herd of horses, and a stallion busy working on a mare. The Lady Helena touches Isaak's sword hilt. Tell me, she says, what do you make of that? That, says Isaak, is no doubt on account of the fire. The fire, says his mistress. Yes, says Isaak, and he points to a house with a blazing chimney below them. The horse wants a better view of it, he explains, so he's climbed up on the back of the mare. I do believe you're right, says the Lady Helena, though she can't stop her giggling. They journey on. At last they reach the warm springs above Heringsdorf. Prince Tewdrig has instructed his daughter to bathe here, for unspecified purposes, so she offs with her clothes, kidskin girdle and all, and into the water with her. Isaak stands watching at a respectful but attentive distance. The Lady Helena splashes about a lot, then she calls out, If you want to bathe with me, undress yourself. Isaak takes off his shirt, his boots, and his trousers, and enters the warm springs. As he sinks into the water, the Lady Helena notes to herself the length and apparent usefulness of his tool. Her high breasts pout like pigeons. Now they are wading about together in the warm clear water, and it's soft and salt and lovely, and the Lady Helena puts her fingers to her lower lips and shows herself to her man and asks him, Isaak, what do you think this is? A well, says Isaak, quick as you like, a wishing well, madam. Yes yes, agrees the Lady Helena, and she reaches down with her hands and makes a grab for him under the water. And what's this then Isaak, she demands, what's this between your legs here? That, says Isaak, gulping hard, is called a horse. A horse! exclaims the Lady Helena with approval, and does your horse drink then Isaak? He does, madam, says Isaak, as dignified as you could expect, in the circumstances. But only when he's thirsty, he adds. The Lady Helena's fingers move up and down the length of him, and round and round the width of herself, her one little hand is warming his member, while with her other little hand she is warming herself, and the water is warm, the air is warm, the hot springs bubble up incessantly, the pool is full of good warm currents, swirling all about their naked limbs as she fingers him, and herself, and her fingers fly, and the water frets and bubbles, and Isaak's member gets bigger and bigger, swelling and lengthening, until he's scared it'll burst, and her other hand is equally busy, preparing and opening, though she needs no moistening, what with all the warmth and the water, the warm warm water, and the whispering currents, and O she wonders O Isaak O O is your horse thirsty now? He is, says Isaak, yes he is, madam, quite. And would he like a drink, enquires the lady, a drink in my well? He would, says Isaak, he would, madam, I believe. Then come in horse, counsels the Lady Helena, only don't go too deep or you'll drown, poor thing. She means, of course, that the extreme coldness of her fissure will be the death of the interesting beast, and she is a-weary of her men dying, but Isaak can't hold back now and he enters her quick and smooth, and the warming water, and the circling currents, and the bubbling springs, and the blandishments and entreaties of these natural things make her open her legs as she has never opened them before, so that Isaak flows in, and the water flows in, and the warm flows in, and it is all flowing warm flowing and flowing flowing warm and O, the Lady Helena gives instruction, O Isaak O make your horse go deeper deeper deeper. So Isaak does, and the horse finds the well is very very deep, but he does not drown, and nor does he freeze, on account of the hot springs and other circumstances already mentioned. They were sorry to leave the water. Nine months later, to that very day, to that very hour, Adam Kadmon was born. His mother, knowing Tewdrig would not take her back with a bastard, returned home to Prussia without him. The babe was left with Isaak, who by that time was betrothed to Sara Mundi. Sara had a good heart, and she brought the child up as her own.

Adam Kadmon's youth was not without the usual diseases. It was left to Friar Goat to cure the little man. The reformer was a great believer in natural cures and medicines. He suffered himself from the ague. He cured it, not by wrapping a spider in a raisin and swallowing it, as you might think, nor by eating sage leaves seven mornings running, as you might hope, but by going at night alone to the crossroads and as the clock struck midnight turning round on his heels three times and driving a large nail into the earth up to the head. Then he walked away backwards from the nail before the clock had completed its twelfth stroke. The ague left him, passing into the tax collector who was the next person to step over the nail. Adam Kadmon had the measles. Friar Goat cured his measles by cutting off the cat's left ear and persuading the boy to swallow three drops of cat blood in a wineglassful of water. Adam Kadmon had the jaundice. Friar Goat cured the jaundice by making the boy eat nine lice on a piece of bread and butter. The other cure – twelve earthworms baked on a shovel and reduced to powder to make a philter to drink every morning – had failed to shift it. Ditto the tench tied to Adam's bare back. Adam Kadmon had a rupture. Friar Goat cured it by going to the ash grove above Zinnowitz and cutting a long sapling longitudinally and getting the lad to climb, nude, in and out of the fissure three times at sunset, then binding up the tree tightly and plastering over the crack with dung and clay. As the hole healed so did Adam. The other cure – the snail stopped up in the hollow oak – did not work. Adam Kadmon had the whooping cough. Friar Goat cured his whoopers by taking a saucerful of brown sugar and encouraging a slug to crawl over it until the sugar was nice and slimy, then got Adam to eat the sugar. The muslin bag full of spiders, worn round the neck, and the hair from his head stuck between two bits of buttered toast and fed to the dog, had both failed to do the trick. Adam Kadmon had the toothache. Friar Goat cured that by chasing him out of the house and making him bite from the frosty ground the first fern to appear in spring. Adam Kadmon had pneumonia. Friar Goat cured it by tying a bullock's milt to the soles of the lad's feet, and burying the milt afterwards. Adam Kadmon immediately contracted the thrush. To cure him, Friar Goat captured a duck from the nearest lake at Swinemünde and placed its beak in the boy's mouth so that when he tickled the duck's throat and it opened its beak it breathed into the boy. The cold breath of the duck cured the thrush. The other cure – reciting the Emerald Table of Hermes Trismegistus over the victim three times three days running – did not work in this case.

The midwife Rachel was a great teller of stories. Every Wednesday evening – Rachel's Wednesday's, they used to call them – would find her seated in her rocking chair in the marketplace at Zinnowitz, the wind blowing gritty from the sandhills, her bottles and her boxes spread before her. First she would eat a spoonful of this. Then she would drink a mouthful of that. Then she would blow her nose, clean out her ears, rub her eyes, gargle, spit, clear her throat, take Adam on her knee, and begin a story. Adam's favourite was the tale of the white raven. It went like this. There was once a prince who lived in a dark palace. The poor people hated him because he was so cruel. One day this prince was walking in his garden. He allowed no flowers there. On the trees no apples grew. The branches were black and bare even in summer. In the heart of the garden was a pool of deep water, where no fish swam. It was always cold in the garden. Even the sunlight seemed scared and full of ghosts. One morning the prince was in a good mood. That is to say, he had ridden out before breakfast on his horse, Satan, and burned eight cottages to cinders. Now he stood brooding in shadow, looking forward to the daily executions. Just then a white raven flew down and perched on a branch of the tree. A fear came into the prince's eyes as he saw it. He picked up a stone and threw it at the bird. A shiver ran down his spine when the stone, in mid-air, turned into a rose and fell to the ground, spilling a few petals. The white raven looked straight at the prince. It threw back its head. Its bright beak fell open. Amen, it said, amen amen amen. The prince drew his sword and took a step towards the tree. Amen, said the white raven. Now the prince was frightened, so he pretended not to give a damn. He leaned on his sword, and roared with laughter. The bird stared at him for a moment, then flapped its wings as though to shake off the shadows of the garden, and flew away. For a week or more the prince dreamed of the white raven and what it had said, but nothing happened and he forgot. He grew richer, murdering and marauding. He kidnapped the pleasant daughter of one of his lords. They were married and in time the prince's wife had a son. The prince hated the child. He gave it to one of the palace guards. Leave it in the woods, he said. But the guard was not as bad as his master. He took pity on the boy. Besides, he had no children of his own and this was a grief to his wife. So instead of leaving the child in the woods to starve or be eaten by wolves, he hid it secretly in his own quarters. Now the prince took it into his head to have a feast. He sent out messengers with invitations. Many who were called refused to come. Some wrote, We do not care to join in your celebration of the murder of your own son. Others made less honest excuses, work or weather. As it happened, only the other wicked princes – the ones who were about as bad as the prince himself – came to the feast. On the night of the feast they were gathered in the great hall of the palace. The floors were paved with human bones. The walls and rafters were draped with black banners. The torches all burned blue. Every kind of meat and every kind of drink was served, and no vessel was brought to the table, brimming with mead or heavy with meat which was not fashioned of silver. The prince himself drank wildly from a blue buffalo horn, rimmed with gold. Now the prince had called two minstrels to the feast. One of these was all that a minstrel should *not* be: hard, bent, and ambitious. He amused the company with his stories and songs in praise of the devil and all his works. They banged with their fists on the tables, laughing sottishly, shouting for more. The other minstrel was different. He was disgusted by the feast, and his heart grew sad at the thought that soon it would be his turn to play. He slipped out of the hall and wandered through the passages of the palace, looking for gentle faces. But everyone was at the feast. Passing a door in the guards' quarters, however, the minstrel heard a child crying. He pushed the door gently, then he pushed it with all his might – but it would not open. Opening closed doors was nothing to a true minstrel. He stooped down and whispered into the keyhole: Open lock, at my third knock! Then he tapped three times lightly with his knuckle on the door and at the third knock it flew open and in he went. The child was a lusty bawler. It was, of course, the prince's son. There's a noise, murmured the minstrel, and sitting down by the cradle he began to rock it with one hand while plucking a lullaby from his harp with the other. Being a true minstrel, he was inspired to sing of a prince who was dead but not dead, lost but not lost, and who would one day come into his own and rule over the lands his father had wasted. The child listened, and stopped its crying. Then the minstrel amused it by letting it play with his fine white gloves. The child loved this game. Before long it fell asleep clutching one glove in its fist, pressed under its cheek. Just then the minstrel heard banging and shouting from the hall. He took up his harp and tiptoed to the door, closing it softly behind him. He had not the heart to take his glove away from the child, now fast asleep. Back in the hall the minstrel began playing and singing. His fingers gathered music between the strings, his green slipper tapped on the bone-paved floor, his voice was strong and warm. But the guests were not pleased with the new man's songs. He sang of Our Lord Jesus Christ and of His Blessed Mother and they did not wish to hear of either. Long live death! Long live death! shouted the prince, pounding on the table with his buffalo horn. Then they all started laughing and swearing and pelting the minstrel with the bones which they had picked clean. The minstrel took no notice. He seemed to have forgotten where he was. The bones did not harm him. An inch from his face they were turned, in mid-air, into roses. The roses fell at his feet, shedding perfume which was itself like music. None of the guests appeared to see this. The prince, though, he saw the thrown things turn to roses. He sat up in his great black chair and stared at the minstrel's face. He seemed to have lost the power of speech or movement. The minstrel played on. He played so fast and sweet that his fingers bled. He sang a strange song – of a prince who was dead but not dead, lost but not lost, and who would one day come into his own and rule over the lands his father had wasted. And all the while the petals rose higher and higher on every side of him and his swaying harp, and he sang as though in a dream. And then his fingers fell away from the strings, and as the last note of the strange song died among the red rose-petals and the black banners, there came a roar of thunder like a hungry beast at the door, and lightning lit the blood-red windows, and a cold wind rushed through the hall, extinguishing every torch and candle. And a white raven rode into the hall on the back of the wind and perched on the minstrel's harp. All in the hall except the minstrel were blinded by the darkness and deafened by the wind, and they blundered about in confusion, but could find no doors. The prince himself was not granted the mercy of being blinded or deafened. He sat still in his high-backed chair, and his eyes in the blackness shone green. The raven spoke. Amen, it said quietly. Amen amen amen. And it flew from the harp to the door. The minstrel sat folded over his harp, his arms about it, exhausted by music. He paid no heed to the bird. The raven flew back and perched again on the harp. Once more it spoke in the minstrel's ear. Amen, it said, amen amen. Again it flew from the harp to the door. Still the minstrel did not move. A third time the white raven flew to the harp and perched on it. This time when its beak fell open it cried with the voice of the wind and the storm, and thunder and lightning filled its throat, and it shook as though it would burst in two. Amen, it cried. Amen! Amen! Amen! Then the minstrel got up, as if awakened from deep sleep. He shook his head and he took up his harp and put it on his back. He walked softly through the rose-petals. He followed the white raven. There are no absolutes, said the prince. His eyes looked pleased and clever in the gloom. But he could not rise from his chair. As for the other guests, they rushed about in panic, hacking at each other with their swords, but they could find no way out. The minstrel followed the white raven. It flew always a little in front of him, so that no matter how fast he ran he could not catch it. The white raven led him safely from the palace. Outside was blackness. There was no moon. There were no stars in their usual places. But the minstrel trusted the bird, and it led him unscathed through thicket and mire and up the mountain. Once the minstrel stopped, because he was tired, but the white raven flew round him, clapping its wings together and crying its cry, Amen amen amen, so urgently that he did not dare to stop again. Then, as bird and man reached the top of the mountain, there came out of the dark behind them a crack of thunder. The earth shook. There was a roaring and thrashing of waters. Mixed with the thunder and the sound of water, the minstrel heard cries for mercy. And, louder than all, one voice that shouted defiance: Long live death! Long live death! But all were soon stopped, and silence fell. The minstrel looked in wonder at the white raven. It returned his gaze. Then, flying towards him, it touched him on the cheek with its wing, and disappeared into the night. The minstrel began to feel foolish. What am I doing here? he asked himself, I'd better get back to the palace, they'll need me for the dancing even if they don't like my songs. Then he wondered how he could be certain that they had not liked his songs. He racked his brain for memory of the night. But he could find none, except – My glove! he cried. And then: The child! Certain that something dreadful had befallen the palace, and the one innocent soul in it, the minstrel started to stumble back down the mountain. But he had not gone twenty steps when he tripped in his harp and fell flat on his face in a murmuring mountain stream. The minstrel was wearied by the night's adventures – some of which were coming back to his mind now, in dribs and drabs of memory beyond belief. He drank deeply of the cold water. Then he fell asleep. When he woke, it was morning. The sun was rising over the mountain. The minstrel turned his head and looked down in the direction of the palace, and he saw that there was no palace. There was only water – water – water – a vast smooth silent lake stretching from one side of the valley to the other. What he had taken for a mountain stream was the nearer shore of this lake. Shielding his eyes against the light of the sun shimmering across the lake, the minstrel saw something bobbing on the surface. It was a something now wafted towards him by the breeze, then drifting away again in the mist. The minstrel knew what he must do. He sat down by the lakeside and began to play his harp. He played a song calling home whatever it was that rode there on the water. The music sped ripples across the lake, and the ripples drew the theme of the harp's song back to the strings of the harp. Presently it came to rest on the shore at the minstrel's feet. It was a cradle, and in the cradle was the prince, still fast asleep, still with the white glove clutched to his cheek. Then the minstrel took the child and looked after him as if he had been his own son. And when the boy grew up he had a new palace built on the shore of the lake, and all was grace and light inside that palace, and the minstrel, an old man now, played there at many a feast, where the hungry were filled with good things and the rich were sent empty away. And sometimes, after the feast, he would sing quietly to himself of a prince who had been dead but not dead, lost but not lost, and who had come through flood and fury following one who followed a white raven.

The midwife Rachel wore eyeglasses and a black hat pulled square across her forehead. She used to sing to herself a lot. Oh tennis, she sang, oh tennis is the finest game and boy and girl believe the game they love is just the same that Adam played with Eve. This woman spoke often to Adam Kadmon also of crickets. The wings of the cricket when folded form long thin filaments, giving the appearance of a bifid tail, while in the male they are provided with a stridulating apparatus by which the well-known chirping sound is produced. The abdomen of the female ends in a long thin ovipositor. House crickets are greyish yellow marked with brown. Field crickets are bigger and darker. It burrows in the ground, the cricket, and in the evening the male cricket is to be seen sitting at the mouth of its hole noisily stridulating until a female approaches, when the louder notes are succeeded by a more subdued tone, whilst the successful musician caresses with his antennae the mate he has won. The cricket's musical apparatus consists of upwards of 130 transverse ridges on the under side of one of the nervures of the wing cover, which are rapidly scraped over a smooth projecting nervure on the opposite wing. The mole cricket is different. Its front legs are like hands.

DAVID
PLANTE

DAVID
PLANTE

*Born 1940, Providence, Rhode Island, into a French Canadian parish;
taught by French nuns in primary school, Christian Brothers in secon-
dary, Jesuits in college. Studied French literature and philosophy at
Boston College and at Université de Louvain. After formal studies,
lived in Rome, then New York (1962–64) where he assisted on
writing a guide book to the city, then in Boston for two years, teaching
French. In 1966, came to London. Work first published in England*
(Transatlantic Review). *Now a British resident. Novels:* The Ghost
of Henry James, Slides, Relatives, The Darkness of the Body.
Stories in Penguin Modern Stories 1, Modern Occasions. *Translated,
with Nikos Stangos, Andreas Embiricos'* Argo, or The Flight of a
Balloon *(London Magazine Publications).*

LETTER TO THE EDITOR

Dear Giles,

I've tried, but I can't stand apart from my writing and make a
statement about it. Every attempt I made rang false. I hope you
won't think it too inappropriate to use this letter instead of a statement, as long as it remains clear that it is a letter.

Perhaps all I can say about my writing is that I'd find it extremely
difficult, if not impossible, to write in any other way. Whenever
I have attempted to write differently—whenever I have tried quite
consciously to 'experiment'—the result has always sounded to me
forced and fake. You may gather from this that I value some
'natural' or 'true' element in writing. I think I do. Certain writing
emanates a sense of *something* which is immediately perceivable
as true, a quality which is unmistakable and yet impossible and
unnecessary to define; some writing sounds false and pretentious.
Of course, there is no absolute way of knowing the difference, and
writing for me becomes ultimately an act of faith. (This is not to say
I don't often betray my own faith, and write in false and pretentious
ways.)

You may also gather that I am not very interested in theories of fiction writing, that I feel the novel as a deliberate artifact is impossible for me; though I *am* very interested in theories, I never apply them to my own work, and though I greatly admire the craft of fiction, there is very little *imposed* system on my writing. I want to stress this because critics of new fiction tend to think it is written on an elaborate theoretical platform; in fact, I would like to think of my writing as very old, and quite 'mindless'.

I don't have an analytical mind. This sometimes worries me and makes me envious of other people's power of analysis. By necessity, I must make an advantage of what may be a weakness: my intuitive faith, based, I think, in a *sense* of what I want to write, a a sense I never quite succeed in realizing. It is what is left out of writing, what writing can't state, which possesses me—certain senses, certain states of consciousness, as real to us as eating and sleeping and working. They are inarticulate, but distinct and powerful. Above all, they are *ordinary*. They are the substance of my work, and my effort is to make them rich and dense.

What I mean is suggested by the following quotation from William James' *The Briefer Course*:

There are innumerable consciousnesses of *want*, no one of which taken in itself has a name, but all different from each other. Such a feeling of want is *toto coelo* other than a want of feeling: it is an intense feeling. The rhythm of a lost word may be there without a sound to clothe it; or the evanescent sense of something which is the initial vowel or consonant may mock us fitfully, without growing more distinct. Everyone must know the tantalizing effect of the blank rhythm of some forgotten verse, restlessly dancing in one's mind, striving to be filled out with words.

What is the first instantaneous glimpse of someone's meaning which we have, when in vulgar phrase we say we 'twig' it? Surely an altogether specific affection of the mind. And has the reader never asked himself what kind of a mental fact is his *intention of saying a thing* before he has said it? It is an entirely definite intention, distinct from all other intentions, an absolutely distinct state of consciousness, therefore; and yet how much of it consists of definite sensorial images, either of words or of things? Hardly anything! Linger, and the words and things come into mind; the anticipatory intention, the divination is there no longer. But as the words that replace it arrive, it welcomes them successively and calls them right if they agree with it, and rejects them and calls them wrong if they do not. The intention *to-say-so-and-so* is the only name it can receive. One may admit that a good third of our psychic life consists in these rapid premonitory perspective views of schemes of thought not yet articulate . . .

It is, the reader will see, the reinstatement of the vague and inarticulate to its proper place in our mental life which I am so anxious to press on the attention.

In being possessed by certain states of consciousness, certain vague and inarticulate senses, at moments I think I am a romantic writer. I think I am a realist in trying to depict, as accurately as possible, very real states, very strong senses, but I am a romantic, or perhaps a romanticist, in believing those states, those senses, imply a vast and overriding world of spirit.

David Plante

PREFACE

. . . This brought about something that made neither words exist for themselves, nor sentences, nor choosing, it created the need of paragraphing, and the whole paragraph having been being made the whole paragraph had rising from it off of it its meaning.

What is English Literature, Gertrude Stein

A circle is easy to visualize, so is a square.

It is less easy to visualize the circle contained within the square; the lines fade. I impose a triangle on the combined square and circle, and try hard to see the figure as a whole. I imagine two diagonal lines crossing the figure, but I am no longer able to see the result; it decomposes into a kind of vagueness, and all I have left of it is a sense, a sense half seen, if at all, as a cloud of bright points in the black from which appear then disappear, in sudden flashes, a simple square, a circle, a triangle.

He and she, in their unhappiness, appear to me such a complex figure — a line drawn from the tip of one of his fingers to the middle of her forehead, a curve extended from the roundness of one of her breasts to one of his closed eyes, a long triangle made from the points of her nipples and his navel — the figure dissolves in my attempt to visualize it, and I am left with a sense only of them, or their configuration.

I loved them, I loved them.

I tried to see this: her sadness, round, circumscribing him, square, the circles and squares revolving on one another, and, finally, separating from them, rising up around their heads in greater and greater arcs and angles, expanding out into the air, over the land, until they might have thought their sadness was the sadness of the country they inhabited.

I don't know why they were unhappy. Perhaps they didn't.

I recall, as though they were components of a vast figure, her eyes, his forehead.

I saw – no didn't see them, I couldn't see them; I sensed them, because, dead, they were elaborated into figures I couldn't visualize – I sensed them, for long after their deaths, in the earth, and though I tried to recall them as they had been when alive, with me, my mind was drawn down into the ground where they were, their eyes and foreheads sinking elaborately. But that elaboration I imagined was not what was happening underground; I had no idea what was happening underground, because I couldn't see there. I could only imagine them, and in my imagination, itself buried underground, their flesh turned to water, their bones to stone, their heads glowed in an enveloping flickering gas.

No. Their dark invisibility was a repudiation of my strained attempts to elaborate them. They were where they wanted to be.

No. I elaborate this.

I assume her life began, physically, as if she came together out of a sudden, erupting mixture of fire and earth, the moment he first turned to her and saw that he wanted her, and she sensed the pull, because she turned to him at the same moment.

Seeing him, she immediately turned away from him. They were among others. Everyone but he and she moved, and he vaguely saw in everyone's movements, away and towards her, extending and contracting distances between herself and them as they moved around her, the lines of a criss-crossing, in-and-out diagram.

He believed that some vast superseding awareness, founded on an enormous abstract diagram of cricles, squares, triangles, brought them into a proximity which enflamed his own awareness of the angle of her bent arm, of the curves of her head, of the zero formed by a closed thumb and index finger. How else could it have happened, out of the many many possibilities, out of his many glancing encounters with women – with women of all ages, because what he was aware of was out of his control, and it was not his, had never been his, to decide what the object of his awareness would or would not be – that he should have seen her and stepped towards her? How, how? He had seen her at a distance, among others, and what he thought first, as if that great awareness had already descended and all the long perspectives around him became lines to a figure, was: why she? why was it she he saw in particular among all the others? He saw in the conjunction of the lines and the curves, projected outward from points on her and his bodies, a configuration he did not understand, but which contained them.

She turned back to him and he stood still. Light, red, white, fell on her, on him. They stood apart, and he thought: we are going to turn away from one another, are simply going to leave one another, because if we come together now we won't be able to pull away from one another. His horror was that they would go to one another. They couldn't help it. They stepped towards one another.
  To what figure did they take the first step?

They married. The ceremony was dangerous, an elaboration from which they excluded anyone but themselves because they knew they were taking a risk in marrying that shouldn't involve others, not even – above all, not – me. They did not even dare to think of me. The sense of risk kept them apart throughout the ceremony, like fire and volatile water, because they knew the danger implied (the danger of their merely touching one another, for she recalled, in an atmosphere loosely composed of bright air turning to fire, of rocks made porous by the melting away of veins of softer minerals, of long stretches of water over which heat-mists shimmered, of wide views from a height about which the wind blew, standing at the edge, having come as far as she could go, he having followed her across distances that were green, yellow, red, white, and she stood still, leaning a little backwards over the precipitous height, watching him come nearer, and with each step nearer she felt a kind of preparation for the moment when he would reach out and touch her, as though his touch might be a slight, thrusting push; but he didn't touch her): the danger of what might happen. They did not know what it might be, but they knew that the wedding, in its elaborations, would make it happen.

In the midst of the ceremony, this happened (as I imagine, from my distance, it happened): she, kneeling, rocking back and forth, her mouth open, her eyes open. He, standing above her, not knowing what to do. I hear, as if from very very far above us, a thin wail, and I look up, narrowing my eyes; the wail, at a great periphery, slowly begins, concentrically, to evolve down to us, slowly, slowly, growing in intensity, then falling more and more quickly, changing its pitch, until suddenly it strikes my mother and she shouts. Crouching, my father takes her in his arms and rocks her back and forth with the same fierceness with which she had been rocking on her knees.

Through him, I was able to live moments of their lives that occurred before I was born – moments only, small, unrelated, but they were to me points to which I could myself relate what I sensed about them in the way one can make a kind of pattern by referring lines and curves to points arbitrarily made, as by drops of rain.

He said: There was a moment, shortly after they married, when she left him. (A moment, he said, because that was what it seemed to him after the long experience rolled itself together into a sphere.) She left him because she knew what would happen if she stayed. It was as though she disappeared into air, because, he said, when someone leaves, and you have no idea where she is, it is impossible to visualize her anywhere, and her body loses shape; so she, apart from him, lost shape, and he tried to find her, knowing that if he himself had any shape it was only in physical relation to her. He looked for her in air. He couldn't find her. He prayed for her. Maybe it was his longing itself that finally drew him to her, or that made her materialize from the air and stand beside him, saying: she couldn't remain away.

Then, he said, he left her, a reflected moment. When you leave someone, he said, you visualize her vividly in the space you left her in, the space you lived in together, and her body becomes as unbreakable as stone. She was stone. He tried and tried to break her. He knew he must break her for her own sake, never mind his own; he must because in breaking her he was breaking the feelings that bound them together, too horrible, he often thought, to imagine himself involved in them. His leaving, as hers, was a kind of geometric effort of will. They knew they had to do something, risk anything, to get out of what they were in. Air and stone, air and stone: she was both. She couldn't get outside what she would have had to get out of to get away from that part of her which, like stone, fixed her in one place, that part of her which, like air, extended everywhere. He couldn't break her. He came back. Of course, of course he came back. He found her lying still. He lay next to her. He could just hear her breathing. He was not sure she was sleeping. She opened her eyes and, not moving, stared at him. She sat up and he sat up. He watched her closely. She raised her hand and smashed him across the face. All his muscles rebounded. He held her down. He beat her, he beat her and beat her. He beat her till he was exhausted, even after she lay, mouth open, eyes closed.

He said:

I tried to talk to her, to talk something out, to surround it with talk, words repeated over and over again with the slightest variations, until the something was a roundness. I talked not simply to exhaust myself of talk – though that had a great deal to do with it, because I wanted to exhaust something in myself – but, by the very circumlocutions of my talk, to isolate what might, if isolated, be put at a distance, and which might, at the distance, serve as an outward point of reference to what was happening to us. I tried to see, as though drawing lines between points, the multitude of connections between her eyes and my eyes, her hands and my hands, her mouth and my mouth, until what I saw reached, when the connections became nation-wide, a complexity of interconnecting lines I couldn't sustain. There are no defenses against the inexhaustible. The complexity dissolved into water.

He said:

If my way was to include everything, her way was to exclude it. She tried to make her presence an absence; silent, she stayed away from me. It was as though she had made up her mind, with a kind of passionate deliberateness, that she wanted nothing, not to sleep or eat or shit, and nothing, not even I, was going to deter her from getting what she wanted. She would reduce, reduce to a roundness, and she would do it with all the force of a will trying to save itself. She did not let me touch her. At night, we lay side by side, awake, and I would sense her mind – sense it in her body – cutting back on itself, as if, having to start somewhere, she started anywhere – with water – then cutting away everything related to water, until everything, everything became water, and I could see her body, in minute jerks, thrash. I didn't touch her.

One evening we took a walk. All around us were crushed rocks. She walked ahead of me, or behind, so I imagined she was following me or I was following her. She stopped to pick up things – flints, I think – then threw them down.

We walked to a height that ended abruptly with a drop over water. She stood at the edge. I stayed away from her. I walked about the place, the rock like dry bone marrow, and stopped where water, as yellow as urine, had collected in hollows. Now and then I looked back at her. There was a wind that blew her hair. She seemed to be leaning slightly backwards over the height, perhaps pressed back by the wind. I noticed, suddenly, that if she moved even one small step back she would fall over. I didn't call her. I walked away from her, then, in a wide curve, circled back to her, my eyes on the rocks as if looking for something. I approached her at an angle, as though by accident, and when I got within arm's reach of her I stopped.

She was looking away. Her hair blew forward, then, the wind suddenly shifting, blew back, exposing her face, her throat, her neck. I raised my arm slowly, and when I got it waist high I extended it towards her, and as I did I felt myself lean forward as if to thrust my arm out and push her. Oh no, oh no. I wanted her to live, and I knew I must struggle, against myself and against her, to keep her alive, would have to struggle for reason after reason for her to stay alive, each reason held up to her like a transparent object, which she, taking it in her hand, would look through. My hand still raised, extended towards her, I saw her look at me, and I saw in her face that something – something she had for so long been waiting for – had occurred to her. I don't know if it had anything to do with me or with that moment, but her face all at once softened, her hands unclenched, one dropping a flint, and she went colourless. I lowered my hand. I didn't touch her.

We walked back slowly, not speaking. Inside, she said she was tired, and went to lie down. I followed her. I lay down beside her, still watching her. Her eyes were closed. She opened them, and I saw immediately that she had succeeded in realizing what she had wanted: she had seen that nothing mattered, me less than anything. There is no use going into how it happened. Say it was just a great abstract occurrence, the result of a mental effort put to an impossible task – bisecting a scalene triangle into two equal parts – and finding, suddenly, that it was possible. She had done it: she had her circle. If there was any expression in her eyes, it was a slight awe in what she had done.

My first reaction was as if to stare at it, that circle, with her, a circumference above our heads. Perhaps, I thought, it was an upside down hole which we were about to fall, to fall as we had fallen, like falling bodies, in love. Or, perhaps we were at the bottom of the hole, and there was no deeper to fall. I turned to her. I touched her ankle with my toes. She didn't react. I grabbed her wrist, lifted it, let go, and her hand fell.

I rose up on an elbow and looked down at her, looked into her eyes, but she didn't see me. I kissed her. She remained still. I bit her upper lip. She didn't flinch. I bit harder. It was like biting one's own numb lip. I could feel my teeth sink in. I rose. I saw little red indentations on her lip. Her hair was all out. Her body was faintly blue, as was mine, I saw, when I glanced down at my chest, glanced as if to make sure my body was there. I noted thick blue veins in my arms as I pulled her hair away from her face. And then, abruptly, I grabbed her shoulders as if to yank her into a sitting position, and threw myself on her. I began to thrash, and all I can recall is kicking with my knees, jabbing with my elbows. She was turned on her side, her legs raised, her arms across her breasts and face, her head lowered. I said, stop it! stop it!

Her body shuddered when I hit her in the back of the neck. I tried to get at her breasts. I tried to straighten her legs to get at her abdomen. I was hot, she was cold. The blood rose to the surface of all my body. I hit her face, and said, look at me! I wanted her to see me. Only that. You see, I had lost her, and I wanted her back. I wouldn't let her go, no, not without me. And suddenly she looked at me.

She reached up and clamped my head in her hands. She pulled me down. I resisted, and tried to hold back. But she was strong, and used all her weight to pull me closer, till I was kissing her, but not kissing her, for she bit me so deeply on the lips a shock ran through me and when I broke away blood and saliva dripped from my mouth on to her face.

Should I have let him go on?

The blood was pumping in his arms, legs, head. He didn't have an erection. Her body was, as ever, cold. And yet, they were making love. She clasped herself tightly to him, wound her legs and arms around him so he couldn't unwind them. He rolled over and over, but she clung on, and what he felt at first was that she was pressing his esophagus together so he couldn't breathe, and then he felt her fingers sink in, and with a great contortioning threw her off, and grabbed her about the neck. He pressed his thumbs in and shook her head.

I wasn't yet born.

He let go of her, suddenly, as though a round eye had appeared above him, and in the reflection of the dark iris he, all at once looking up, saw what he was doing. He let go of her throat. He turned away from her. He thought: we must do something. The moment he thought it, he realized the *something* would always remain unqualified. He felt his muscles loosen and all his body go slack. When, finally, he turned round to look at her, it was as if he were looking at someone he didn't know, and he saw that she, too, looked at him as if he were a stranger, that she was wondering, in the way she might suddenly wonder what the weather was, who he was. He got up and left her.

While he was out, he realized – the idea appearing like a sustaining figure in the air before him – what would save her: me.

He found my mother lying as if she had thrown herself from a height. He raised her up to her feet and held her up.

He wanted to make love to her, and he knew their love-making would have to be different from all the love they had made before, and he had to convey to her the difference, a difference widening out in the awareness that they were making love for a reason that hadn't before occurred to them, not with such a presence, as if what he wanted, and what he wanted her to want, were already there, or the outline of it was, and their love-making gave body to it.

Their love-making, before, had been as though to get behind each other's lungs, livers, hearts, where dimensions, vastly and inwardly expanding, went deeper and deeper, until they were no longer knocking on flesh, but water, but stone. I know, I know.

Now, he held her and kissed her around the eyes, along the jaw, along the edges of her face. He kissed her delicately. He had to say what he wanted without saying anything, had to surround her with a desire that now went beyond all his other desires, and yet not say what it was, because how could he, how could he explain when the desire circled and circled, and multiplied in the circling, and not one part, separated from the others, meant anything, only meant anything when everything swarmed together. In making love to her, he had to surround her, not with words, not with feelings accented by a touch or a look, not even with sentences, not even with emotions elongated to give the individual feelings a greater scope to reach round her, but with whole long paragraphs, with a dilated sense that, like a great drifting wind, like a flame shot off from fire, like water slowly evaporating, like stone calcinated to a fine rising powder, floated off the paragraph too dense and too involved to be undone, floated off and swept her up, swept them both up, and they would know, without being able to say, what they were making love for, what, suddenly, made their love different: that presence of something, half-seen as a thin, luminous outline, to which they would give roundness.

I was born.

They gave me all their attention, and if I screamed, thrashed, raged for more, they gave me more. I was a great infantile black mass, too dense to support its own weight, which was collapsed in on itself, and they risked collapsing in as well, bodily, as they pressed closer and closer to give me what I needed – no, not needed, to give me what I couldn't help demanding.

They got – as though that density, involuted to the impossible extent that it was a black hole, all at once reversed itself, and what had been outside went in, and what had been inside came out, the dark just as suddenly turning to light – a bright sphere.

It was bright, it was simple, it was an orbicular nothing that hung as a centre about which their lives revolved. It was not an affirmation of anything. It was, if it could be called anything, a round negation, but a negation filled, over-filled, expanded in their awareness that there was as much, if not more, to be got from saying no as saying yes. In any case, they loved me by saying no, no to the colour of my eyes, no to the tone of my skin, no to my looks, no to my sex, no to my voice, no to my feelings, no to my intelligence, no to me entirely, for even in giving and giving to me, even in paying attention to me as if their very attention were necessary to sustain me, what they gave and what they paid was too vast to have had anything to do with me, and I was to them an open, a deep, a round nothing about which all the gleams fell. They wanted everything.

They wanted everything.

And what do I see of them, through a big eye that blurs, from this beginning?

I see them, seeing them through a blur, as seeing nothing, and holding to it as if it were something, to it as if it were a promise of everything, to it as if it, it in itself, became a thing in itself, there, there and for me, now, here, and wondering, all of us, if there were such a thing, and, if there were such a thing, they would, I would, never let go of it, never.

He observed her and the baby, me, closely, and once, while she bathed it, he noted that something had come over her, as if, having been drained, rich blood suddenly rose up in her and filled her. She splashed the water against the baby; it laughed, and she laughed. She slipped her hands round and round the plumpness, not simply to wash it, he saw, but to feel it, over and over. He stood above her watching. She held each of its hands in her hands and splashed the water with them, and the baby laughed more, then splashed with its feet, so the water hit its mother's face. She looked up at her husband. He would not have been able to diagram the signs of something having happened to her, but he knew they were there, the lines altered about her mouth and eyes, the shift in the angles of her cheeks and jaw, as if her face had opened, and he saw a different face to the face he had known. The water dripped from her cheek and nose. She took up the baby from the water, its body shining, and at the sight of it in its mother's arms there passed through him a suffused sense that they would get what they longed for.

Then —

They were walking together. My mother was carrying me. Shadows were projected before them into the bright air, bright as with an opacity of floating, flaring particles, and caused alternating planes of light and dark, so we went from light to dark, from dark to light. Because of the opacity of the bright planes, it was impossible to see through them. The light and shadow passed across my eyes. My mother walked slowly.

My father stayed behind. Perhaps he had seen something, someone he wanted to see more clearly. My mother continued, through plane after plane. When my father looked for her he couldn't see her. He went ahead, the succession of light then shadow acting on his eyes strobe-like, so everything appeared to him in static images, in moments, and he suddenly wondered if the images, the moments, might be discontinuous, if, after the next flash, he might all at once find he was no longer where he had imagined he had come with his wife and their baby. He rushed ahead to find them.

He found my mother – no, not found, because it was as if she abruptly appeared before him – he discovered her, motionless, her long shadow extended before her into the air. She was looking away. He approached her quietly. He didn't want to jolt her. He saw, near enough, that she was unaware of him, and her line of vision was itself a long shadow down which she looked. He sensed that she was someone else, because her arms were empty. The moment was disconnected, large, and as stark as the image of her.

She turned to him, and as she did he saw come over her the awareness of what he suspected in her: what she might do to the baby, what she might not be able to keep herself from doing to it.

He said, the baby.

She pointed. She might have pointed at the air, at water, at a flaring brightness of light, at a stone. An unqualified panic made him suddenly tremble.

He quickly picked it up from the ground as if to save it from drowning, and, holding it, looking it over to see that it was all right, because it was silent in a way that indicated a fear deeper than what screaming would have indicated, it occurred to him that he might have, then and there, just found a baby, and though it had nothing to do with him, he knew it was in danger.

Something had happened, some shift in the gravitational pull which suddenly rearranged the elements: the ground gave way a little as if beneath it had turned to a liquid, the water stirred like gas, the air seemed about to burn up, and a flickering, a coruscation that revealed, or was itself, a high concavity, spread out and up like a thin aether. Did my parents notice? Did I? No, we didn't. My father handed the baby, me, back to my mother, and we went on. My father felt, however, tinglings about his body, as though gravities and pressures, minutely altered, drew him and pressed on him in ways that made him wonder, as he wondered about feelings that suddenly, unaccountably altered, if he, if the country he inhabited, were changing. The wonder was enveloped in the superseding awareness that, no, nothing was changing. And yet, he thought, how could he account for the sense that something *had* happened, and because it had happened, he and his wife and the baby were dying? There came over him the horror of what the baby had been born into, the horror of its nationality, from which it must be saved.

It must, he thought, though it would be like trying to hold together a sphere as it dissolved in the midst of a pervading confusion. He must save it; they must. He must convince her that they must, that if she didn't matter and he didn't matter, the baby did, simply because, with the force of all his concentrated will, he imposed it he made it matter.

They slept with the baby between them. (I imagine, as they slept their bodies, in the darkness, decomposed from bone and blood and flickers of thought to a merging of stones and earth, of water sinking and suddenly rising, or eruptions of fire, of steam and a slow dislodgement of lava, of gases and of layers of enveloping atmospheres.) He didn't let the baby out of their presence, out of her sight, as if to impress the plump body on himself as well as her. She accepted it. She did nothing else. One day – one day? perhaps one week, one month, one year, perhaps, all together, one moment – to call her back from her withdrawal, he held her in his arms, the baby squeezed between them, and said her name over and over again again and again, until, in its repetition, it was an incantation, and the name ceased to be her name, became a sound, circular, that drew her attention towards the centre of his forehead, towards the tip of the baby's chin, towards the backs of her hands. He tried to sustain the attention. He repeated, over and over, his voice modulating the sound so that, though it was always the same, it was always different, and if he could keep it up, keep it up so it continued ever after he stopped, her tenuous attention would hold, and he would have her.

He sustained the repetition, he barely sustained it, but he did, and he saw in the centres of her eyes her attention clarify, and with that he continued, he made his appeal. I do not know what the appeal was. I reach back to the knowledge that it was made, as though I were reaching back through layers and layers to what now sustains me: they struggled for me and with me to keep me alive, and there's my pity for and terror of them, because they struggled against all their deep and wild desires to give up. I do not hate them. I imagine the appeal evolving in him, in his concentration, like an evolving gravity, which not only drew her attention to it, but rearranged it, so she, too, might wonder what was happening. It was not an appeal to her emotions, not an appeal to what might have been thought her sensibilities as a mother; it was not an appeal to her arriving at a conclusion by thinking her way to it; it was an appeal to that part of her which recognized a circle, a square, a triangle. He wanted her to see that what they must struggle for was the recognition, a recognition of shape, and, more, of shade, of beat, which promised, not only rearrangements, but shapes not known, shades not seen, beats not heard, not for them – no, for not even he, now, believed in the possibilities – but for me. Because I mattered. Because I mattered. Because I would know, see, hear what they didn't know, see, hear. She must come out from wherever she had gone, and she must help him do whatever had to be done to allow me to know and see and hear – They tried. He said to her that they must try, and, repeating it till the repetition rolled itself into a globe that vibrated as with audible rays pulsing from it, she finally sensed what he was insisting upon, because, her eyes widening, she responded, she wept. She shook as she wept. She didn't emit a sound.

I must be saved – be saved, perhaps, from their love for one another, from which they themselves couldn't save themselves, and I return again, as I return always, to why they fell in love, and can only think it was because they couldn't help it, couldn't help falling. This is everything I know, and it is an everything I can in no way grasp. My parents abide in that hollow, and I have difficulty now imagining what they looked like as they retreat deeper and deeper to where the hollow, concave, reflects in its curves its own emptiness. There is nothing about them, especially not their love for one another, which I might be able to stratify; their lives are a moment.

They fell in love in a moment.

I remember this: watching them from a distance, they in the middle of a wide, perhaps slightly tilting plane, and around them darkness. He was sitting. She stood behind him. I think they were talking, but I was too far away to hear more than a kind of modulated hum rising and falling like voices. Then she touched him – touched him on the shoulder or at the back of the neck – and he groaned. She touched him again – I couldn't see anything in her hand – and again he groaned, and groaned yet again when yet again she touched him, a groan that seemed to rise not from any pain she might have been causing him, but from a depthless desire to groan, to emit some sound which would make his desire whole and project it out, a desire always unlocalized, a passionate desire for he had no idea what, a desire he imagined at least being rid of by a deep internal sound that rose up from behind inside organs, from dimensions that would remain even after heart, liver, lungs, brain, sex were removed – and what would remain? everything would remain – and it was from there, that empty dimension, that he groaned, again and again. She touched him on the back of the neck, about his head. He raised his head, stretching his neck, but otherwise didn't move. He shook his head from side to side as if this were all he could do to stop her from touching him. She didn't stop, and suddenly he jumped up and grabbed her, and when he grabbed her the groan became a strange harsh gurgle, and I saw her step back from him. He advanced, and she held out an arm, either to keep him from falling or to ward him away. He came closer; she touched him on the chest; he screamed. She was silent. He screamed and threw himself on her, stumbled to the ground with her. I did not know what they were doing. I don't know now what they were doing. I saw her arms rise up and come down, again and again, and saw him twist his body from side to side. They could have got up and run away from one another – it would have been so simple, so easy – but they didn't. And then, her whole body abruptly arrested, I saw my mother look towards me, and freeze, She said something to my father. He all at once lay still. They had become aware that I was watching them.

That was the end. That I should have seen them doing what they didn't want me to see, what they had sworn I would never see, was the end. I saw it all, from my distance, as a landscape into which I knew I could never go without taking risks too vast for me to associate them even with being killed – I felt they were greater than that – and yet I knew I could never turn away from the landscape. It was my country, to which my allegiance was assured, because I had been born into it, as I had been born into my own blood.

My mother rose, violence radiating about her, slightly hunched up, her fingers separated one from the other, and came towards me. I see her as through distortions that magnify her face, her eyes. She said, expressionless: GO AWAY! GO AWAY!

I thought I saw – I think I saw – my father, in the distance, raise his hand and point at me.

ANN
QUIN

Ann Quin was born in 1936 in Sussex. She was convent educated, then worked in various publishing houses, and on and off as a part-time secretary for a number of organizations including the Royal College of Art. She published four novels: Berg *(1964),* Three *(1966),* Passages *(1969) and* Tripticks *(1972). She published short stories in* Nova *and the* Transatlantic Review. *Her novels, all published in Britain by Calder & Boyars, were also published in America, France and Germany. In 1965 she received the Harkness Fellowship, which took her to the USA for one year, and also the D. H. Lawrence award, and she spent some further time in America in the late 60s, which gave her the material for her novel* Tripticks.

Her publisher, Marion Boyars, writes: 'Her novels Berg *and* Three *were extremely well received by the press in Britain and elsewhere. She was compared with such diverse writers as Graham Greene, Nathalie Sarraute and Samuel Beckett. She had, however, a very individual style and if any influences are to be found in her later work, it seems more appropriate to name people like Robert Creeley and John Cage rather than those writers named above whom she told me she had not read seriously by the time she was compared to them. She did feel, unjustifiably in my view that she lacked formal education, and in the last year of her life she went to Hillcroft College to prepare herself for university entrance. She should have started at the University of East Anglia in the English Department in October 1973, the month after she died, tragically, by drowning at the age of thirty-seven.'*

From THE UNMAPPED COUNTRY
an unfinished novel

'Good morning and how are we today?'

'Bloody rotten if you must know.'

'Why is that – tell me more?'

Silence. Patient confronted psychiatrist. Woman and man. She looked at the thin hair he had carefully placed over his yellow husk. Thin lips, almost no lips. Thick hands, bunches of spiders on his knuckles. He wrote or doodled, leaning forward, back.

'I don't like your madness.'

'What do you mean by that, Sandra?'

Pen poised, ready to stab yet another record. She could not see his eyes, the light bounced, spiralled in his spectacles. Black tentacles crept from his nostrils. In the distance a woman screamed.

'Won't you explain further, Sandra – tell me what you are thinking?'

She did not hear him, did not choose to, she waited with the walls for the screams to subside. She saw the hospital staff in their hygienic armour of white approach a struggling body. The raising of a needle, the filling of it, hands holding the body down, eyes unable to see when the needle would sink into the flesh. Soon the whimpering would fill in the cracks, bury itself in some closet room, behind a locked door.

She knew he would continue writing even if she did not say anything. Every gesture noted. She looked towards the window. Out there another world; were they still there waiting? No, they had gone, and meanwhile she had to cope with this clown. Those tentacles crept out of his ears. She stared at a stain on his waistcoat, like semen between the wrinkles, above the separation over his paunch.

'I really don't like you and I have nothing more to say.'

He smiled, showing a hole where a lizard struggled between rocks. In a space between clouds some gigantic bird wheeled, then plummeted down. White on white the snow against walls. As white as God's beard. She closed her eyes. Prismatic colours rose and fell.

'Tell me about the journey you took – why did you . . .?'

'No.'

Wind ruffled snow. The north wind bringing the sound of ice. She saw again three gulls circle the ship's mast, and heard the movement of wood against ice; saw the icebergs like fallen statues move slowly past. Points of light from islands pinpricked the disturbed darkness. Gull cries echoed the endless cries of the dead from the ocean depths. How many of the dead had she awoken from their full-fathomed dreams? 'Bless you all,' she muttered.

'What was that?'

'Fuck you.'

He laughed, a gasping kind of sound escaped through the hole.

'That's your reaction in analysis to me, don't be influenced, don't be moved, don't be lured into reacting to me.'

'It's not how you live that matters it's how you die that's important,' she said, watching him scratch the paper; a nicotine-stained finger curled round the pen, or tapped it with mechanical precision. He pulled back his sleeve and scratched his hairy wrist. She knew he was really looking at his watch.

'Well I think that's it for today Sandra.' He took his spectacles off; perhaps his eyes went with them? She could see nothing there that might even resemble eyes.

She escaped into the corridor, where Thomas waylaid her. At least he had eyes, washed-out blue, focusing always on some point to the left of her head.

'You believe me don't you, even if no one else does, you do don't you?' he said, catching hold of her arm, 'you believe that I'm Judas Iscariot reincarnated, you see I have positive proof, the evidence is all in my book, at least it will be when I've written it, and God is Mrs Carr, and my friend Bob is Jesus Christ.'

'What are you going to call your book Thomas?'

'God's Joke.'

They walked into the ward, where she joined the queue for her medicine.

'Blessings on you from the Holy Mother of God herself oh Jesus Christ have mercy on your sins you cunt you bloody fucking cunt.' Said Mrs Carr, undoing her nightdress.

'Now Annie you know you musn't do that – be a good girl do yourself up.' A nurse said, placing her hand on the woman's shoulder. Somewhere above a man groaned; somewhere else a woman laughed. Nearby a high-pitched voice cried 'Where's mummy where's my mummy I want my mummy.'

'May the blessed Virgin shit on you – shit shit shit.' Shouted Annie Carr, frantic fingers plucked at her nighty.

Sandra awaited her turn for the pills she would later spit out in the lavatory. A new patient entered the ward, screaming between two orderlies. 'I don't want to come here – what are you doing to me – I'm going home right now – leave me – let me go you can't keep me here you have no right – no right whatsoever – I want to go home.'

The patient's voice trailed off, rose again as white coated robots surrounded her. The needle produced, raised. The screams into inevitable whimpers, as one more person was subdued into drugged submissiveness; would later wake up, dazed, glaze-eyed, nod into helplessness before the authority of 'feel better – that's right – no need to worry you're in good hands now – we're here to help you'

'I had a dream about you last night Sandra,' Thomas whispered 'where your head had been cut off, it was delivered to me all bandaged up with blood dripping through – perhaps you are John the Baptist – yes that must be it.'

'But Thomas last week I was the Virgin Mary.' He did not reply and wandered off down the corridors of his Jerusalem.

Sandra bent over the lavatory and watched the pills fall, she flushed them away.

'Sandra – Sandra are you there – your mother is on the phone do you want to speak to her?'

'No.'

'She sends her love.'

The Red Queen breathing through the tunnel. Her face at the bottom of the lavatory, grinned up. Flush her away. Sandra sat for some time in the lavatory, the only place she could be by herself and not be distracted, and go back over the journey; even so their voices interrupted 'It's all in the head you must realize that – in the head in the head inthehead inthehead inthehead . . .' and she saw the doctor's faceless presence behind his desk, like the painting 'Le Principe du plaisir', by Magritte, except the figure in the painting was infinitely better, more pleasing. Then there was the Red Queen's face, one eye open; even when dead her mother, no doubt, would be watching her. And Clive – what of Cilve? Frightened of his own madness; seeing her actions, reactions as an interpretation of what he considered a madness just round the corner for himself. Young, younger than herself, blond and beautiful with a little old man tucked away somewhere, who popped out unexpectedly and snarled at her, or worse: turned away, back into his next master-piece. Then all the spectres who possessed him throughout the night, all with different ways of snoring, various positions in sleep. She had grown to love them all, admittedly she feared a few, especially the little boy part of him that stood apart, helpless, frightened, while they in white coats pinned her down. He had never forgiven her for that, for losing control, and unable to forgive himself allowing it to happen.

'Sandra lunch is ready – Sandra are you all right – what are you doing so long in there?'

'What do you think I'm doing – I'm flushing my dreams away.'

'Well hurry up dear lunch is being served.'

'I would prefer not to have caviar today Nurse just a little of the duck with orange thank you.'

She opened the door, the nurse looked suspiciously in.

'If you want to see the remains of my dreams why don't you look in there?' Sandra moved aside. The nurse clicked her teeth, and took mental note of the patient's words.

'You can add to your brief that the patient did not resist to having her dreams looked at.'

The nurse pushed the patient out, back into the ward, where the sound of knives scraped the edge of plates. Some knives remained as motionless as the persons confronting the food.

'May the Holy Mother of God bless you and be food for what we praise in God the fucking father and Satan in the Holy Ghost lamb brought to slaughter.' Annie Carr shouted, pushing out her left breast, dipping it in the gravy.

'Naughty Annie, now you know we told you that if you don't behave yourself you will have to have your meals by yourself.'

'Oh forgive me for what I have not done – on your bended knees and may God strike me dead if I tell lies.' Annie Carr slid under the table, tore off her nightdress, and on all fours gave herself to the linoleum. Two orderlies rushed in. They struggled with the heaving mass of flesh. The other patients carried on eating, chatting to themselves, or each other. Sandra looked across at the young boy who had only arrived yesterday, who had not spoken a word, had not eaten anything. He stared back, through her; what dream screen did he see? Curly dark hair showed through his pyjama top. As if he knew she wanted to place her head there, her fingers in the warm moist nest, he placed his hand on the hairs, and smiled.

'You must be ready for the invasion they are disguised as dwarfs and walk about in the parks, I've got my hammer ready for them, so at least I shall be all right, and I'm making a special bomb to destroy them.' Said an old man at the end of the table. No one took any notice, they had heard his warnings day in, day out. The bomb he kept under his bed, at least that's where it had been until they took it away. A contraption that had been improvised out of lead piping, ball-bearings and wire.

Someone started crying. Another person laughed. Sandra left the table and went into the dormitory. She lay on her bed and stared at the ceiling.

'You can't lie down now dear, it's time for your occupational therapy – painting isn't it for you this afternoon?'

'I don't want to.'

'Well you can't go to sleep now Sandra.'

She felt under the mattress, yes the journal was still there, she took it out and began writing.

'Sandra please get up now and go across for your painting session.'

'Sandra it's time to get up. Sandra your meal is ready. It's time to go to bed. Sandra take your pills. It's time for your treatment. Sandra get your potty. You're late. Sandra do your homework. Pick that up. Are you in there Sandra? Don't do that. Stop snivelling and whining like a child. Sandra do her peepees now. Sandra do her two-twos now. Sandra don't wear your best dress. Put on that coat Sandra. Put that book down when I'm talking to you. Don't go around like that in your bare feet you'll get athlete's foot. Don't go in for petting with men Sandra it leads to other things. Sandra do you hear me . . . ?'

Yes I hear you all my mothers and fathers will you never stop? Stop.

She made her way to Block C, but did not enter. Instead she walked the grounds and made paintings with her footprints in the snow. A solitary bird, a hooded midget nun, on a bare branch looked down and seemed to wink. Once she had understood the language of birds, now no longer, it took all her time to understand her own language, and that of those who attempted communication. Once there had been the subterranean language with the underground forces. If speech at all then it was the spaces between words, and the echoes the words left, or what might be really meant under the surface. She knew, had known. No longer knew. Only remembered. In the recollection, pictures, words, visions, thoughts, images built themselves into citadels, gigantic towers that toppled with the weight of it all; the top heavier than the foundations. Last events came first, the beginning at the end, or suddenly reversed, or slid into panels midway. Had ECT done that – damn them? She shuddered, as though the wires were attached to her head there under the branches. Branches shaped in a design by the wind. They shape one into a walky talky doll with all the correct responses. Squeeze me here and I squeak. She squeaked, and watched the nun fly off. Snow sea-sprayed onto her face.

The boy, who never spoke, approached. He held out a box of chocolates. She thanked him. He smiled, inclined his head, like a

B.T.W.—I

dog, waiting for her to throw a stick. Then she saw what he was really applying himself to; he had his own stick to play with. She walked away quickly, nausea rising. The Exit gates were wide open. If she ran past the porters' lodge perhaps . . . but the sound of traffic defeated her; sound of heavy Red Army boots would be out there, they would be waiting for her. She threw the chocolates into an area of untrampled snow.

She sat in the rose arbour and opened her journal.

Today I do not know the date

There is snow, heavy on the surrounding hedges. I can no longer remember how long I have been here and yet I count the days for when I am discharged. They say 'soon'. 'You are making progress.' It is all pretence on their part, as well as mine.

DIALOGUE WITH ANALYST

A1: Come in. (*Long pause*) How are you today?

P1: I had this dream last night.

A2: Yes?

P2: I was playing the piano and suddenly the keys went soft, I noticed they were my fingers, that in fact my fingers had changed into keys. I looked over the keyboard, inside the piano was my father wrapped in cellophane. He was dead, at least I thought he was until I bent over and peered closer, he rose and his hand broke through the cellophane, tried to grab me and pull me down.

A3: Ummhuh.

P3: And, ahh, I thought I'd bring that up. (*Pause*) Bring the, ahh, dream up I mean, not him, my father.

A4: Ahh, it makes sense.

P4: Then I had this fantasy (*pause*) that is, ahh (*pause*) after ahh woke up.

A5: Yes.

P5: I would find my father and stab him in the back, which of course means I really want him to fuck me (*pause*) ahh and then I was angry because of the guilt.

A6: The logical sequence.

P6: The logical sequence, fits into the pattern (*pause*) doesn't it?

A7: More or less – yes.

P7: Against myself primarily, but (*pause*) ahh well I've planned it all out I know where he works for some death-aid place (*pause*) sorry I mean ahh deaf-aid – it's along Miller Street, and you know how crowded it can be there.

A8: Yes it can get very crowded.

P8: Well, ahh, I would (*pause*) wait for him to come out of his office at 5.30 – his office isn't actually on Miller Street but in Bond Street (*pause*) Do you know it?

A9: Yes, I know the street.

P9: Well there's a little question there, ahh, the decision of this as a possibility is becoming more crystallized.

A10: Ummhuh.

P10: So this fantasy has triggered all sorts of other things off (*pause*) for instance, ahh, if I project my father image onto someone else.

A11: Ummhuh.

P11: But that's another dimension.

A12: The other side of yourself.

P12: Not myself at all (*pause*) I see the whole situation as an outsider looking on. I have not felt myself as the individual in the situation. I only see myself, what, looking as though at another person.

A13: Ummhuh. (*Pause*) So there's a kind of, it's sort of the existentialist approach.

P13: I have to sort of, what, struggle around to try and find something that describes it all and the terminology used, I make no guarantee of its accuracy.

A14: O.K. now Wednesday at four?

P14: Wednesday at four.

A15: Goodbye.

P15: Goodbye.

Patient and Analyst satisfied. But myself? Only impatience at his stupidity in listening and believing in the radio he switches on.

Sandra closed the journal. Opening her mouth she waited for the snow to fall in. She heard footsteps of someone approaching. The old man shuffled by, furtively looking over his shoulder.

'Ah did you see him – one of them actually here disguised as a dwarf, I must get my bomb?'

He wandered off. In the distance she saw flames, which she went towards. A rubbish heap being burnt. She could smell the burning

of flesh. Perhaps they cremated those who were never discharged?
Something scurried into the bushes – a rat. She felt hungry,
remembered the chocolates, and went across the lawns to where she
had thrown them. Like a thief she quickly put them in her pocket.
In a lavatory she crammed them two by two into her mouth.

Disinfectant, steel trolleys, closed doors, shouts, murmurs, screams.
Scurry of porters, orderlies, nurses. Patients in dressing-gowns
stared out of windows, or were fascinated by something on a wall,
in the stone floor. Smells of urine, cabbage and rubber. So many
wards, all looking the same; corridors upon corridors. She wandered
along an endless one, dark, empty. A door opened. She was pulled
into a pitch-dark room. She recognized the boy's smell – the smell
of water dead flowers leave, as he pressed her against his body. She
pushed him and heard him cry out. She fled.

In Block C she joined the half dozen patients who were in the middle
of describing their paintings.
   'This is me in the middle.'
   'But it looks like a horse.'
   'It's me and above are two moons in eclipse.'
   'That looks more like you.'
   'Hello Sandra where's your painting – the one you did last week?'
   'I destroyed it – I've done another though it's outside.'
   'Well fetch it and we'll have a look.'
   'I can't – anyway the wind has probably wiped it out.'
   'Very well, if you feel like doing one now Sandra you have
time.'
   She thought of Clive's paintings; the need for posterity. How
much better to create like the Navajo Indians, beginning at sunrise
in the desert, a sand painting that would be rubbed out by sun-
down. A desert landscape with wild horses galloping across. Sand
rippled. Landscape only disturbed by the wind. In a grain of sand
the whole universe – something like that, Blake put. He had visions.
A God who laughed, belched, snored and picked His nose. Her
God had been straight out of Blake, long snowy beard and snowy
locks, and in His face every conceivable landscape.

'That's a funny face Sandra.'

'It's God.'

'Looks like a lump of shit to me.' A patient said, making up her face with paint brushes. Someone else suddenly woke up and cried out 'The light, the black one, ahh, that stabs in the dark, ahh, because, ahh, I haven't, what, looked at them from the outside, of what this is a step towards, in that if I don't make these reasons.'

'Now Charles what have you done today?'

'I've switched off the connecting line to the President.'

'Yes well – but I mean you haven't done any work have you Charles, you've been asleep the whole afternoon?'

'The connection has been switched off.' He collapsed over the table and went back to sleep.

It was time for tea. They filed out, back to their wards. Back to the trolley where the wolves pounced on pieces of cake and biscuits.

'There's a visitor to see you Sandra.'

She looked up and saw Clive stride in.

'Hallo how are you?'

'Fine – and you?'

'Fine.'

Silence. He sat down on the edge of the chair. On the edge of the bed she spread out her legs as he bent over her.

'Cold today isn't it?'

'Yes colder than yesterday.'

'Yes – temperature has fallen.'

'Yes.'

'Cigarette?'

'Thanks.'

Silence. He pulled her off the bed, carried her towards the mirror.

'Still you're nice and warm in here – best place to be really.'

'Yes.'

Silence. Body to body. Body part of body. One body. The spaces between limbs.

'The food O.K.?'

'Oh it's all right.'

Silence. She took him in her mouth. He moved with the rhythm of her tongue.

'Oh I forgot – something for you – just a little something – here.' She took the box of chocolates from him, and smiled, looking at his hand. Fine boned, veins showing through like a Chinese water-colour. What other skin had that hand explored?

'Been working well?'

'On and off – you know.'

'And the teaching?'

'Just the same – same old rut.'

'How are your parents?'

'Fine – sent their love to you.'

'Well I . . .'

'Do you still . . .?'

'Sorry you were saying?'

'Ought to be going.'

'Yes.'

'Well goodbye – take care – see you again soon.'

'Goodbye.'

'Goodbye.' He bent over and pecked her on the cheek.

'Don't eat them all at once.' He said, indicating the chocolates, and strode out.

'Time for group session.' A nurse shouted. Shuffle of feet, chairs put in a circle. Patients from other wards came in. Three doctors surveyed the scene. Annie Carr tripped in and made the sign of the cross over each person.

'Sit down Annie – now who would like to begin?'

'I would like to say that I think the food here is pig's muck.' Said an enormous woman.

'It's better than what you'd get in the nick I can tell you.' Said another woman.

'I think there ought to be two televisions it's not fair just having the one and Mrs Whatshername hogs it all the time I never see what I want to see.'

'I want to know when I can leave?'

'I don't think it's fair being woken up at six in the morning.'

'Someone has stolen my slippers.'

'I have a poem here I'd like to read it's called "The Trees Aching Green" – when the trees move . . .'

'We don't want to hear any of your crappy poems.'

'When the trees begin to walk . . .'

'I want to know when I can go home?'

'Naked I stand in the roots . . .'

'Imagine him naked ahhha.' All the patients laughed. The doctors remained silent, yawned, or doodled, or looked at the clock.

'An earwig crawled into my ear Doctor and it's eating away my insides – I wish to have an X-ray please.'

'Looks as though it's eating away the outside as well.'

'The roots of my heaven leave holes in the sky . . .'

'You've got holes in your socks if that's what you mean?'

'Can we please have our eggs soft boiled?'

'I want to know when I can be discharged?'

'Two televisions instead of one.'

'The branches of my hell leave traces in the mirror . . .'

'Not surprised the way you look.'

'Someone's stolen my pearls.'

'Can we have two eggs instead of one for breakfast?'

'I want to go home.' Someone shouted, rose, and made for the corridor. A nurse brought him back.

'Has anyone anything else to say?' A doctor asked. Silence, apart from coughs, clicking of knitting needles, and someone snoring.

'Well I think that's it for this afternoon – thank you.' The doctor said, smiling round the circle. He and the other doctors marched out, followed by a few patients, whom they ignored. Cries of 'When can I . . .?' 'Please tell me Doctor when . . .' 'I demand an X-ray so you'll believe me you'll see the earwig for yourself . . .' Cries that bounced back onto the patients, leaving them with each other, from whom they turned away, turned into themselves, or the walls, the floors, the windows that looked onto concrete blocks.

Sandra went into the dormitory and lay down. Someone opposite muttered in her sleep. Someone else bent over paper bags. In the distance a man shouted 'No don't do it I don't – don't want it –

leave me alone.' Two nurses entered with the Charge Nurse, they marched down the line of beds.

'What's this Sandra aren't we feeling well?'

'I'm tired.'

'You can't sleep here now you know.' She went back into the ward and sat in a corner near the window. An old woman in a wheelchair stared at her, without blinking. Oh God, she's dead, Sandra thought, and turned away. Somewhere beyond the buildings Clive would be striding towards a yellow circle enclosed in a green triangle. Or perhaps a yellow triangle between white circles, a triangle he would enter.

A dry rasping cough startled her. She turned round and the old woman bent over. Sandra moved away and went into the area for television. The boy was there, staring at his fingers, motionless on his knees. She walked up the corridor, back again.

'Sandra come and sort out some counters.' A nurse called out.

'No.' She went and looked for Thomas, he was busy writing.

'Hi.' She bent over and tried to see what he had written, minute words crawled into each other across the paper. 'Is that God's Joke you're writing?'

'Just some notes – I think I've reached the point where I realize that I am betraying myself.'

'I should think by now Christ has forgiven you Thomas.'

'How can I know that He – Bob – I mean He can't speak and whenever I try and speak to Him He has such an accusing look in his nose.'

'How do you mean I mean eh how can you see that in his nose?'

'It points straight out at me.' He continued writing.

'I've seen God's face Thomas did you know that?'

He did not answer, but went on writing. She moved away, and went back to the ward. A young girl was silently crying. The old woman had gone back to her death-like mask. A group of women sorted out the coloured counters, putting them in polythene bags. A woman was trying on a wig.

'What you want that for – it's exactly the same as your own hair?' Someone asked.

'Well I got this lobotomy op coming up and they shave the head you see – nice isn't it – they designed it specially so it would look like my own hair?'

Sandra opened her journal at random.

I don't remember that day as a day – not surprising – for a long time no day seemed like a day, no night seemed like a night. But that particular day has no shape in my memory. I used to mark the time by meals, but as I believe we are given several sets of meals in each real day – about half a dozen sets of breakfast, lunch, tea, and dinner in each twelve hours – this was not much help.

She turned several pages and continued reading:

CONVERSATION WITH TWO DOCTORS

Dr X. Sandra, I wish to ask you something. I'm holding a pen here. Do you see this pen?

S. No.

Dr X. Dr Y, do you see this pen?

Dr Y. Yes, I see the pen.

Dr X. Sandra, how is it when I show you the pen, you say, no you don't see it, and Dr Y says yes, he does see it. How is it he says yes and you say no?

S. Well . . . ah the doctor says he doesn't see it?

Dr Y. I do see it.

S. You do see it?

Dr X. What do you say, Sandra?

S. I do see the pen.

Dr X. You do see the pen?

S. Unnhhh.

Dr X. No, wait, you tell me. I've got the pen here. Do you see the pen?

S. No, I don't see it.

I see an endless road, white-glittering under the sun's rays, glittering like a needle; above the remorseless sun weighing down the trees and houses under its electric rays. How can I explain, describe that to them? They would never understand. How ridiculous he looked holding that pen, nodding, grinning up at the other doctor. What a relief to get away from them and hear a newly arrived patient exclaim 'I am St Michael the Archangel and the Red Horse of the Apocalypse. You might say I have delusions of grandeur, but like Christ, I glorify myself for my Father's sake. For additional proof, I refer you to metaphysicians and Jehovah's Witnesses. I am in diguise and one might say a blessing in disguise.'

Sandra turned the pages over, and began writing.

Have just seen C, and saw myself seeing him, saw him seeing me, or rather not seeing me. His visits now have become a duty; as soon as he's here he wants to leave, obviously can't stand the role of visitor with sick person. I shall write and tell him not to come here anymore. No point. Nothing. If I love him still it is only love in memory.

Sandra paused, looked out of the window, some gulls circled above the grey buildings, tips of their wings caught in the fading light. She thought she heard the sound of waves breaking, the rush and sliding of pebbles, but it was only the rush-hour traffic. Out there was a world that carried on its daily duties, and somewhere they might be waiting for her, waiting for her to help in the Cause. But what Cause? She had almost forgotten what it was all about, what it was they wanted of her; like a dream now, the electric waves that had sent messages through her body had disappeared, the Cosmic Forces gone – gone. But not her memory, they hadn't obliterated that with their injections, pills and tentacles on her head. She looked across at the woman with her wig, she held it up for other women to admire. What would she be like after they had operated on her brain? And all because she was a compulsive house cleaner.

She suddenly felt claustrophobic, the smell of women penetrated her nose, mouth, ears and eyes. She went again into the dormitory, where it was dark, silent. She lay down and slid into black velvet. A sea of velvet that tossed her gently, and somewhere above her the sound of ice breaking. If I go back to the beginning of it all . . . but there is no beginning, and in the description I lose the threads. How many days, nights she had attempted going back over the journey, always it appeared in flashes, like a film running backwards, at top speed, a few pictures were stills, frozen, hovered there while others piled up. A landscape with snow, and the north wind god telling her to move in another direction. A ship's mast in a park, no, wrong again, a heavy cross leaned towards the west, and there was the mast, a ship sliding into dock, moving slowly below the town, in air it seemed. A hotel room overlooking rail tracks, the shuttle of trains, wagons throughout the night. Before then, before I arrived there, how did it begin? Let me see. . . .

Someone groaned across the way. Sandra opened her eyes and peered into the darkness, a huddled shape moved, jerked towards her. She sat up. The smell of stale bread and beef breathed over her.

'Go away.' She shouted at the old woman. 'Go away do you hear?' The old woman laughed and crouched over the bed.

'Nurse she's at it again.' Sandra screamed and sprang off the bed, and ran out.

'Listen that old hag has got out of bed really she can walk she's there go in now honestly if you don't believe me go in now . . .' The nurse shook her head, clicked her teeth, and marched into the dormitory. Sandra behind her. The old woman lay snoring in her own bed.

'Well she's just got back – honestly she was up a minute ago.'

'Poor old thing she's asleep as usual Sandra you must have been dreaming.'

'I wasn't.'

'She hasn't got out of that bed for eighteen months she's quite incapable of walking Sandra so don't be so silly.'

Ugh, the monster, a clever monster at that, Sandra thought, and went back to her bed.

'You can't sleep now Sandra – you know you're not supposed to be in here at this time of day so come along now.'

She went and watched the television. A newsreel shot of bombs being dropped in an area the pilot had marked out for him on a map. Someone started laughing.

'Shutup.' Someone else said, and concentrated on the picture that had changed to a girl rising in slow motion out of a sparkling sea, following an animated bambi.

'The doctor is human you know yes he's human I know now he's human 'cos he farted today when I saw him.' Someone said, and collapsed into silence.

'Yes she left it all to charity it's a mortal sin that shouldn't be

allowed but these old people get cranky don't they funny that how
they go all queer when they get past a certain age.'

'Such a shock for her . . .'

'A loud fart it was and the smell was strong.'

'Shutup.'

'And I told Jack to see a lawyer not right leaving it all to a dog's
home is it?'

'Have you seen Beryl's wig it looks just like her real hair – less
trouble it will be really?'

'So Jack's going to see a lawyer and get it sorted out.'

'I mean when you hear a fart and smell a fart then you know a
man's a man and he's human.'

'Will you shut up.'

'Just like her own hair, same colour and everything, cost a bomb
I'm sure – had it specially designed for her – can't tell the difference
at all.'

Someone changed the television channel. Screams of protest.

'Well you weren't watching anyway just natter natter natter.'

'That's not fair we were watching.'

'No you fucking wasn't.'

'No need for that.'

Silence. A picture came on of a table laden with food.

'Looks nice doesn't it?'

'Not poisoned like it is here.'

They leaned forward and watched the picture intently.

They leaned back and swallowed their saliva; carried on chattering, nose-picking, knitting; fingers plucked at buttons, cigarettes,
fingers at fingers, a battle of insects.

Sandra moved heavily away, and looked at the clock. An hour to go
before supper. She saw Thomas staring into oblivion.

'What you thinking – you look miles away?'

He did not answer, nor look at her. Obviously in one of his
moods. She persevered.

'Thomas tell me about God's Joke?' But he persevered in his
silence. She put her hand out as if to touch him, but there was that
feeling again – overpowering from his body – his grey mottled

skin would not feel like skin to touch, but some horrible substance that would congeal under her hands. She looked round the ward. People slept, or muttered to themselves, to each other, or were transfixed by some part of their anatomy; a lot seemed concerned with their hands, as though they were palm reading. Some nurses laughed behind a closed door. She looked again at the clock. Soon it would be supper, soon it will be over, and the long night crawled ahead of her.

She went into the dormitory once more, hastily looked over for the lump of senility — the old woman was not there. Sandra looked quickly round and saw a shadow move or rather lurch from other shadows, and the old woman, cackling, stumbled towards her. Sandra quickly went over to her own bed, brought out her journal and ran out.

She found an uninhabited space where she pulled up a chair and table, but someone entered her new-found territory. It was Thomas, blinking like a bat behind his spectacles.

'Wondered if you'd care to read this and let me know what you think about it?' He handed her a wad of paper covered in his spider writing.

'Is this God's Joke?' She asked, looking at the pages, moving her hand quickly away from his that still held on to the paper.

'Yes — just rough though — notes really.'

'But I can't read it — your writing is absolutely illegible Thomas.'

'What if I read some of it to you?'

'If you like.'

He pulled up a chair, cleared his throat, cleared it in such a way she half expected to see a frog jump out, or some of the grey inner substance.

'In the beginning when all was space, space not as we know it, but an infinite space, with nothing, no light, no darkness, God had a dream. The dream was a desert with horizon, and then He woke up, and felt very lonely, very bored and . . .'

'What a load of old bullshit.' Someone passing by, shouted. Thomas paused, bit his lip, frowned.

'Where was I – oh yes – bored and He thought if He could dream such dreams why couldn't He create the dream into reality. So He . . . are you listening?'

'Yes, yes go on very interesting.'

'He created the desert and the sky, and again he felt lonely, and very bored, so he went to sleep again, and had another dream . . . oh damn it's supper time – I'll read some more after O.K.?'

Sandra nodded, and followed him to the dining hall, where she joined the queue and awaited her turn. She ate quickly, amidst the usual babble, scraping of plates, coughing and spluttering.

'I'll see you back in my ward Thomas O.K.?'

She went outside, and stood on the entrance steps. In the distance a dog howled. The snow made points of whiteness in the dark, and the stars reflected their points, but no longer did they charge her pulse; the transmission had been cut off. There was no moon. She no longer moved with the weather, no longer a creature of the night. The wind changed its direction of its own accord. The dog's howl entered her. Whining, she ran into the grounds, across frozen lumps of earth towards the North star that hung suspended beyond the gates.

The gates were shut. She moved along by the railings, in deep snow, shivering, and looked at the row of identical houses the other side. She stood for some time looking in at a window where the curtains had not been drawn. A woman watched television. A man on a bed, read a newspaper. A naked light bulb burned between them. The woman turned round, got up, and drew the curtains. Sandra moved back slowly to the entrance steps, and sat down on the top step, breathing over her hands. No signs. No messages. Where had they gone? Supposing if they – the doctors – everyone were right, it had all been in her head?

She peered through her fingers at the white and black landscape, and watched the snow fall. Already her tracks had been covered, but those made by cars on the winding road remained, thin rust-coloured patterns. She rose and went inside, up to the ward, or rather into a parrot house. Those who were not chattering, stalked the room, or fluttered on chairs, made stabbing movements with knitting needles, skeins of coloured wool spilled onto the floor, dribbled yellow and red between flapping arms. Someone croaked, another barked. A mouth opened, closed, opened again, no sound came. But eventually a howl did emerge. Doors opened, and in rushed the keepers. The howl continued. People turned their heads, froze in contorted positions, as the keepers bent over a young girl struggling on the floor; her head curiously twisted; the white of her eyes showed through dark feathers, damp with sweat. The howl changed into a gurgle, the gurgle to gasps, as the body writhed in the net of arms. And like a huge octopus the group moved slowly out of the room. The girl's shoe remained, on its side. Someone kicked it across the floor. The knitting needles pierced the air, click click click, and bodies took up their preceding positions, and went through the motions of survival of the fittest.

Sandra went into a lavatory and sat down. She watched her legs shake, her hands came up as if warding off blows. She heard someone come in, being sick, coughing followed, then muttering.

'Damn them – fuck 'em bastards – more earwigs, not just one – nurse – nurse come here and see thousands of 'em, it must have been that shepherd's pie – they must have come from that – nurse come and see.'

Sandra looked at her knees, as if they belonged to someone else, they nudged, knocked against each other, in some strange communication of their own.

'Come along dear – it's all right – there now feel better?' A nurse said.

'Look at 'em wriggling away down there – that's evidence for you.'

'Now don't be silly dear come and watch television we like watching telly don't we now – come along.'

'That thing is plugged in you know and watches me they think I don't know about the earwigs they are planting.'

'Yes yes come along now there's a good girl.' The good girl shuffled out.

Sandra stood on the lavatory seat and opened the tiny window, where she looked out on a narrow space of darkness. The window sill had a hard crust of snow impregnated with pigeon tracks, a part ruffled in the middle, where the bird's feathers must have brushed against the snow. She looked up and saw the edge of the moon, like a broken off finger nail. A train rattled by and left an echo between the buildings. Someone next door breathed heavily, loud farts filled the air. Sandra closed the window and jumped down. She went out and washed her hands. A woman was sticking false eyelashes on, swearing under her breath.

'Don't know why I bother she never looks at me now.' The woman said, twisting her mouth, smiling at herself.

'You don't have to bother do you dear you're still young you don't have to bother with makeup – lovely hair you have is that its real colour?' The woman looked at Sandra in the mirror, moved over to her, and still looking in the mirror, she stroked Sandra's hair.

'Lovely and soft – you're lovely and soft – what's the matter – oh well be like that.'

Sandra moved away, followed by the woman shouting, swearing. Through the swing door, in a backward glance, Sandra saw a crumpled face, an eyelash quivered on a rouged cheek.

Music greeted her in the ward. A party jerked people into action, or non-action. A table laden with jellies, small grey sandwiches, and jugs of orange juice. Women danced with women, the men smoked and watched, or slyly went off to their secret horde of hard liquor. Thomas came up, bowed, and asked if she cared to dance. She shrank away.

'I couldn't find you after supper – wanted to read you the rest – ahh I . . .'

'Perhaps tomorrow Thomas?'

The girl who had earlier thrown a fit was brought in, stiff, glaze-eyed, she sat down and contemplated her fingernails. People moved away from the girl. They knew who to avoid, not to avoid, so that little groups formed round the room, watched over by a few charge nurses on the fringe. Two or three men swayed in, burping, spluttering with laughter.

'Enjoying ourselves are we then – that's right?'

Before Sandra could answer the nurse moved along, nodding, smiling at everyone.

In the alcove Sandra noticed the boy, who had given her the chocolates, he stared at the television, which was not turned on. She walked into the dormitory, and sat on her bed, eyes closed. Laughter and music from the ward entered, drifted away, entered again. Two women came in, whispering. Sandra pretended to be asleep, and watched them through half closed eyes. They gently embraced at first, but soon they clawed each other, like animals in a fight. Sandra shut her eyes tightly, but she heard the two women panting, swearing, and soon the bed creaked. She felt the sweat run between her breasts. She opened her eyes, shut them; did not want to look, but looked. She held her breath, as the women's breathing came heavy and fast. Arms and legs flew everywhere, or mingled. One of the women crouched in a praying position between huge thighs, mottled skin marked with bruises and thick purple veins.

Sandra got up and moved quietly down between the beds. One of the women shrieked with laughter.

'Getting bored darling – come and join us?'

Out of the corner of her eyes, she saw a puffy red face, a pink and yellow tongue curled about itself, protruding.

Back in the ward someone offered her a piece of jelly. She refused, and sat down. The atmosphere was hot and smoky. A group in the middle attempted Knees Up Mother Brown. Another group sang old songs. Annie Carr sat on the floor, between her spread legs a long orange strip of wool dangled; she was conducting with the knitting needles, and singing a in strange cracked voice 'All Things Bright and Beautiful'. Sandra turned towards the girl and asked her name, there was no response, apart from a slight twitching of the girl's hands. Thomas came over, and sighing, sat down next to Sandra.

'How can you say Annie Carr is God, Thomas – I mean look at her now – just look at her?'

'We all have our disguises.' He replied, taking his spectacles off, and wiping them with a grubby handkerchief. The needle in the record stuck in a groove and the words 'All I need is love' blared out over and over again. Someone stopped it, people hardly seemed *to* notice, but went on kicking into the air, swaying, bumping against each other.

'I have this buzzing in my head – strange it doesn't seem to go – had it for days now.' Thomas said, shaking his head from side to side. 'As if a fly has got in or something.'

The strains of a last waltz came over, and everyone drifted apart, and looked at the remains of food, crumbs on the table, the floor. A few couples moved slowly round, with eyes closed, trying to kiss, avoiding kisses. One old man collapsed, smiling happily. Another man helped him up, holding a whisky bottle to his mouth. The old man gurgled, then sucked on the bottle, Sandra edged her way into the dormitory. The women were no longer there. She undressed and got into bed. The others came in, giggling.

Soon there was just the sound of the clock, and breathing, wheezing, dream murmurs, and bodies turning over. The long night stretched out. Wind rattled the windows, and snow mixed with hail pounded like small fists against glass. In the middle of the dormitory, a nurse read or slept under a lamp. Sandra stared at this light until it spun from its orbit and approached. Right at the very beginning – but there was no beginning. Vague notes for a basis of shape. The first section interrupted by the last. No continuous movement. A starting point somewhere. Chords superimposed on chords. The pendulum swung back.

MAGGIE
ROSS

Maggie Ross was born and brought up in Essex. She went to art school, then to the University of London. She taught art before turning to writing as a career. In 1968 she won the James Tait Black Memorial Prize for the year's best novel, The Gasteropod *(Cresset Press, Penguin). She has been fiction critic for the* Listener. *Her short stories have appeared in magazines and on radio, in England and abroad. They have been published in* Penguin Modern Stories 6, Fifth, Sixth, Seventh *and* Eighth Ghost Books *(Barrie & Jenkins),* Factions *(Michael Joseph) and* Covent Garden Stories *(Covent Garden Press). Her poems have been published in* Transatlantic Review, New Statesman *and* Sunday Times. *Her plays for television include* The Cupboard, The China Boy, Lovely in Black *and* Sweetheart, *and for radio:* The Museum of Man, The Promotion Game, The Dog Academy *and* The Boss. *She has one daughter, and is married to the playwright Barry Bermange. They live in London.*

INTERVIEW

Do you like talking about your work?

Thinking aloud constructively can be useful. Especially if you've reached a point where there are several directions you might want to follow. I find present possibilities interesting and diverse. Again at the crossroads, so to speak. I wrote *The Gasteropod*, a novel, in 1968. Since then I've moved on to other forms. The reasons are complex, but it has to do partly with a desire not to be pigeon-holed too soon. To be free to work in whatever medium is best suited to the presentation of an idea. *The Gasteropod*, in any case, marked the end of something, not the beginning. The end of my flirtation with writing, during which I'd written stories, articles, pieces for broadcasting, in which my main aim seemed, in retrospect, to be to work within the established order of things. After *The Gasteropod* I began a real engagement with the business of freeing my work from self-imposed sometimes abstract restrictions.

B.T.W.—K

Was it a difficult book to write?

Technically it was. But I like that kind of problem – writing something that requires you to give more than you thought you could give. Perhaps that's why my output compared with other writers is modest. And I've had my failures. To add to the world's already vast sum of literary works can sometimes seem an act of folly, unless one feels the thing so deeply that writing it out of your system is your only solution.

Do you like being at the crossroads again?

It's important to think about the way you shouldn't go. Having written a book thought 'stylish' by some people, I would do well to heed the warning signs that style might overcome everything, become my sole preoccupation. That method and not content would dominate. Being well aware of this, I try to choose my way accordingly. I'm interested in theatre, that is radio theatre, television theatre, and the stage. I find the forms exciting for different reasons. Utilizing them to the full could be a really testing task. Television, for example, is a brash, ephemeral medium. One's work becomes part of the daily visual-verbal bombardment. What is seen on the screen must imprint itself immediately on the mind in a powerful way, or be lost. I wrote *Sweetheart* bearing this in mind.

Was it in your terms successful?

The result seemed complicated, abstruse. I wrote it really striving for clarity. Appealing to the lowest common denominator of understanding, or so I thought, with what I believed to be direct and simple means. My idea of simplicity isn't everybody's. Only in a limited way was it successful for me. But working with the director, the actors, the technicians, gradually putting clothes on the skeleton of my script, this was interesting and worthwhile, instead of presenting a beautifully finished piece of written work with nothing else to do to it. The script was the start, not the end. It should be possible to work in this way more widely. More freedom should exist within the writer/producer relationship in order to get the utmost out of a production. There's an innate sterility in a system in which roles are too clearly defined, where a writer at a certain specified stage is forced to relinquish power. Rarely is he allowed total freedom of expression and directorial control.

As your husband Barry Bermange achieved in his memorable productions of Invasion?
The classic example.

Tell me about The Dog Academy.
The concept was a radio play in which sounds predominated. It was composed and presented in the form of a quadrophonic montage, showing man as a social animal being manipulated by his fellow men: a man and dog enactment, if you like, of responses to orders within the framework of an intolerant society. The action takes place in disorientated space. One of my instructions was that the performance should be in the spirit of Frank Zappa's *The Return of the Son of Monster Magnet*, phrases and sounds interweaving to suggest the atmosphere of a military training school. The script was like a groundplan, very basic, and it was put at the disposal of a musical director in Wisconsin to treat as he thought best. Writing it was a liberating experience. I'd like to produce it in collaboration with a pop group, or a classical composer.

Are you musical?
I was a Fine Arts student. References to painting, to visual phenomena, can be found in all my work. It's important to me, this world, something I shall never lose, that will always interest me. *The Gasteropod* is set in a portrait gallery. Our house is filled with pictures, picture books, books about optics and the science of colours. The movements in Art today I find absorbing. There are so many, as many as there are ways to look at and think about them. It isn't easy to chart the course these movements might take. Every so often a change occurs which adds to the confusion. Only occasionally is it possible to see a movement that may cause an important shift in the centre of gravity. The work of Warhol, for example, whatever your views are about it. The New Realists are also a good example. They are turning our attention once again towards naturalism, order, and things that endure. Towards a world both orderly and likely to last. Multiple Art and Expendable

Art is suddenly on the wane. Perhaps we've absorbed mechaniza-
tion and its depersonalizing influences, and are ready once again to
revert to an earlier, more durable aesthetic. The move is towards
the precise presentation of reality. If literature follows, we may
expect a return to a more traditional approach. It wouldn't surprise
me. In the sixties we had political and social unrest on a universal
scale, suggesting we were in the thick of revolutionary change. The
wave gathered momentum and volume. Where is it now? Now the
desire among ordinary people is for the reinstatement of authority,
the re-establishment of order in the world, whatever the price.
Meanwhile we find ourselves in the undertow. Will there be a return
to rigid rule, the mass return to a cold conservatism? I'm not
optimistic about the outcome.

Does it affect you as a writer?
The outside world? With all of us the barrage is constant. A lot
floats down into the subconscious and, given the chance, floats up
again. We live in the world and must take notice of what goes on
in it. To lock ourselves away would be cowardly and irresponsible.
Several of my poems deal with specifically political subjects. I'm
deeply interested in the work of committed writers and politically
engaged film-makers, poets and painters. *Battle of Algiers* was an
unforgettable indictment of French Colonialism. The paintings of
Genoves, the poems of Hans Magnus Enzensberger, the life and
work of Solzhenitsyn, all help to clarify my own thinking. Who can
say where influences begin and end?

Would you describe your work as being emphatically English?
The tendency, when thinking of English writing, is to think in
terms of writers who are emphatically non-political. But this is
changing, I hope, as are the boundaries between what is, and isn't,
deemed fiction. The written word follows slowly on the tail of the
other media. For a long time now the cinema has made use of
documentary footage, and the reconstruction of actual events within
a fictional framework. *Z*, *A State of Siege* and *Executive Action* are
three fairly recent examples. And Norman Mailer has employed this
technique, and so has Truman Capote, both quite effectively in
their writing. Again it's a question of the removal of demarcation

lines, the freeing of the means of expression. The more I'm aware of the changes, the less of an English writer I'll become.

Why do you write?

It clarifies my thoughts, my feelings. I'm unhappy if I don't write. It's an obsessive thing. It is a way of speaking to people, a lot of people, all at once. And although at times I've been accused of being dense and unreadable in my writing, it's never been my intention to be so. Given the choice, and the ability, I'd rather be thought of as a writer of infinite clarity. We write in the only way we can. There is a very beautiful and moving Czechoslovakian story, Hrabal's *Closely Observed Trains*, a masterpiece of simplicity and clarity. It was so impressively simple. How had Hrabal achieved it? Had the translation anything to do with it?

What are your feelings about translations? Taken out of their social and political context, do you think that literary ideas can travel truthfully?

A great deal must depend on what we know of that context. In translation much is lost, or presented in the wrong perspective, or shown in a false light. Not because of the translator. His contribution is frequently overlooked. I think the trouble lies rather in our distance from the original ideas, the basic philosophy underlying them. A good translator can become more than the mediator between us and another culture. He can guide us towards much more than a superficial understanding of it, but we are still forced to question our own understanding. Poetry in translation is particularly interesting. Here the translator is faced with the double difficulty of having to translate very accurately the shape of ideas and feelings as well as rhythms. The result is often more interesting than the original might have been. In some poems one finds a certain quality of strangeness which perhaps the author didn't intend. Perhaps poetry in translation is another form of poetry and shouldn't be confused with the original.

What are your future plans?

I find myself more and more involved with the subject of women in society. I'd like to continue writing about their problems and their attitudes. About the roles they should be free to play compared to the roles they're forced to play. And about how they see themselves – especially how they see themselves. This subject is still in its infancy. A great deal needs saying and clarifying and removing from the realm of dogma. I'd like to be heard as an individual, not as a cog in a movement. It's unfortunate but inevitable that every movement has its detractors, and the Women's Liberation Movement has many. The strength of feeling this movement arouses is symptomatic of the fear it engenders. But can women be looked at *en masse*? We're all at different stages along the road to emancipation. No, not all of us, some may never wish to be responsible for themselves. We must therefore, in my opinion, consider as many problems in as many ways as possible, in order to reach anything resembling the truth of our collective situation. I try to do this through my work. In my play *The China Boy* I looked at the relationship between an older and younger woman, both astray in the disaster area of mistrust and jealousy. In *Lovely In Black* I examined the dream-thought-day-dreams of a bourgeois housewife who sees her escape through widowhood. *Sweetheart* was about the contender for a beauty title – an essentially male manifestation – doll-like and dumb, and the willing but sad victim of her own and other people's greed.

Is 'Fire' about female emancipation?

It's a story in which I've tried very hard to distance myself from the subject, in order to see more clearly the overall pattern of women in society. Although the story is in the first person, it concerns many different women. Each has a differing attitude to the situation in which she's found, and in which she finds herself. By turning the story into something futuristic, I've tried to show how they might respond to the notion that they're captive without resorting to contemporary references. The notions and responses are presented as abstractions. It also gives me plenty of opportunities to indulge in an imaginative reconstruction of a society entirely man-made. It was enjoyable to write.

Do you enjoy writing generally?
I find it both a pleasure and a pain.

When is it a pain?

When there looms before one the spectre of the past, and all the words that have ever been written, and all the things that have ever been said, and whether it's possible to say something again. Something that matters to one personally, something that's worthwhile saying and can be said in a worthwhile way, and whether when one has said it, others will listen, and what they'll make of it.

When is it a pleasure?

When I forget all that, and there is flow, and things look bright, and good.

FIRE

We were captive a long time. Many of us believed this captivity to be the natural order of things, and were only slowly made aware it could be changed.

At first I was one of these, being hard put to it to remember whether I had been born into captivity or whether, in early childhood, I had once been free. There was a picture in the recesses of my mind which I held close and told no one, of a child on a warm and distant day. She is walking in a stream in which the water is swirling dangerously round the tops of her boots. She is making good progress against a strong current and watching with interest the way it constantly threatens to flood her feet. She feels nothing but the excitement of the moving stream and the sunshine which burns her neck. Suddenly she thinks 'I am unique'.

We were captured and herded together with older women who, we were told, were our mothers. I learned this later from one of them who told me many things she shouldn't have done for fear of punishment. From the mothers to whom I was allocated I remember nothing but gentle treatment. Indeed this seemed the general case. Very rarely did any of us have cause to complain of physical force being used upon us. That is why it was difficult for us children to know the truth, that all of us, young and old alike, were captive.

The mothers' task was to educate us with gentleness in the ways of our masters. To see to it that when the time came for us to become part of the work force we were well prepared. Our childhood days were carefully divided between Education, Recreation, Competitive Play and Sleep, over which the mothers presided and whose divisions they decreed. Any major deviations from the norm were always referred to the masters. Major changes in policy were their concern and theirs alone. All this I was told by the old woman to whom I'd gone with a childish question. I had wanted to know

why we children were never allowed outside the walls from where
I could hear coming what sounded then like the rumbling roar of a
mighty giant laughing. I wanted to see this laughing man who
could house so much mirth inside his frame. 'Who is he? Why does
he laugh like that? Why can't I see him for myself?'

She bent her head and whispered so that the others could neither
see nor hear she was whispering. She told me I had sharp ears to
hear such a distant sound. Many, she said, would never hear it
because of the thickness of the walls. She advised me to keep what
I'd heard to myself and not to mention it to anyone. With her my
secret was safe. She'd been classified as Old and her danger quotient
was therefore low.

'I like the sound of the laughing man.' She smiled and whispered
like a sigh in my ear 'How do you know he's not being tickled?'
And she led me to a corner out of the way, having first asked my
mothers if she could tell me an educating story. She told me about
a giant captured by little men the size of ants. They tied him down
to the ground with ropes across his arms and legs. They pegged his
hair. And every time they ran between his fingers or scuttled across
his chest, he laughed and laughed because he couldn't bear the feel
of their little feet. 'I want to see for myself.' She said the story was
better than the reality. When she took me back to the mothers and
they asked whether I'd been good, she touched my face with a
wrinkled hand and told them yes. They suspected she was lying
and told me not to trust her.

From then on it became my greatest interest until I was in my
teens to watch the mothers and the way they behaved. They seemed
collectively to constitute a perfect police force of complete depend-
ability, not only policing the children but each other. Nothing
delighted them more than to be in charge of a group of quiet, clean,
obedient charges with whom to play their favourite formation
games. We were arranged in rows and made to form complicated
moving patterns in competition with each other. Points were
awarded for precision and perfection. Since there was no arbiter
the mothers spent as much time arguing the merits of their individual teams as directing the activities. We were encouraged to notice
and point out the opposing teams' defects in order to gain more

points for ourselves. Any differences in individual looks were considered faults and frowned upon. If any child appeared different from the rest she was closely examined and her clothes, hair – her very features – were rearranged so that she would more closely resemble the rest of the company.

At those times when there seemed a danger of the games becoming wearisome, when the mothers felt perfection had been reached, they would devise fresh ways to keep us occupied. But always I remember the formation games, some of beautiful complexity, and the way we were witness to the mothers' arguments. They were forever, it seemed, trying to decide which of us was the cleanest, prettiest or most malleable. In this way we grew up learning the ways of our mothers, ready in our turn to take their places when their time came to be reclassified as Old.

From our mothers we learned many useful things which helped us in our captivity. From them we learned control, which one must have if one is to serve the masters. They taught us the value of silence in the face of outside forces, and proved that collective action can bring results. But all this within the bounds of a captivity which they accepted as the natural order. When I grew older one mother said to me 'Why don't you enjoy what you have? Look at the rest of us. You don't see us complaining.' She meant I should enjoy my servitude and be grateful for the masters' compassion. I was shown pictures of other tribes in distant colonies far less advanced than ours, whose captives were forced to work long hours at primitive machines, producing artefacts intended for other planets. We were allowed to choose what we made from the materials supplied us. It was said our skills were handed down through many generations, and indeed we produced many diversely beautiful things. But it seemed to me no great thing to make what someone before me had already made, for our choice was always limited to what had gone before. If I wished to warp with a new colour, or compute a new culinary flavour, the masters' advice was always sought. It was they who told me yes or no. And they always asked why I should want change when there was such variety and choice already. It is true that the joy in craftsmanship often blinded me into thinking I was satisfied.

It was considered meritorious to spend a long time working on a single piece of fine embroidery, or a complicated Reticella intended only for exhibition in the Hall of Craft. I went there once on cleaning duty and stood in wonder before the sheer quantity of work. I saw before me the sum of centuries of useless labour. The proof that if we turned such industry to other things we could become a powerful force.

The Sculptor

Over the years of my captivity I saw very little resentment of the sculptors. They came and went freely among us for the purposes of their work. They made use of us in any way they thought fit, not at all concerned by anything other than their own interests. They never tried to probe our lives, never asked us how we felt or what we thought. Always, it seemed to many of us, they depicted only our most superficial aspects, contenting themselves with the obvious differences between us of form and structure. It was apparent even to the simplest of us how much they prided themselves on the way they represented a species they considered had been provided for their art and nothing else. That this representation was intended to prove their prowess, and not the innate qualities of their subject, was taken so for granted that many of the captives totally approved. They didn't want it any other way. I have seen many of the younger captives actually place themselves in the path of the sculptor, hoping to please his eye and thereby be perpetuated in bronze or chrome or fibreglass. Little did they realize how many hours they would be forced to stay motionless, shouted at if they so much as moved a finger while the work was in slow progress. I have seen some in contortions more like the inner armatures than anything human. They have been used and abused and still thought it worth while. Who could blame them for thinking that their short lives might at least be perpetuated in a more lasting material valued more highly than their own?

One day a sculptor came and stood among us and closed his eyes. We waited breathless, wondering what new tortures he might impose. Then he opened his eyes and said 'I have it all in here.'

With his finger he drew a line from the front of his hair through to the back. 'When I want you,' he said, 'all I have to do is call upon this graph. No one need pose for me any more.'

Immediately there was a flurry of frightened voices. He needed us no more. What was to become of us? One stripped her cover to show him her back, asking whether he was capable of remembering such subtle beauty as hers. Another begged him not to forget how much she had suffered for him in the past. A braver one asked why someone so rich and free should reject the basis of his riches. 'I must always give them something new,' he said, 'or they will stop paying me. For the moment you are expendable.' He told us our turn would come again when the masters had tired of his new offerings. He said he was forced to give them whatever they required. Up until that time I hadn't known that he too was a captive. I asked whether his was a special class and he said yes. But he told me privately there were others living outside the walls whose lives ran to a different pattern, some of whom were captured every season and brought in. I asked how long he'd been a captive and he told me to mind my own business.

When he left he threw down a handful of coins which we scrambled for on the floor. We were sorry he had rejected us for we knew the others would do the same. And we would be deprived of diversion. Only Janin laughed and said she didn't care. She had been to the Artemporium and seen herself in chrome. She was questioned excitedly and asked what the sculpture was like. 'Chrome!' she said and laughed. She said it was very pretty.

The Toy

The artist brought us a toy one day and spent much time showing us how it worked. He said it wasn't a new invention but an old idea reshaped and modernized and perfected over the centuries. He thought it might relieve our duller times. We could see from his manner how well he understood the nature of our service, how well he saw its effect upon the more sensitive among us.

Division of labour on the whole was fair. We had little to complain about the work load since any of us, at any time, could put in a request for less work and have it granted. We were generally strong and healthy and felt ourselves capable of great endeavour. Yet for each and every one of us younger ones the work we undertook was a heavy burden. Some thought the masters fed us bromides in order to weaken our will. Others that the loads we carried, the machines we operated, the calculations were special tasks designed to drain the strength of would-be troublemakers. Each evening after food we lay together, our bodies collapsed where they'd fallen. Those who had requested leave from work, those who had done nothing for many weeks, lay with us as if they too had worked hard, complaining of muscular fatigue. It was like a strange disease afflicting the body so powerfully that only by exercising the strongest will could the mind be forced to operate at all.

In his demonstration the artist was very patient with us. He pointed out the individual beauties of his toy, going so far as to lift our unresisting fingers to make us feel its lovely surfaces. He said we might look upon it as we liked – a box or receptacle, a doll, a cupboard of delights. We might, he said, when we felt a little less relaxed, explore its many drawers and shelves, discovering for ourselves its versatility. It had a pretty patina which drew us to it. We found the energy to raise ourselves to gaze at its rainbow colours. We saw ourselves reflecting in its facets, and felt the energy returning.

'I'm making you feel better,' the artist said. He pulled a lever on the toy and out slid small panels holding palettes of coloured powder, red and green and blue and yellow which he came and mixed in the palms of our hands and printed on our foreheads. He was very kind and gentle, telling us to play and smile. Smile and be happy, he said. By smiling you give pleasure which you're sure to receive in return. His words chilled me a little. But the others did as he asked, crowding round the toy, their energy returning. They asked how long they could keep it and he said as long as they liked. He said he'd have to come back from time to time to make necessary alterations. 'We like it just as it is,' someone said. 'Why can't it stay this way?' He just smiled and shook his head as if she were foolish. 'Play pretty!' was his answer.

It was a wonderful toy which gave us much pleasure. It stemmed the loss of energy and animated many an evening's conversation. Sometimes within the rooms in which we worked nothing was discussed but ways in which we might explore it further. We discovered it was mechanical and could be activated by turning a key inserted, had it been human, in the basal region of the neck. Then it set up a delightful sound of indescribable pleasure. It made us feel alive. Someone said 'it sounds like Now' and we understood. Avit described it as 'that infernal Thing', but did as the rest, gathering round it after work to touch and wind and finger its colours and listen to its music. She said it took up too much time. She said Time was our ally for only a short while. She reminded us that the artist too was in the masters' service and victim of their will.

'I do as I want,' the artist said. But the masters approved his toy. Of course they were pleased it gave pleasure. Wasn't one of their Statements: Pleasure is in Giving? They believed in kindness. It was the only way to get the rules obeyed. They never desired unwilling servants who kicked against them.

When the artist wished to modify our plaything, they sent him to ask our advice. The serious way he listened to us made us feel important. We did our best to help him produce the most ingenious, the most lovely toy of all time, unaware of exactly how much of our new-found energy was being consumed in this fashion. Some of the younger captives, hardly more than children, would follow him in admiring groups, begging him to think up further innovations.

'He's transistorized the Thing,' Avit said one day. 'It's rolling through our quarters like an old locomotor.' What excitement then. We found it could play formation games, chase us into corners, bundle us into rows and shuttle us like seven-pins. The little ones loved it. It could push us all into perfect formations and figures of eight in less than a minute, while we laughed and gave each other points for perfection.

When it was discovered broken and lying in a corner, Avit was accused. The others might have punished her severely if the artist hadn't intervened and hastily mended his toy, adding a few extra antennae from which he hung small banners which spun at a touch. Our smiles quickly returned. Avit swore she hadn't broken the thing, claiming she'd too much contempt for it to think of touching it. To me it was harmless enough, once I had recovered my strength and spirits and could look on it for what it really was – a plaything and not the centre of a small universe. Eventually one of the quieter captives was discovered trying to break it with a building bar. No one gave her a chance to explain her motives or feelings. She was taken away and kept in solitary confinement for many months, general opinion being that she was mad.

As far as I know, the artist's toy is still in existence, and still excites as much fervent enjoyment. When I occasionally long to see myself reflected in its pretty surfaces, or wish to hear again its warbling, or want to feel its arms pushing me into orderly play, I pick up a leaf instead, brush it gently on my maculated skin and think myself fortunate to be here, so distant from it.

The Masters

I first observed them from a window in our quarters overlooking a section of the Great Square. Many times the window was boarded up, but as often as it was closed and by whatever means, someone somehow managed to unblock it again. It was the only opening at the end of a long corridor down which some of us were afraid to pass. Indeed there was little reason to pass that way unless something had to be obtained from one of the storage rooms which this part of the building housed. Frequently I volunteered to fetch equipment from a place the more timid were loath to enter. I said I was stronger and not fearful of the dark. The corridor itself was grim enough because of its length and the gloom which neither day nor night affected. Only at the end did faint rays of light from the window cast a path by which to find the way. By this light could be seen the heavy bronze doors of the storage rooms, forbiddingly powerful with their combination locks and secret handles. The locks were simple to open once one had learned to decipher the set of figures devised by masters long since dead. Even when not required to fetch something from these fascinating rooms, I would quietly find my way to them along the dark passage, an excitement in me far greater than the fear of blackness. I spent many hours in these rooms and learned much about their contents. So fascinating were they that it took me far too long to realize that the small, blocked window in the wall held things of greater interest.

The masters were truly gigantic. My first impression of them was of their amazing size compared to us captives who seemed to have been stunted in growth. I imagined they fed on special substances, an unknown protein-rich bean perhaps, which had built them from birth into these gargantuan specimens. I immediately decided to secure some of these beans for the purposes of experiment.

Then I saw that many of the masters were richly clothed in fabrics which I recognized as having been made by us. It pleased me momentarily that our work was being put to use. But then I saw that each individual was clothed in so many layers of cloth that most of our labour was being utilized to make him appear larger than he actually was. In effect all we'd done was pad him out until he resembled a giant bullfrog.

This square was obviously the place where the masters took the air. They walked at leisure round and round the statue of the Captive, some talking together, others indulging in various forms of rough play. Some were sitting in the sun, others busy over board games or intently studying maps and books. I envied them and admired such a display of contentment with a way of life.

My window afforded me many opportunities of studying them, during which time I came to many and often differing conclusions concerning them and what I thought they were. At first I must confess they seemed a race so superior that all I could do was look on with longing as they played, gambled, conversed, argued within the precision of an area designed expressly for them and from which all outsiders were excluded. There were days when they appeared more like children squabbling over toys, or unfettered animals indulging in unseemly romps. I saw how they too played formation games as we had done in our youth. But to them the games were intensely serious. There were continual fierce arguments over scoring and the allocation of individual scores.

I saw that the whole square was laid out in sections of differing designs so that, from any vantage point, it resembled one of those multi-coloured boards on which counter games are played. Some sections were of marble, others of sand. In the distance I could see areas of green and brown interspersed with walkways of unfinished aspect. Often the masters measured and trod these sections, discussing ways in which to improve their designs. They were after some idea of ultimate perfection which seemed to occupy much of their time. On these vast boards I saw them play many games similar to chess, using themselves as pieces. For me it was interesting and instructive to observe them considering and completing moves, and watching their difficulties. I never tired of these games, becoming skilled myself in the complexities of play.

It was late evening on a dull day when I saw the first real fight. Since the light was so dim, and partial boarding of my window had made it difficult for me to sustain a prolonged view, I first heard the uproar. There were shouts of Traitor! followed by the clash of metal. Many voices began to shout, some trying to keep the peace, others urging everyone to battle. I looked through a crack and saw a phalanx of the masters moving rapidly across the square towards others forming themselves into battle order. The square was rapidly filling with an excited confusion of fighting men whose cries and screams were terrible to my ears. Smoke began to fill the air, hanging low over the mass of writhing combatants. It began to filter through my tiny viewing space masking much of the dreadful sight.

I crouched in the corridor below the window, afraid to look, while above me the dark wall glittered with the bright and vicious illuminations of their guns. The noise was terrible and I covered my ears, hiding in fear until it had abated.

At last I ventured to look again. The square was emptying. Through the lingering smoke of battle I saw broken masters lying in liquid pools. The living and half-dead were dragging themselves away or being carried off over the shattered remnants of stained marble. The war was over.

I went back to the others and told them as best I could what I'd seen. Some of them already knew such things took place. The told me it was the captives who were expected to tend the wounded.

In the beginning I was alone when I watched from the window. But from the time I grew tall enough to see without effort, and had the strength to break any barrier across it, I was being joined by others. At first we were timid together, afraid of being betrayed. Later many friendships grew within that small area of light. I met Leah there, and Janin and others whose names now elude me. We helped each other to see more clearly by trying to analyse collectively the masters' behaviour.

The masters frequently caused us much amusement and made us forget our cares. When we saw them indulging in ridiculous behaviour we laughed and shouted rude names. Our vantage point made us feel too secure.

One day a group of them heard us shouting and looked up. I was ready to run but Leah held me there. She stood at the window smiling down, defying them while they began to gather in a crowd below. 'No rules forbidding it,' she said. 'They didn't block our window.' So I stayed clinging to her as the crowd increased and began to call up to us. Leah laughed at them so I laughed too. Below us came back the echo of our laughter and the roar of voices urging us to come down. 'Down!' they shouted. 'Now!' We could see them jostling and calling and pointing and pushing like a nest of spiders.

Several of them left the group, quickly returning with bundles on their backs which they placed beneath our window. They were building a pile of twigs and branches. When it had reached twice the height of the tallest among them, someone ran forward with a flaming brand and set it alight. Immediately it began to shoot upward in a beautiful curling flame. Soon the whole pyre was ablaze, lighting up their faces with its glow. We could feel its warmth where we stood. I wanted to put out my hands and let the tongues of flame lick my fingers. Sparks rose and circled us, falling at last into the calling crowd and adding to the confusion. We saw how some of their clothing caught fire, and how they leaped at each other crying warnings. Yet they seemed to be enjoying the danger.

'They're just like us,' Leah said.

We stayed at the window watching them long after the warning bell. We saw how they were exhausting themselves in keeping the fire high. And we knew they were trying to build it high enough to consume us. But Leah tore the wood from our window and threw it down to the centre of the heat. She shouted to one of them to get it, and he snatched the already burning plank from the flames, held it aloft and dashed round the square with it as if it were a torch. They called to us to throw down more fuel. They urged us to throw anything inflammable – our uniforms, ourselves. Nothing mattered but the continuation of that great blaze.

Eventually the flames began to die into a heap of glowing ashes as the masters one by one, stood back or sank exhausted to the ground, overcome by the heat and the smoke and their fruitless efforts. Leah's runner still staggered round the square, holding aloft a stub of smouldering charcoal. I left her still standing at the window watching him. As I went down the corridor I could hear her screaming at him, like a woman possessed, to keep on running.

Since that time I have witnessed many fires and spoken to others who have seen many more. We have seen them in many places and taking many forms, and each of us is unable to describe the exact effect of such sights. When I asked Leah how she felt after that first time she shrugged as if it had meant nothing. Yet it took me a long time to remember it without a shudder of mixed enjoyment and apprehension. She was my friend with whom I shared many experiences. It was often perplexing to me that our separate memories of them could be so different.

Reclassification

When the time came for me to be reclassified, I was called before the masters, as I'd been warned I would be, and told about my future. They told me I was one of the lucky ones. I must admit this knowledge had been with me long before this time. It was almost as though I'd grown up aware of a difference between myself and the others, as if I belonged to a select group nourished in special cells. I was one of the lucky ones, they said, considered intelligent enough to be given the power of choice. Bearing in mind the many restrictions and taboos incumbent upon my class I could, if I liked, discard the common uniform and don the special colours which signified change of status. I could be servant to a single master. I would be allowed to choose him.

It was as if they already knew I wished for change. They stressed the great honour, as if they were already certain I had no desire to stay within the compound, living my life exactly as before. That was the alternative. But I had seen others make this choice, and seen their lives wither. I had seen how the performance of menial, repetitious tasks year after year had turned these poor creatures into dried up sticks like so much kindling. I had seen them crumble into dust. When I asked one why she had chosen this way she said she'd done so out of fear. She was afraid of the unknown. Some said they'd had no choice at all. They thought choice an illusion.

This knowledge was with me on the day they took me out. I went to a building ringed by deep pits dug all around it. They left me there. I saw fires burning in the pits and felt a wonderful elation. I chose one of the more fiercely burning fires and ran at it fast. With a leap I cleared it, feeling the heat burn my legs. Then I ran, as I had been told, towards the building which I could scarcely see through the smoke from the pits. It was a place I'd never before been to, but only heard about from others who had made the journey. I expected so many things that disappointment at whatever I found had no place in me. My mind was in confusion. Would it be hall, or palace or prison, or museum? There had been so many conflicting stories about this building that I had been forced to the conclusion that the masters altered it in order to confuse us. I half expected another square similar to that where I had first observed those over-padded, strutting creatures at their games.

It was no marble square. It was like nothing I had previously experienced, nor like anyone's descriptions. I was met by no welcoming crowd, as one captive has been, to take me in procession through a decorated labyrinth. Nor was I blindfolded at the door and hurled into a mob of monsters.

I found a wide door and entered into a place so artfully ringed by trees and lit so bright that if there was a roof above it was disguised as sky. I smelled the burning instantly, and instantly was on my guard as I felt the accustomed thrill. I saw palm trees rising round me in infinite variety, and plants with leaves like shining plates. Tropical flowers with waxen trumpets grew together with strange fruits. Tiny birds flew in front of me quite carelessly as they sought out the honey and perched on the curiously twisting vines and creepers. As I walked in this exotic place I felt metal beneath my feet and saw how everything was growing, not in earth, but through gratings in the floor from which issued smoke, or steam. I was in a vast conservatory which, for all its size, constricted my breathing and gave me thoughts of suffocation. I remember it still that place – that special mixture of perfumes and smoke and steamy moisture. I can still, by concentrating hard, conjure for a brief moment the special excitement I felt there, and which has never quite been repeated.

As far as I know I was alone, or unaware of being watched. I did not feel as if I was being put through a sort of test and awarded marks for behaviour. Other captives believed this was the case despite my reassurances that I spent some time wandering among the foliage looking for an exit, completely hidden from any view. They said I was lucky to have had such an easy trial compared with theirs. I told them how I found another opening in a wall, across it a narrow pit from which sprang a sheet of flame. As I jumped I remember how unafraid of the fire I was, yet somehow demeaned by passing through it. The burn I suffered on my leg took some time to heal, becoming nastily infected before I gained control of it.

My leap took me into a narrow room or corridor, quite brightly lit and wide enough for me to pass between two rows of stationary figures which at first I mistook for the masters. They were so life-like that had I not seen the actual masters I might have been fooled. They stood so tall and real that I mistakenly imagined their eyes following me as I passed. But they were only models, made with such precision that I hardly dared bring myself to make a closer study. Yet I knew instinctively that from these figures I had to make my choice.

I walked up and down not knowing what to do. If the real masters were not going to present themselves, then I was committing myself, to what I believed would be a lifetime's service, to a shadow. As I walked slowly perusing them, only slowly did I come to the realization that this parade was expedient not only for them but for me. I knew that once having committed myself in both mind and body to something or someone, it was difficult for me to remain detached in any way. I came to the conclusion that choosing one of these replicas was no choice at all.

Considerably cheered by this thought, I spent much time examining details – waxy hands with finely modelled fingers, the careful ridging of nails, skin on which I thought I could discern the finest beads of sweat, eyelids from which sprouted individual hairs – wondering at such craftsmanship. Finally I selected what, to my mind, was the most handsome specimen. The way he was standing, the set of his head held my imagination. I liked his dark gloss, the shine of him, the perfection with which an over-zealous craftsman had worked on his clothes. He was the most genuinely artificial of them all. He would suit me well.

Janin asked me to describe the occasion of my reclassification in detail. When I did she said I was being unspecific. She wanted most especially to know if I'd noticed the shape of the room in which the selection had taken place. She asked if it was a tesseract with an intermediate or cross-sectional square in each of its cubes. To me at the time it was only a floor surrounded on three sides by flat walls of unknown dimensions, and peopled by creatures equally as flat. It was later that we spent much time discovering the beauties of the fourth direction outside the generating cube.

And so, in an environment almost wholly unobserved, I selected my particular master from his shadow, and went into his service.

The Books

I served this master for two long years, during which time I rarely got within six feet of him, except to perform personal duties. We captives spent our lives bounded by rules from such an early age they were second nature to us. As far as I know few rules were written ones. They seemed to be passed on by word of mouth from generation to captive generation, accepted as if they had originated from higher beings, and therefore rarely questioned. When a new rule was introduced it came in the disguise of custom. Precedent was always claimed for it. It wasn't really a new rule they said, only an ancient one revived. Many of the captives were conservative in their thinking, preferring what they liked to call Traditional. And so that we never felt overburdened, one of the newer rules would be allowed to lapse until such time as it was needed again to keep us in check.

One of the more hallowed rules was that we never went within less than six feet of a master unless specifically requested. A captive might be asked to wrap a master's body robes, shine his boot skins, serve his food or sleep with him. Some made constant use of their captives, others hardly any at all. It was also usual to sit at the prescribed six feet and listen with head bent to readings from the Masters' Books of Statements. Readings might take place occasionally, once a month perhaps, or at regular daily intervals, depending on the individual. Each had his own reading times and tastes.

Statement: An eagle does not catch flies.

Statement: He who is silent gives consent.

Statement: In fleas the salivary glands are four in number.

Statement: Out of the strong came forth sweetness.

Statement: Happy is he who has been able to learn the causes of things.

Naturally enough our own tastes were to some extent formed by what we heard. If the same Statements are repeated over and over often enough, it takes a strong will to resist them totally.

Statement: The reflecting power of a surface is measured by the ratio of the amount of regularly reflected radiation to that of the incident of radiation.

Statement: There is no such thing as chance. A door may happen to fall shut, but this is not by chance. It is a conscious experience of the door, the door, the door, the door.

Statement: War is nothing more than the continuation of politics by other means.

Some captives were subjected to the constant reading of Statements, and many suffered in spirit because of it. Others like myself rarely heard them. And although sometimes I longed to be like the others and share the assault, I realized that the more frequently the Statements were heard, the more they paralysed the listener's will. I remember standing near a group of captives released from their daily work and gathered together for mutual comfort. I had had many lively discussions in such groups. But this evening I thought I heard them speaking in that curious tongue the masters use for highly formal occasions, when they wish to seem superior. The sing-song tones were the same, but it shocked me to discover that I could recognize the words. They were repeating, over and over, lines from the Books of Statements, on their faces the light of pleasure. First one, then another group would take up the chanting, until young and old alike were intoning their lines like incantations.

I crept away and thanked the darkness that my master's sluggish brain in an active body kept him away from me.

When work was done I had the time to take down his books and consider them for myself. Each master was supposed to have the entire collection of Statements, but since this ran into possibly thousands of books, it was more usual for each master to own only his special favourites. If, like mine, a master lacked the interest or intellect to choose, a selection was provided by some higher authority. This selection was considered by the hierarchy to be catholic and sufficient. There was much in these books to admire and ponder, and much that could have been the start of useful argument. But captives never argued, and rarely spoke to their masters except in admiration. I thought how worthwhile it would have been to share the deeper meanings and explore the subtleties, for alongside the frivolities and stupidities were new and exciting ideas. Some of the books were bound in curious cloths and printed in old Metal Letter. I found in them signs of amendment and addition and heavy deletion. I wanted to know why. I wanted to share their fascination.

On several occasions I tried to engage my master in discussions about his books. I would run alongside him through the echoing rooms, forced to finish the last braid plait at a gallop, he was so impatient to be gone. He was unaware that I knew his destination – the Great Square where he thought he was free. There he must have felt himself safe from me.

As I ran with him I tried to formulate my questions into simple sentences which wouldn't overtax his brain. I asked him 'Why do you run?' or more boldly 'Why do you run from me?' and 'Who are the Statement Makers?' But he never seemed to hear me. If I tried raising my voice it was as if a sheet of glass existed between us through which he could hear faint cries. Once or twice he gave me a little sideways glance of real alarm. On one occasion he smiled at me with a look very near compassion.

For all his size and simplicity he was gentle in his ways. He handled me softly enough. When he rolled me in his bed and the questions still tumbled from my mouth, he never became angry. His expression merely changed from one bewildered look to another. 'Where do children come from?' I asked him. 'Who has the babies?' I learned nothing from him in those two years.

Amali told me the masters were barren. She said she'd heard it from one of the older captives, a strange creature who always sat like a watchful bird in her own special corner. She said the babies were brought in secretly, as we had all been brought, through a special channel connecting us to the Outside. Although none of us had ever seen what was beyond the distant outer perimeter, we believed her story of the existence of another race out there, whose children were abducted and brought into captivity. We wondered how far away they lived to be in such constant danger. We sought out the old woman secretly and questioned her further. She told us fragmented stories of a dim childhood spent in a different land, and I felt the flicker of recognition. I saw myself carried screaming into an alien society. She said that although this had been going on for centuries, those beyond the perimeter could never find complete protection against such a powerful adversary, whose most powerful weapon was fire.

They lost their children yet they had more. More were always being caught but some remained. Outside our captivity there lived a people who defied the masters and who still survived.

Escape

They were such tentative beginnings. Leah, Janin and I must have made our discoveries at much the same time, but each thinking herself unique, or doubting the value of her findings, valuable time was wasted before collective action. Together we had gained as much information as we could about the so-called Open Lands. Old women dredged their memories for clues as to where they might lie. We searched our masters' Books of Statements and found many clues to help us. I wanted more.

On many occasions I had asked my master to supply me with more books, or direct me to the Central Bibliokamer. He ignored my requests, sending me instead into the pleasant countryside which immediately surrounded our dwelling. He hoped my desire would fade. He left me to myself and I began to search his empty house when he thought I was sitting in the sun. In his vaults I found charts, maps of the city system, its roads and monoways and underground links. I began devising ways of escape, drawing careful plans to take me through the central complications of a city intricate and frightening to the frail and vulnerable captive I considered myself to be. Ten months I wasted in this way, excusing my slowness to act by telling myself I must be sure.

Leah made a more important discovery which she too kept to herself. Later she told how one day she had inadvertently stepped closer to her master than she should. As was usual in such instances he stamped his foot, this being the traditional sign for the captive to regain position. For some reason, possibly irritation, Leah stayed where she was. He stamped again as loudly as he could. She stepped a little nearer, watching him closely. She said she could see him thinking. Suddenly he spun round, put his back to her and folded his arms. He remained in that position ignoring her until she became frightened by her own daring and retired. In defence of her it must be said that hers was one of the stronger masters, a known fire-raiser whose brand we had often seen from the central towers when he came back from his marauding.

Janin experimented boldly with her master, first turning her back on him to test his reactions. When he did nothing she tried advancing on him, and was amazed to see him retreat. She told how she had made him run, he throwing off layer after layer of his clothes to reduce the weight he carried. Feeling victorious she allowed him to return and was astonished when he tried to continue their life as if there had been no change in the relationship. She repeated the same experiment many times. It always produced the same reactions. Finally she felt the time had come to make her escape from him.

So while we were searching and experimenting, each of us was coming to individual conclusions on the best way to escape. I began to see how it might be possible for me to leave by a secret route. On the map I had already located the tunnels I would take, starting from beneath my master's outer towers, running under the city itself then through the fire lines into designated Open Lands. The extent of these lands caused me some surprise. There were huge areas of territory unmarked by the masters' fire symbols and therefore uncolonized. Written across them somewhat hopefully were the words Domain of the Masters. I made them my goal.

Many of us chose the same day on which to leave, but each devised her own method of escape. We determined to meet together as soon as we possibly could on the other side.

My master caught me at the entrance to his outer towers, where I was snatching a minute's rest before attempting the intricacies of the city system. I was off guard for a moment, bewildered by the realities of a city previously seen only on paper. I was attempting to make sense of the warren of connecting tunnels before me, trying to trace them on the plan and relate them to my knowledge of overground. I heard the soft stamp of his foot, to which I made no response. Softly he called me. I turned and saw his bulk darkening the entrance. He made no move but called again, still softly. He was incapable of violence. For the first time I ignored his voice, remaining where I was, continuing to sit and stare at him. I felt sorry for him. He remained very still, resembling exactly that glossy statue of himself which I had chosen on reclassification day. Still watching him I rose and began to move away from him, trying to be unafraid. I felt heavy and tired as I forced myself away. He did nothing but watch me go.

So it was easy. I walked away. But I walked slowly and warily, unable to cope with the feeling of freedom. I found myself circuiting by mistake the cellars of his towers, until I forced myself to stop and make a more careful study of my plans. I was aware that many of the more open-seeming ways led back directly to beneath the central city areas. Some of these ways were designed with such cunning they resembled the clear paths to the Open Lands. My way led through what at first glance looked like impenetrable walls which, in fact, were composed of tesseract cells in groups, through which a route could be found. I had discovered it first by accident while reading the Statement: Consciousness is moving in a new direction. A small diagram had been attached to it, and an amendment in another hand: Consciousness is moving towards the conquest of a new space.

So it was simple. All one had to do was forearm oneself with knowledge then act with caution, and it was possible to pass from captivity to what we foolishly supposed at the time to be complete freedom.

I met my friends again in the beautiful Open Lands, and many others joined us, escaping by numerous routes of varying difficulty. Some had found leaving so easy they insisted it was no escape at all. Janin said we had only made one more necessary move in the right direction.

The Beginning

But where were these other people supposed to be living outside the jurisdiction of the masters, who had survived against such heavy odds ? If we were their offspring we should join forces against a threat we understood so well. I thought we would surely find them among the remote hills and fertile valleys of the Open Lands. Janin said no. She said we wouldn't find them in so vulnerable a place. She warned us to beware. She said that here the masters could come for us. She showed us how our roofs might burn, and told us to keep watch at night.

They came in a roaring blaze which caught us totally unprepared. They burned our puny shelters and followed us as we ran screaming into the unknown.

Each time we thought ourselves safe from them they found us and came with their fire to carry us back to captivity. Some were caught, others found the strength to flee, to rebuild and carry on. Wherever we went they found us as if, however hard we ran, their strength would always outstay ours. For although we became with time more adept at avoiding them, there lingered in many of us a small secret wish that the chase might always continue. Whenever

I saw the lines of torches flickering like night flies across the land, I felt in me an insane longing to move closer, to stay and watch our houses burn.

Amali admitted herself she shared the same sensations, saying she preferred to stand watching the first flames colour the sky like desert dust than run for safety. When she and I watched from a hillside the burning of an entire collective, it seemed much easier than flight. To be captured so much more preferable. As the fires raged we felt them inside us. The upward movement of the flames lifted our spirits with a rising excitement. Leah said she watched from another hill, and shouted for joy as the tallest roofs caved in, and the giant chimney descended in a slow, crumbling curve of dust. Some of our younger friends perished in that fire, but whether by accident or design I don't know. How many were consumed in that great conflagration we never discovered. All I know is that there were similar fires in many parts of what we had come to call Our Country, taking their toll of many of our kind. It is understandable that there were those who made the decision to return, unable to withstand the pressures and the pain.

Some compared the fires to earthquakes or floods, natural phenomena to be endured or even worshipped since they were outside our control. Leah said that understanding came with time. The fire was nothing. But I spoke to another whose eyes were still bright despite the terrible things she'd seen. Had she been a captive she would have been classified as Old. She told of many ordeals. And she was of the opinion that the fire was at the very centre of the masters' philosophy. Everything they thought or did was directed by the idea of fire. And it would always be the same. It was not possible to have more than a brief conversation with her. All I know is that she spoke with conviction saying 'Always beware of the fire. Without it they are nothing.' On her skin the burns had healed badly, leaving it brown and delicately puckered like fine needlework. I too bear the marks of burning.

We are now moving along the farthest edges of the Domain of the Masters, still running, still not safe from pursuit, still drawn to that which we should abhor. Our numbers change all the time yet constantly grow. We are becoming a force which, we have decided, will one day be sufficiently strong to make peace. I believe this. Some of us still wish to go on seeking that race of people from whom we came. Their goal is to find them. Many are content with what we have already found. We have found joy in being together. And pleasure in being ourselves. We are as much a cohesive group as we shall ever be. The fire is our link.

Q7